design and use of computer simulation models

design and use of
computer simulation models

JAMES R. EMSHOFF • **ROGER L. SISSON**

McKinsey & Company, Inc.
New York

Government Studies & Systems, Inc.
Philadelphia

THE MACMILLAN COMPANY • COLLIER-MACMILLAN LIMITED, LONDON

*Since our accomplishments are determined to a
large extent by the environment of our early
childhood, we dedicate this book to our parents—*

Doris and **William Emshoff**
Rachel and **Jean Sisson**

The Macmillan Company
866 Third Avenue, New York, New York 10022

Collier-Macmillan Canada, Ltd., Toronto, Ontario

Library of Congress catalog card number: 72-96739

First Printing

preface

1545640

This text grew out of a course in simulation presented by one or the other of the authors at the University of Pennsylvania and the University of Waterloo numerous times. The reader is assumed to be interested in industrial engineering, management science, operations research—basically in improving management. He is assumed also to have at least a basic facility with FORTRAN, statistics, and calculus.

In a few sections mathematical presentations are used that require knowledge of advanced statistics. These discussions have been set in a different typeface (see, for example, page 29) and may be skipped without interrupting the continuity of the chapter. The practical consequences of their content are summarized in the regular text.

Like all techniques, simulation can be learned only by trying it. Readers who want to be able to use simulation should follow the examples in detail and do all of the exercises. A computer that can run FORTRAN and GPSS language programs will be required for some exercises.

We want to thank all of the students who contributed to our understanding of simulation and who helped develop the examples, particularly Fred Smith and Peter Hamm for their work on the example in Chapter 10; John Castle, Don Holland, and Steve Russell for their work on the example in the Appendix; and Hari Johri for work on Exercise 5–6 and Section 9–2.

In addition, we would also like to express our appreciation to James L. McKenney of Harvard and Paul S. Greenlaw and Robert L. Stafford of Pennsylvania State University for their helpful comments during the development of the book.

Typing of the manuscript was under the direction of Marilyn Dalick who was assisted by Billie Myers and Sandra Smart. Louise Rowland retyped later drafts.

Our special thanks go to the people at Macmillan, particularly John C. Neifert and Elisabeth H. Belfer. Their efforts on our behalf have greatly improved the final product.

We want to thank the Computer Centers at the Universities of Pennsylvania and Waterloo for computer time and for their general support.

J. R. E.
R. L. S.

contents

1
systems, decisions, and models
1

2
simulation and symbolic models of dynamic systems
23

3

simulation methodology
49

4

model building and use
61

5

developing the simulation model and program
75

6

simulation languages
115

7

model design
159

8

analyzing a simulation run
189

9
experimental optimization
209

10
a simulation model of a computer center's operations
225

11
simulation models of human behavior
243

12
the future of simulation
263

list of tables

list of figures

1

systems, decisions, and models

business complexity and the need 1-1
for analysis

Commerce, industry, and government have become exponentially more complex since World War II. One obvious reason is the tremendous increase in the number and variety of products and services being made available. In today's world of diversification, it is rare to find a manufacturer who produces and distributes only one product. As a consequence of this diversification and rapid growth, businesses have tremendously complex organization and control problems.

It is unlikely that the increase in complexity will slow down; therefore, it is foolish to argue that the managerial problems of today are only transitional and will sort themselves out in time. Management has begun, and must continue, to change its methods to meet the problems created by the complexity of present-day business.

Since 1955 the computer has been, without question, a key factor in improving some management decisions. However, computer usage has been limited primarily to providing management with quick and accurate access to status information, thereby making existing methods of decision making more effective. Only in a few specific applications has the computer been used in conjunction with managerial expertise to improve the actual process of decision making. Computer simulation is a technique to facilitate such improvement. It is a method for predicting the dynamic characteristics of an organization and thus improves the basis of the decision process.

Managers, who are living in a world of rapid change and extensive interaction, must continually improve their own decision-making skills or end up reacting to crises instead of controlling activity. Apprentice-ships and experience are not enough; today judgment and intuition are barely put into use before change occurs. A formal and efficient technique is needed to augment the manager's experience. The technique must be formal—that is, capable of precise documentation—so that it can be learned quickly and applied directly to new situations. The technique must be efficient so that its cost does not increase in proportion to the complexity of the situation. Although the modern manager is faced with a more complex world than were his predecessors, he has even less time in which to make decisions and therefore can less afford the luxury of time-consuming, manpower-consuming decision aids.

The central thesis of this book is that computer simulation is a technique that will fulfill these needs. Computer simulation is a formal decision-making aid that is adaptable to the complexities and change of modern business and can be developed and communicated efficiently.

Simulation is a natural development in the discipline of operations research. Operations research evolved out of efforts to provide formal, efficient decision-making techniques for the design of air defense opera-tions in Britain during World War II. Since that time methods of operations research have been refined and its areas of application expanded until today it is being successfully applied to a wide range of problems. Oper-ations research techniques use symbolic models and mathematical deduc-tive processes to predict the effects of alternative solutions to a problem and to determine the best (or approximately the best) solution [Ackoff and Rivett, 1964*].

Operations research has progressed both in military and in industrial applications by improving middle management decisions—decisions that are constrained by existing systems and policies. In industrial applications, operations research is particularly useful in inventory control, in designing product distribution systems, and in some areas of production planning. Techniques have also been developed for other well-defined processes, such as waiting line and equipment replacement problems.

As techniques for the solutions to middle management problems were developed and utilized, the operations researcher turned his attention to the higher level management decisions. In trying to apply existing tech-niques to problems such as capital investment or product planning, operations researchers discovered that neat mathematical procedures could no longer be found to perform the necessary analysis. One of the reasons for this difficulty is that the system by which higher decisions are made operates with fewer constraints. Difficulties also occur in applying mathematical techniques to such middle management problems as the scheduling of jobs through a shop. Although scheduling appears to be straightforward, operations researchers have yet to provide a complete solution. Decision makers who face these problems and somehow make decisions are the first to admit that the basis of their decisions is quali-tative and could be improved if appropriate quantitative aids were avail-

* Names and/or dates in brackets refer to publications listed at the ends of chapters.

able. This need for quantitative techniques for complex situations, combined with the ready availability of large electronic computers, led to the development of simulation.

models and the scientific method 1-2

Operations research (O.R.) is based on the approach to decision making outlined in Figure 1–1. The process starts when someone in the organization recognizes a problem and decides to investigate the possibility of using the O.R. approach. The situation is formulated in this way.

- A *measure of performance* is established by which the value of a decision is judged.

- The decision is specified by identifying those factors or variables which the decision maker can control; the *controllable variables*.

- The rest of the world is summarized by relevant *uncontrollable variables.*

- An objective function relates certain variables to the measure of performance; it tells how to estimate the relative value of the *outcome* of any decision.

- A *predictor* is then needed to predict outcomes (certain uncontrollable variable values) for any decision.

After the problem is defined we ask, "Does any standard operations research model fit the problem?" If one of the standard models does fit, the optimum decision can be found very efficiently since procedures for solving standard models are known. In this case, the right-hand sequence of steps in Figure 1–1 is followed.

(1) The problem is set up in the standard form.
(2) Data are gathered to provide the inputs for the model.
(3) Any necessary adjustments are made in the model to account for the particular situation.

A standard model implies a certain range of alternatives. For example, a linear programming model assumes that the available alternatives are any fractional or whole combination of activity levels. In a typical inventory model, each possible reorder quantity and reorder timing is an alternative. The model is solved by deducing which is the best of the entire range of possibilities. In a complete operations research study, the solution derived through the model is confirmed by field tests, and this solution, if it proves out and is acceptable to management, is implemented.

If none of the standard models fit the situation (which is a common occurrence), then the analyst chooses one of three procedures.

3

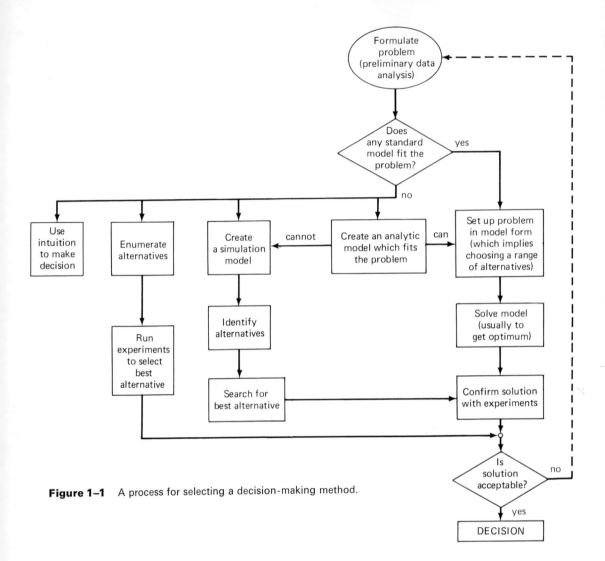

Figure 1-1 A process for selecting a decision-making method.

(1) He can try to *create* a suitable mathematical model. This may involve deep applied mathematics, and in many cases, behavioral research. Such analysis is a high-risk alternative; a suitable model may not be created within the time frame available for decision making. However, if a model can be created, then the steps on the right side of Figure 1-1 apply. If not, one of the other alternatives must be chosen.

(2) When no standard model fits, the analyst may choose to use simulation. The steps involved in this choice will be covered in detail in Chapter 3. A simulation model is designed, alternatives identified, and the model is used to search for the best alternative. When found, the alternative may be confirmed by field tests, as is any other model.

(3) If the analyst decides not to use a simulation model, the direct experimental approach remains. Here, alternative courses of action are identified and the best is selected by direct experimentation in the real world.

Finally, if none of these approaches are used, the analyst and the decision maker can resort to intuition—which means they have decided not to use operations research.

classification of models* 1-3

Since the construction of models is an essential part of the operations research approach, it is useful to distinguish between the different types of models that are available to the analyst. A classification of model types will enable us to more clearly define simulation and examine its relationship to other techniques.

Any explanation of a method of modeling has two parts. The first part describes the form in which the model is to be expressed; the second part describes the way in which the model is to be used to make predictions or to determine optimum solutions. Of interest in evaluating modeling methods are factors such as the relative cost of the use of the models (their efficiency), the ease with which the models may be communicated between technical people and from technical people to practitioners, and any special limitations on the application of the models. Table 1–1 is a taxonomy of model types based on these factors.

Descriptive models (which are expressed in native language) have many limitations, perhaps the greatest being that the method of prediction is usually internal and thus cannot be communicated easily or replicated. The greatest advantage of descriptive models is that the cost of making predictions when they are used is extremely low; therefore, they are the most commonly used model for decision making.

Physical models range from floor plan layouts to complicated aircraft wind-tunnel models. The method of optimizing with physical models is to search among alternative designs in the following way:

(1) Performance criteria are established.

(2) Estimates provide an initial combination of controllable variables.

(3) The model is then used to predict the value of the performance criteria under these conditions.

(4) A search rule, which incorporates all results to date, resets the controllable variables. The rule for search is designed to move the controllable variables in directions that will lead to the greatest improvement in performance.

* Adapted with permission from Chapter 2, "Simulation: Uses," in *Progress in Operations Research*, Vol. III (ed. by Julius Aronofsky), Wiley, New York, 1969.

Model (Form of expression)	Method of Prediction	Method of Optimizing	Cost	Ease of Communication		Limitations
				Technical	Nontechnical	
Descriptive (Native language)	Judgment	?	Low	Poor	Poor (appears good but often misunderstood)	Cannot repeat the prediction process
Physical	Physical manipulation	Search	High	Good	Good	Cannot represent information processes
Symbolic	{ Mathematical	Mathematical	Low	Good	Poor	Needs previously developed mathematical structure
	{ Numerical approximation	Mathematical	Medium			
Procedural	Simulation	Search	High	Fair	Good	General properties not easily deduced from the model

Table 1–1. Taxonomy of Model Types

(5) When maximum performance is found the search has found an optimum, and the values of controllable variables that give this optimum are the desired operating conditions. Search procedures are discussed in Section 1–5.

One significant advantage of the physical model is the ease with which its structure can be communicated to people with a nontechnical background. However, for modern decision-making purposes it suffers from an inability to represent information processes. Furthermore, there is often a high cost in the construction of a physical model, and, usually, the model can be used only for the particular problem for which it was designed.

Operations research, like other scientific disciplines, has progressed by use of symbolic models [Ackoff, 1962, Ch. 4]. These models use concise mathematical symbols to describe the status of variables in the system and to describe the way in which variables change and interact. Predictions are made from these symbolic representations by means of mathematical procedures. An important prerequisite for the use of this type of model is the calculus that applies in the situation. (Here we use the term calculus in the general sense; that is, a formal structure of axioms, theorems, and procedures.) Such a calculus permits deductions about any situation that meets the axioms. If a model fulfills the axioms of a calculus, the calculus can be used to deduce values of the variables that predict or optimize (or meet other specified criteria). Mathematicians have developed a number of calculi, the most famous and also the most useful of which is differential and integral calculus. The cost of using symbolic models is often low; for example, we do not have to reinvent the simplex algorithm every time we apply linear programming. The existence of a calculus also means that many general properties of the system can be deduced as well as the specific predictions.

The conciseness inherent in symbolic models makes them particularly suitable for communication between technical people. On the other hand, the symbolism is not a form familiar to the average decision maker, and so communication between the technical person and the nontechnical person is difficult. (This situation is changing, however, as more people are becoming trained in the use of symbolic languages.)

In many problems the mathematical manipulations required to derive consequences from a symbolic model can be carried only to a point where the optimizing values of variables are stated in terms of a complex functional relationship, in particular, an integral. Formulae for specific values cannot be derived. In these cases, it is possible to obtain the optimum values of the variables by means of a numerical approximation. Although this requires an added expenditure for computing, the results can be shown to produce the optimum which the mathematical theory predicts.

There are two common methods for numerically approximating an integral: (1) iterative approaches that are based on the fact that the value of an integral is equal to the area (volume) under the function curve (surface) and (2) the Monte Carlo approach [Hammersley and Handscomb,

1964]. This latter approach uses the knowledge that the probability of certain events may be expressed as an integral and, therefore, the integral may be approximated by a sampling process from the probability distribution. Analog computation methods, a third form of numerical solution, are discussed later. We would like to emphasize the point that Monte Carlo methods, which refer to a procedure for integrating a function by means of a sampling technique, have no direct relationship to simulation as defined in this book. The often-seen phrase *Monte Carlo simulation* is improper and usually refers to a direct simulation that contains stochastic (randomly varying) elements. In direct simulation, as we shall see, no closed-form mathematical calculus is applicable, and the numerical procedure *is* the model. A solution to an explicitly stated integral is not involved.

The fourth model type identified in Table 1–1 is procedural; however, it is generally referred to as simulation. The model is actually a *procedure* expressed in precise symbols; the term *simulation* refers to the method by which the model is used to make predictions. In a sense, every model is a simulation of reality, but in this book, in consonance with current operations research usage, the term is restricted to mean the procedural model and its execution process.

A procedural model expresses the dynamic relationships that are hypothesized to exist in the real situation by means of a series of elementary operations on the appropriate variables. These operations are usually stated in a computer-like flow chart but may also be expressed in the form of decision tables [McDaniels, 1968] or other procedural languages. The prediction of outcomes is made by actually executing the procedural steps with appropriate initial data and parameters. This is the essence of simulation. The execution process may be carried out clerically; however, it is generally done using a computer. The computer is programmed to perform the procedure (which is the model). Running the program creates the prediction. Concisely, *a simulation is a model of some situation in which the elements of the situation are represented by arithmetic and logical processes that can be executed on a computer to predict the dynamic properties of the situation.*

As with other model forms that do not utilize an explicit mathematical calculus, optimum combinations of controllable variables must be found by a search process or some other form of enumeration. This is a consequence of the structure of the problem, for if there were a mathematical theory for finding the optimum, simulation would not be needed. Simulation is expensive in terms of both the model preparation time (although this has been reduced significantly by use of simulation languages) and the cost of the computer time necessary to make the predictions during the search for the optimum. However, an important by-product of a simulation model is that, properly written, it facilitates explanation of the model and its conclusions to people with a nontechnical background.

Simulation models can be created for almost any situation in which a researcher can precisely state the relationships among variables, no matter how difficult it might be actually to obtain the data for such models. For example, the methods by which humans process information has been simulated (reviewed in Chapter 11). This does not necessarily mean that the simulations are valid; but, at least, the models can be written, the consequences derived, and the results communicated to other people.

It is possible to mix model types. For example, there are simulations that contain within them a mathematical, symbolic model. In plant-location studies, the overall process is a simulation. But within each trial plant-location scheme, linear programming is used to find the least-cost transportation pattern.

simulation and analog models 1-4

The use of analog methods (which may or may not mean analog computers) to solve decision-makers' problems can be viewed in three ways. First, an analog may be a physical model (for instance, an electrical network) that is thought to behave in essentially the same way as the system being studied. A second way of looking at an analog model is that it is a method of obtaining approximate solutions to sets of complex integral-differential equations. The model type is symbolic and the analog, usually in the form of a computer, is used to obtain a numerical approximation to the integration problem. The analog might be a circuit in which voltage, say, can be calculated by integrating the same function as in the problem under study. Or the computations might be performed on a digital computer. Finally, an analog model can be viewed as a simulator. The procedural model expresses the relationships between the variables in terms of operations such as integration and differentiation. The analog is designed to carry out these operations directly. The situation is simulated by the analog computer executing this procedural model.

Each of the foregoing ways of looking at an analog computer are useful; however, the analog computer users refer to their activity as *simulation.* The analog computer journal is called *Simulation.* The advent of digital computer programs that simulate analog computers makes it clear that there is really minimal distinction between computer methods for carrying out a simulation. Either case starts with a procedural model. If the operations are described as a series of summation and difference equations, the analyst may use either an analog or a digital computer. Where most of the operators are arithmetic and logical, digital computer execution is generally more suitable.

Analog methods are particularly useful for representing dynamic, continuous processes and for searching for optimizing parameters. The literature on analog computation is replete with discussions of methods for experimental search [Korn, 1965].

prediction, optimization, and search 1-5

Models that are to be useful to decision makers must predict the consequences of specific actions or inputs. The ability to predict accurately a system's behavior is, however, not sufficient to satisfy the decision-

9

maker's needs. He always desires the optimum action—that combination of inputs which will most nearly obtain his goals. His method of optimizing is often intuitive and therefore not explicit. Operations research is based on the assumption that the need to optimize is part of every decision-making situation.

The word *optimum* may be somewhat misleading. It does not mean the best solution in any absolute sense, but instead refers to the best solution that the decision maker can attain with the resources and time available. It is almost always possible to see, in retrospect, how a better decision could have been made. It is a view of operations research that model construction, even without absolute optimization, is important because it results in a forward-looking point of view; it tries to provide the tools that will permit the decision maker to arrive at even better decisions next time.

An example that we will explore in depth in the next chapter is that of a bottling process in which labeling machines fail from time to time and must be repaired. The decision maker is faced with a design problem. He must design operating procedures so that the total costs (maintenance costs plus idle time costs) are as low as possible. This minimum value is constrained by the knowledge and techniques available to the decision maker at the time. To solve this problem, the decision maker can change the number or the skill level of the maintenance people or their schedule of work. A model, simulation or any other type, would first predict what the costs would be if a certain number of maintenance men with given skills and work schedules were employed. However, the decision maker must go further. He must explore different alternatives; that is, different combinations of repairmen with different skills and work schedules until he finds one that produces the minimum costs.

Basically, four ways exist of finding an optimum once a model has been developed. The first and most commonly used method is the intuitive procedure. This method is not capable of formal statement and, therefore, will not be discussed further here.

The second most commonly used method for finding an optimum is differential calculus, a branch of mathematics with a long history. To use differential calculus, however, it is necessary to formulate the model according to specific axioms. Assumptions must be made about the continuity of the process; that is, the process cannot have discrete changes of value. These assumptions do not hold in many business situations. The techniques of calculus, apparently so powerful for studying the physical world, fail in many elementary business situations.

A third form of optimization is known as extremum-finding. The linear programming procedure is the prototype extremum-finding algorithm. Linear programming, which became significant with the discovery of the simplex algorithm, assures that the optimum will be found efficiently in linear allocation problems. Other extremum-finding procedures are available for optimizing decisions about inventory levels, equipment replacement, and some simple queueing situations. Extremum-finding algorithms require that the model be formulated according to specific assumptions.

When a model does not fulfill the requirements for either calculus or extremum-finding, a direct search for the optimum becomes necessary. In this book we will deal in some detail with search in conjunction with simulation. (The word *search* here is not to be confused with *search theory,* which is a particular type of model dealing with situations in which one object is searching for another.)

The problem of searching for an optimum can be compared to that of finding the peak of a mountain. A better analogy for business situations is finding the peak of a range of mountains in multidimensional space, of nearly equal height on a foggy day, under conditions where landslides and earthquakes keep shifting the terrain. In the calculus we are able to describe the shape of the mountain with algebraic equations and can compute the location of the peak. With an extremum-finding algorithm we take advantage of certain properties of the mountain so that by going from ridge to ridge (to press the analogy further) the search always proceeds uphill in an efficient way to the peak. In some cases we do not know the shape of the mountain nor any particular property of its surface and, therefore, we must simply search around for the peak. We can sometimes, as we will discuss, take advantage of the fact that we can tell uphill from downhill and that the peak is always on the uphill side.

Developing a simulation is only half the battle. The other half is using the simulation to search for optimum decisions. Sometimes this search is purely intuitive; sometimes it is made under a set of guidelines or rules of thumb (called a heuristic search); sometimes it is made by using more formal techniques, such as hill climbing or random search. In Chapter 9, we will deal with these search problems in detail.

If you are still vague about what a simulation is read Appendix 1A.

the characteristics of simulation models[*] 1-6

To clarify the nature of simulation, a number of the characteristics of simulations are defined.

Static–Dynamic

A simulator may be used to represent both dynamic and static situations. In most operations research studies, we are interested in dynamic models; for example, a simulation describing the sales of a new product. Occasionally certain static problems are of interest, and, typically, these are problems of space allocation or plant design.

Aggregate–Detailed

One of the most important characteristics of a simulator is its degree of aggregation. In simulating a manufacturing company, for example, we can represent every operation performed by each person, the transfer of every piece of relevant information, and all the other details. On the

* Adapted with permission from Chapter 2 of *Progress in Operations Research,* Vol. III, *op. cit.*

other hand, we can construct a very aggregate model in which only the gross quantities—total sales, total materials, and people flows, overall costs, and so forth—are represented.

The level of detail in a model is usually determined by the specific objectives of the modeling effort. In a study of overall resource allocations, a detailed model may be inappropriate by being too expensive to construct and run in relation to the information needed. On the other hand, if the problem is to evaluate alternative manufacturing methods, a detailed model of at least a part of the enterprise will have to be created.

Physical–Behavioral

The situation being modeled may contain only physical processes, such as orbiting vehicle, or it may involve only human behavior, such as decision making in the United States Senate. Most simulation models involve aspects of both. Simulation has been used quite successfully in operational systems containing physical systems and a behavioral component that is limited to routine decisions made by lower level management. The potential of simulation for the analysis of more complex behavior is very great. We will discuss this in Chapter 11.

Computer–Human

The kind of mechanism used to carry out the simulation procedure is an important factor. At one extreme there is the all-computer simulation in which the entire procedural model is executed on a computer. However, there are also models in which some of the behavioral subroutines have not been specified; here, the analyst allows a human to carry out these subroutines on line as the simulation proceeds. We define *gaming* as any simulation in which there is a human-determined component of the model. Thus, at the other extreme are the all-human simulations, often called *games.* Many studies of political situations are carried out through the use of such games [e.g., Guetzkow et al., 1963]. In recent years there has been a growing use of combination simulations in which a computer represents the physical, economic, and other well-defined processes, and humans, through role playing, represent the decision-making components. In some cases, human participation is included to educate the player to the difficulties of making those decisions dictated by the role [Greenlaw, et al., 1962]. In other instances the players are introduced because the researcher does not have sufficient information to create the procedural model for that part of the system. The players then simulate the part of the process not well understood so that the entire model can be used to make predictions [Bass, 1964].

Recursive–Quasi-equilibrium

There are two approaches to the operation of dynamic models: the recursive and the quasi-equilibrium. The recursive approach requires that the state of the system at any given time be derived *within the model* from the conditions at earlier times. In very complex situations, (such as models of the economy), however, econometricians have found it useful to take a different approach. In models of a national economy the interactions between the variables are very complex and the time interval being simulated is quite large (e.g., a year). The economy involves the operation of large, decentralized markets where goods or services are offered and purchased. Wages and prices at equilibrium result from the net effect of many transactions in several interacting markets. These interactions are represented by a set of simultaneous equations that must be solved each time period [Naylor, 1966, ch. 6]. Thus, the computations for a single year are lengthy; the analyst usually examines the results after each year (or other time unit) and may adjust the values of key coefficients according to judgment or special information not put into the model. This approach is called the quasi-equilibrium method. Economists are now using recursive models more extensively, as they are more explicit and permit longer range extrapolations.

Continuous–Discrete

The variables in a simulation may change in any of four ways: (1) in a continuous fashion at any point in time, (2) in a discrete fashion, but at any point in time, (3) in a discrete fashion and only at certain points in time, or (4) in a continuous fashion, but only at discrete points in time. The nature of the variables used depends upon the situation modeled, the purposes of the model, and the kind of computational facility available. In general, more aggregate models tend to use variables that are continuous in value, but often discrete in time. For example, difference equations are used typically in econometric models. For many studies of whole enterprises and of socio-economic phenomena, continuous variables lead to valid, low-cost models. For more detailed models, the discrete nature of the real world becomes evident; there are individual orders, machines, people, and transactions. These models will be discrete in both values (e.g., machine number) and along the time dimension.

Size of Time Quanta

In models with variables that change at specific times the simulation provides a snapshot of the system at each point. A dimension of a simulation is the size of the time unit (the smallest time between two points) to be used. This size relates directly to the degree of aggregation in the model. In aggregate models the time quantum is often a year, sometimes a decade. Detailed models use time quanta of days, minutes, even microseconds.

Deterministic–Stochastic

Most situations in the real world have stochastic (randomly varying) properties because of real (or assumed) ignorance of details. Sometimes these properties must be modeled explicitly, but it is often sufficient to model situations as if they were deterministic by using expected values of the variables. Both deterministic and stochastic simulations are used.

13

1-7 overview

In this book we will concentrate on simulations that are dynamic, detailed, and generally contain a behavioral component. We deal with all-computer simulations that are recursive. In general, we will concentrate on representing processing of discrete units in operational situations so that the appropriate unit of time is a second, a minute, or at most, a day. We will examine both stochastic and deterministic simulations.

The word simulation to us *implies* a dynamic process. There are many static problems that have been solved by a series of numerical computations that might be called a simulation. For example, consider the problem of laying out machinery on the floor of a plant. We may lay out the model of the floor on graph paper and represent machines by small cardboard cutouts. We may then do a search of alternative layouts to find the optimum one in terms of flow and other criteria. The result, however, is a static layout not a dynamic on-going process (as we would have if we were to represent the *operation* of the shop).

Dynamic models are generally built upon the analyst's understanding of the elements of *sub*systems. The understanding of each subsystem is expressed by a symbolic representation of the interactions. The analyst's understanding of a subsystem may be theoretically derived; it may come from observation and experimentation; or it may simply be the formalization of the analyst's experience. The procedural model combines these submodels into a complete model. Solution to the complete model by simulation provides an understanding of the overall system that, a priori, the analyst does not have.

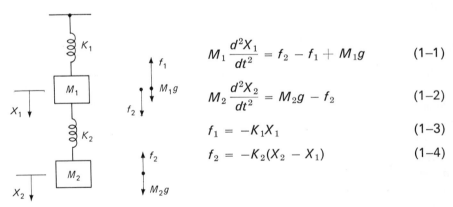

$$M_1 \frac{d^2X_1}{dt^2} = f_2 - f_1 + M_1g \qquad (1–1)$$

$$M_2 \frac{d^2X_2}{dt^2} = M_2g - f_2 \qquad (1–2)$$

$$f_1 = -K_1X_1 \qquad (1–3)$$

$$f_2 = -K_2(X_2 - X_1) \qquad (1–4)$$

Figure 1–2 A typical physical system which can be analyzed using classical mathematics.

The classical approach to dynamic systems uses differential equations as the modeling framework. The subsystem or element relationships are expressed as algebraic relationships between differentials. The element dynamics generally require the assumption that (1) the variables and most of their derivatives are continuous and (2) the relationships are stable over time.

Figure 1–2 illustrates a typical classical analysis. The equations express the interactions for each subsystem. Equation 1–1 represents the dynamics of mass 1; equation 1–2, mass 2; and equations 1–3 and 1–4 of the two springs. This set of equations becomes the model to predict the motion of the masses X_1 and X_2. These relationships are assumed to hold over all time. The solution to the differential equations provides the prediction of the dynamic behavior of the *entire* interacting system.

In simulation the philosophy of approach is the same. Understandings about the subsystems are incorporated into a model to produce predictions of overall system behavior. In simulating, however, a computer program rather than a set of differential equations provides the model framework; furthermore, simulation models do not require specific forms for the subsystem relationships. Continuity is not required and relationships can change with time. In simulation we look at how subsystems change over a finite, but small, time rather than at an *instant,* as in classical analysis. (We can deal with instants only if continuity can be assumed.)

The most significant difference between procedural and symbolic models is the method each uses to characterize time. In symbolic models, time is one of the variables in a set of differential equations. The equations represent the system in a static (multidimensional) time-space. The entire path of the system can be derived, and time could go backward or forward. In simulation, time retains a unidirectional characteristic, and the operation of the model period by period represents the dynamics of the system.

There are a number of other differences as well as a number of similarities between procedures for constructing simulation and symbolic models. The following eight chapters explore the simulation approach. In Chapter 2, the difference between symbolic and simulation models for representing dynamic systems is illustrated by an example. Chapter 3 is devoted to an overview of the strategic steps required to construct and use a simulation model. In Chapter 4, we examine the model-building process that applies to the construction of all model types (i.e., descriptive, physical, symbolic, or procedural). Chapters 5 and 6 examine the question of selecting the best computer language for programming the simulator. Chapters 7, 8, and 9 discuss detailed questions concerning the construction of a simulator, the analysis of its output, and the design of experiments to gain information from it. The last three chapters present examples of simulation uses and discussions of possible future uses of simulation techniques.

references

Ackoff, R. L., *Scientific Method: Optimizing Applied Research Decisions,* Wiley, New York, 1962.

Ackoff, R. L., and B. H. P. Rivett, *A Manager's Guide to Operations Research*, Wiley, New York, 1964.

Bass, B. M., "Business Gaming for Organizational Research," *Management Science*, Vol. 10, No. 8, April 1964, pp. 545–55.

Greenlaw, P. S., L. W. Herron, and R. H. Rawdon, *Business Simulation in Industrial and University Education*, Prentice-Hall, Englewood Cliffs, N. J., 1962.

Guetzkow, H., et al., *Simulation in International Relations*, Prentice-Hall, Englewood Cliffs, N. J., 1963.

Hammersley, J. M., and D. C. Handscomb, *Monte Carlo Methods*, Wiley, New York, 1964.

Korn, G., "Hybrid Computer Monte Carlo Techniques," *Simulation*, Vol. 5, No. 4, October 1965, pp. 234–47.

McDaniels, H., *An Introduction to Decision Logic Tables*, Wiley, New York, 1968.

Naylor, T., et al., *Computer Simulation Techniques*, Wiley, New York, 1966.

exercises

1–1 Review recent operations research literature (e.g., *Management Science*, *Operations Research, Journal of Industrial Engineering*) and identify about ten applications of specific models. Classify these models as symbolic (and, if they are, indicate whether or not numerical methods were used in finding their solutions) or procedural (simulation). Also, describe the simulation models according to the scheme in Section 1–7.

1–2 Survey the literature to determine if either physical models or analog computation has been used to model operational systems in industry, the military, or government.

appendix 1A

A Do-It-Yourself Simulation*

The best way to understand how a computer can simulate an operational situation is to work out a problem. Consider a situation in which machines fail from time to time. As there is only one repairman, sometimes a machine is out of use for a while before repair starts.

There are only three machines. Thus, the failure of a machine changes the odds for another failure. (For example, if all three machines are out of order, there is no chance for another failure, until at least one of the machines is repaired.) We will assume that the statistics for the repair time are of a type not easily analyzed.

Let us now create a simulation for this situation and see how we could begin to accumulate data about machine utilization (the percent of time that the machines are actually available).

Numeric Representation of Shop Conditions

We will create our simulator by use of some three-by-five cards, which will represent the data being manipulated, and by a specific procedure which you can execute. This procedure is analogous to a program to be executed by a computer.

* Extracted with permission from R. L. Sisson, *Management Science Selections*, Data Processing Digest, Inc., 6820 La Tijera Blvd., Los Angeles, Calif., 90045, 1967.

First, consider a layout for the data as shown in Figure 1A–1. The locations represent a card or deck of cards. The nature of each of the cards involved is described as follows.

Time. Number the cards from zero to, say, thirty and place this deck, in sequence, in the upper left-hand corner of a table. These numbers are clock times. Turning one of these cards over will represent the passage of fifteen minutes. Thus, each card represents a time unit as measured in quarter-hour periods.

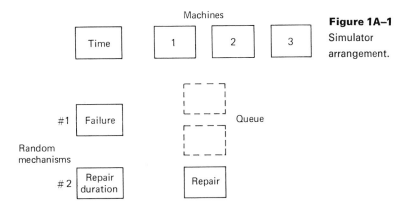

Figure 1A–1
Simulator arrangement.

Machines. Create three cards labeled "machine one," "machine two," and "machine three," and place these in the three spots as shown in Figure 1A–1. These cards will represent the status of a machine. Note that they do not represent the physical position of the machine. When the machine cards are in these normal positions, the machine is operating. When the cards are moved into the queue or repair position, the machine is waiting for repair or being repaired, respectively.

It is convenient also to place on the machine cards a table for accumulating data. This table would have a column for entering times at which the machine fails and the times when the machine is returned to operating condition.

Machine two		
Down time	Return time	Down duration
_____	_____	_____
_____	_____	_____
_____	_____	_____

The last column, which is the difference between the first two, will represent the duration of down periods. At the end of the simulation, the down time may be accumulated and used to compute machine utilization statistics.

Representing Uncertainty

We will need two other mechanisms that generate numbers according to a statistical distribution. Let us look at the one for generating failures. Assume that experience has shown that a machine fails in an unpredictable

17

way, once every ten quarter-hour periods. We might represent this mechanism by creating a deck of ten cards, nine of which we mark with "no," and one marked with "yes." Create such a deck and place it in the random mechanism area—for failures. Your intuition will confirm the fact that if we shuffle and select one card at a given time period, we can determine whether a particular machine has failed at that time or not, and that this procedure will approximate the statistical distribution we had derived from machine records. We will, of course, repeat this procedure for each machine in each period.

Let us assume that our study of shop history has shown that the statistics of service time are these: Out of every ten repairs (on the average), three are serviced in one fifteen-minute time period, two are serviced in two time periods, three are serviced in three time periods, one is serviced in four time periods, and two in five time periods.

In order to simulate this kind of a service durations statistical distribution, we can create another deck of ten cards.

On 3 cards write 1
" 2 " " 2
" 2 " " 3
" 1 " " 4
" ·2 " " 5

If we shuffle these cards, draw one, and interpret the number on the card as the repair duration for the particular case under study, then we have a mechanism for representing the statistical distribution or the variation in repair time as we believe it to actually occur.

Simulation Procedure

Now we need a procedure that will cause this data and the random mechanisms to represent our repair process. The formulation of this procedure is critical and a part of the simulation process that requires some skill. However, an examination of the procedure will illustrate some of the principles of developing a simulation.

Read over the procedure for simulating the shop in Figure 1A–2. Let us follow it through. We start by advancing time. This is represented by turning over a time card.

Failures

We now have to examine the various machines to see if any have failed. Steps 2 through 7 accomplished this activity. We observe whether machine one is operating or not. (If it is not, it cannot fail again.) If it is, we use our first random mechanism to determine if the machine fails at this time (step 3). We do this by selecting a card at random. If it does not break down, we will go on to step 6. If it does break down, we can represent the change in status by moving the machine card from its operation position to the queue area. In order to accumulate statistics, we will record the current clock time in the down-time column on the machine card. Clock time is the number on the time card facing up.

Set up: Put the cards in place. Set all the machines in operating positions.
Start the simulation.

(1) Turn over a time card. If there are no more cards, go to step 15.
(2) Is machine one operating? (Is there a card in operating position?)
   If no, go to 6; if yes, go to 3.
(3) Select a card at random from random mechanism 1.
   If it says "no," go to 6; if "yes," go to 4.
(4) Record the clock time as the down time on the machine one card.
(5) Move the machine one card to top of queue.
(6) Repeat 2–5 with two in place of the underlined one, i.e., for machine
   two. If two is just completed, then:
(7) Repeat 2–5 for machine three.
(8) Is there a card in repair?
   If no, go to 11; if yes, go to 9.
(9) Does the return time (last entry) equal the clock time?
   If no, go to 1; if yes, go to 10.
(10) Return the machine card to its operating position.
(11) Move all the cards in the queue down so that first one enters repair.
   If there are no cards in the queue, go to 1; if there are cards, go to 12.
(12) Select a card at random from random mechanism 2.
(13) Add the number on the selected card to the clock and enter the sum as
   return time on the card in repair.
(14) Go to 1.
(15) Compute down durations: (return time) − (down time).
(16) Sum down durations = total down time.
(17) Compute average machine utilization =

$$\frac{3 \text{ (last clock time)} - \text{(total down time)}}{3 \text{ (last clock time)}}$$

(18) Stop.

We now repeat this process for machines two and three. (We have
abbreviated this process in steps 6 and 7.) We now have adjusted part
of the shop for the current time period; namely, we have adjusted for all
failures that may have occurred. Now we must examine the repair process.

Repair

In step 8, we determine whether the machine in repair, if any, has
completed service. We can do this by matching the clock time with the
return time noted on the card in the repair position (if there is no card
there, we skip this step). If the service is completed at this time period,
we would return the machine card to its operating position as identified
by the machine number (step 10).

These steps represent the change in status of the repair process due
to the completion. Since the repairman is now free, we have to determine
whether there is another machine that is down and requires his services.
We do this by observing whether there are any machine cards in the
queue (step 11). If not, we go back to step 1 and advance to the next
time period. If there are one or more machines waiting in the queue, we
move the last one into the service position. (Note here we are assuming
a first-come, first-served process. We could use the simulator to examine

19

other methods of determining which machine to service next.) All the other cards in the queue must be moved down one. Now determine how long this particular repair will take (step 12). Use our second random mechanism. Shuffle and select one card from the second batch. The number on this card will tell us the repair duration. By adding this repair duration to the current clock time, we can predict the completion time of this service.

We make this addition and write the completion time on the machine card as the "return time." (Even though the machine has not returned, we can, in our simulator, predict exactly when it will.) This serves both to

Figure 1A–3
Typical simu-
lation history.

Time	Events
1	—
2	—
3	—
4	—
5	—
6	—
7	—
8	Machine 1 fails Repair duration = 4 (12)*
9	—
10	—
11	—
12	Machine 1 returns
13	Machine 2 fails Repair duration = 5 (18)
14	—
15	Machine 3 fails
16	—
17	Machine 1 fails
18	Machine 2 returns Machine 3 to repair Repair duration = 3 (21)
19	—
20	—
21	Machine 3 returns Machine 1 to repair Repair duration = 3 (24)
22	—
23	Machine 2 fails
24	Machine 1 returns Machine 2 to repair Repair duration = 2 (26)
25	—
26	Machine 2 returns

*( ) = completion time.

record the data and to provide a notice for later processing as to whether this machine service is completed or not. (Recall how we used return time in step 9.) We have now adjusted the simulator to represent the repair process and we can advance time and see what happens next.

Steps 15 through 17 compute the output—machine utilization in this case—at the end of the run. Set up your cards and try executing the simulator for twenty or thirty periods in order to understand the process of simulation.

Figure 1A–3 lists the results of an actual simulation run for twenty-six periods. No failures occurred for the first seven periods. (Was it proper to start with no machine in repair?) At time 8, machine *one* failed, moved directly to the repair area, and a repair time of four was computed. This would give completion at time twelve. To examine the process in more detail, notice time eighteen in Figure 1A–3. Machine *two* has completed its repair time and returns to the operating position. Machine *three,* which has been waiting in the queue, moves into the repair position. The repair duration is computed as three and the completion time, therefore, is twenty-one. The simulator has simulated the process of the queue and repair service procedures.

At the end of the twenty-six periods, the machine cards would appear as shown in Figure 1A–4. The machine utilization turns out to be twenty-five down periods out of seventy-eight total machine periods, giving a machine utilization of approximately two thirds.

Machine one

Down Time	Return Time	Down Duration
8	12	4
17	24	7
		11

Machine two

Down Time	Return Time	Down Duration
13	18	5
23	26	3
		8

Machine three

Down Time	Return Time	Down Duration
15	21	6
		6

Total down periods: 25

Total periods 3 machines $\times$ 26 = 78

Machine utilization $\dfrac{78-25}{78} = \dfrac{53}{78}$

Figure 1A–4
Machine status at time 26.

21

We could rerun the simulator with a different set of service statistics in order to determine the improvement in machine utilization resulting from, say, a faster repairman. We could examine different procedures for selecting the next item from the queue. This might be useful, for example, if we wanted to be sure that machine *one* was up as much as possible.

Needless to say, the simulator should be run for many more than twenty-six periods in order to be sure that a good average picture of the situation is obtained; that is, that the results are not due to a chance sequence of events.

simulation and symbolic models of dynamic systems

introduction 2-1

Our purpose in this chapter is to compare the characteristics of simulation models with analytic methods and to introduce some basic concepts of simulation. The example chosen for this comparison is a production problem which, although hypothetical, is representative of a class of situations to which operations research has been applied effectively.

The initial problem can be represented by a symbolic model but such a representation does not permit analysis of all the interesting alternatives. When the solution to the problem is thus restricted to a particular subclass of available alternatives, the symbolic model can be solved by mathematics to deduce which alternative is optimal. However, when we consider slightly more complicated alternatives, the analytic procedures become intractable (no mathematical calculus is available for deducing solutions). After examining the characteristics of the complications that negate an analytic solution, we show how a simulation model enables us to handle the more complicated system. We then construct a simulation model of the total system and demonstrate the structural and functional properties of this model.

the problem situation 2-2

XYZ Company produces a variety of preserves (jellies and jams) for the retail trade. Recently, new equipment has been installed to automate the final packaging operation. The packaging operation involves four parallel production lines. The production lines are identical in processing capacity and sequence of operations and are independent of each other. XYZ offers a wide variety of products and a number of jar sizes; the scheduling is such that it is unlikely that more than two of the lines would be handling the same product or package size at the same time. All four lines operate twenty-four hours a day, five days a week.

A relatively high proportion of XYZ's production expenses are in the packaging operation. Management felt that costs were high enough that they could justify new equipment for automating the packaging operation. However, some difficulties have been encountered in integrating the components of the new system. In particular, the operation in which labels are attached to filled jars has not been satisfactory. The labeling operation is an intricate one and the equipment often needs adjustment so that the glue is positioned correctly, the labels go on straight, and the jars move smoothly through the unit without breakage.

Whenever such adjustments are required, the flow of products through the packaging system is disturbed because backlogs begin to build at the labeling operation. These backlogs create three adverse conditions: (1) they decrease the efficiency of packaging operations after the labeling operation because the through-put of products is below normal; (2) the number of broken or damaged (and therefore unusable) jars of product is increased; and (3) if the backlog is serious enough, it may force a reduction in the rate at which jars are processed in operations prior to labeling.

From previous experience with problems in the labeling operation, XYZ Company management designed the improved product packaging system with two features that they felt would minimize the adverse effects of labeling failures. First, the system was designed with excess labeling capacity; that is, there were more machines available than would be necessary to meet the demand of unlabeled jars if labelers were 100 percent efficient all the time. Analysis of the rate of arrival of unlabeled jars and the rate at which labeling machines could attach such labels showed that slightly more than four labeling machines operating all the time for any one production line could effectively handle the labeling operation. Management decided to install six labelers per production line. Thus, if one labeler was not operating the flow could still be handled by utilizing a stand-by labeler. If two were inoperative, unlabeled jars would begin to stack up at a slow rate. With three or more labelers not operating, the back-up would increase linearly with the number of inoperative labelers. Management felt that the extra capacity resulting from the additional labelers was worth the cost. (The question of how many excess labelers to have is an operations research problem, but will not be discussed here.)

Having installed this automated packaging system, XYZ management wanted to be sure that it was being utilized most efficiently. In particular, they are interested in the number of men to whom they should assign the task of adjusting the labeling machines. Because of the physical arrangement of the machines and the existing work rules, an adjuster cannot attend machines on more than one production line at a time but can be scheduled to shift periodically from one line to another. The labeling system is illustrated in Figure 2–1.

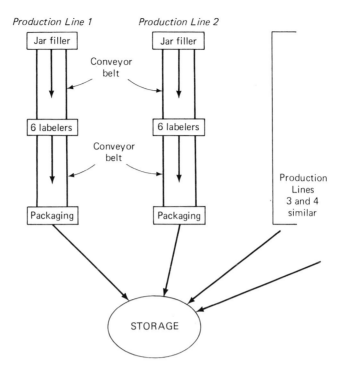

Figure 2–1
Production
labeling
operation at
XYZ Company.

Production Line 1   Production Line 2

Jar filler   Jar filler

Conveyor belt

6 labelers   6 labelers

Conveyor belt

Packaging   Packaging

Production Lines 3 and 4 similar

STORAGE

information required to determine 2-3
the optimal number of adjusters

In order to determine the system operating costs we must:

(1) Isolate the variables that affect these operating costs.
(2) Predict how these operating costs are affected by the number of adjusters employed (i.e., how costs are affected by the factor under control of the decision maker).

Observation of the current operation of the labeler system provides information about the costs under various operating conditions, the frequency with which machines require adjustment, and the time required to adjust a machine that is inoperative. Each of these factors is discussed in the following sections.

Operating Conditions and Costs

The cost factors that appear to be relevant to the solution of this problem include:

- the wages of adjusters
- the cost of idle machines
- the cost of decreased through-put
- the cost of damaged or otherwise unusable products created by the labeler being down

25

Before collecting cost data, some model has to be proposed so that we know what data to provide. Three models at three different levels of aggregation can be considered:

(1) Total costs = [Cost factor × Average number of labelers down per hour (among the six labelers)]
+ Labor costs

(2) Total costs = [Cost factor 1 × Total time 1 labeler is down per hour]
+ [Cost factor 2 × Total time 2 labelers are down per hour]
+
$\vdots$
+ [Cost factor 6 × Total time all labelers are down per hour]
+ Labor costs

Before stating the third and most detailed cost model, we will state the foregoing more concisely in symbols and also introduce the fact that down time is a function of the number of adjusters available.

$$TC(A) = C \cdot E(D_A) + A \cdot L \qquad (2\text{--}1)$$

where $TC(A)$ = Total cost per hour of operation when A adjusters are tending the labelers

L = Labor cost per hour for adjusters

C = Estimated cost to the system per machine hour of down time

$E(D_A)$ = Expected number of hours of down time, accumulated among the six labelers, per hour of system operation when A adjusters are tending the labelers

The second model can be stated

$$TC(A) = \sum_{j=1}^{6} C(j) \cdot E(D_A(j)) + A \cdot L \qquad (2\text{--}2)$$

where $TC(A)$ and L are as just defined, and

$C(j)$ = Estimated cost to the system per hour spent in the situation where j machines are inoperative and $6 - j$ machines are operating

$E(D_A(j))$ = Expected portion of an hour of system operation in which exactly j machines are inoperative when there are A adjusters tending the machines

The third model takes all cost effects explicitly into account. It represents: backlog length, which causes damage and reduced through-put in prior processes, and down time, which is costly in terms of unused capacity at the labeler and in subsequent facilities.

(3) Total costs = [Cost factor A × Individual labeler down times]
+ [(Cost factor B + Cost factor C) × (Individual labeler down times + Product backlog conditions)]

Or, symbolically,

$$TC(A) = \sum_{j=1}^{6} C_t(j) \cdot E(D_A(j))$$

$$+ \sum_{j=1}^{6} \sum_{q=0}^{\infty} (C_d(j, q) + C_p(j, q))E(D_A(j, q)) + A \cdot L \qquad (2-3)$$

where $TC(A)$, L, and $E(D_A(j))$ are defined as in Equation 2–2.

$C_t(j)$ = Cost of delayed *through-put* as a function of j, the number of machines inoperative

$C_d(j, q)$ = Cost of *damaged product* attributed to the backlog as a function of j, the number of machines inoperative, and q, the quantity of product delayed at the labeling operation (here q is termed the *backlog*)

$C_p(j, q)$ = Cost of *production delays* prior to the labeling operation as a function of j and q

$E(D_A(j, q))$ = Expected portion of an hour of system operation in which exactly j machines are inoperative and the backlog at the labeling operation is q items when there are A adjusters tending the machines

Earlier cost models needed only predictions of the proportion of time when 0, 1, 2, . . . , 6 labelers were inoperative. This model, however, requires an explicit measure of the likelihood of any particular backlog configuration occurring. To do this, we must estimate the joint probability $P(j, q)$ of j inoperative labelers *and* a product backlog of q items.

As we use successively more detailed models, we gain in accuracy of representation, but create two problems. (1) we require more detailed cost information, and (2) it becomes more difficult to predict the required probabilities of down time. The detailed cost information is more expensive to collect. It requires observations of more situations, each for some duration.

We can estimate the overall down time required in model 2–1 (that is, the $E(D_A)$) to a large extent by direct observation. The factors in model 2–2, $E(D_A(j))$, can be estimated for some conditions by queuing theory, as will be illustrated. Even for this model, however, it is difficult to estimate the factors mathematically if there is any complexity in the assignment of adjusters. Estimation of the factor in the third model, $E(D_A(j, q))$, is impossible by analytic means, but can be accomplished by simulation.

Assume that the staff of XYZ Company has found that the second cost model will give sufficiently accurate estimates and that the individual cost factors have been determined. These factors are given in Table 2–1. We will now turn our attention to estimating the down-time characteristics, that is the seven factors, $E(D_A(j))$ for $j = 0, 1, \ldots, 6$ and for typical A's: 1, 2, and 3 adjusters.

Table 2–1. Estimated Cost to the System per Minute of Inoperative Labeling Machine Time.

Number of Labelers Not Operating	Cost per Minute of Idle Time
0	$0.0
1	0.0
2	0.03
3	0.06
4	0.17
5	0.50
6	1.20

Distribution of Machine Failures

We make two assumptions about the conditions when machines require adjustments.

(1) There is no difference between the machines in regard to their patterns of failures, time required to make adjustments, or productivity rates when operating; that is, the machines are identical.

(2) When a labeler is operating, its chances of needing adjustment in any instant of time is a constant that is independent of the time elapsed since the machine was last adjusted; i.e., all machines fail completely at random.

For this example, assume that each machine requires adjustment on the average of once every fifteen minutes of operation (i.e., the mean time between failures is fifteen minutes).

Distribution of Adjustment (Service) Time

The assumptions regarding adjuster characteristics are similar to those for the labeling-machine failure rate. Specifically these assumptions are:

(1) There is no difference between adjusters in the time required to make an adjustment on any of the machines.

(2) When an adjuster is repairing a machine, his chances of completing the repair in any instance of time is a constant that is independent of the time when the adjustment was started.

For this example, the average (or mean) time required to adjust a machine once work is begun is five minutes. The mean time between failure and mean adjustment time are determined by observations.

Having presented the assumptions about the labeling operation, let us turn to specific models for representing the effects of alternative numbers of adjusters. Following the approach discussed in Chapter 1 (see Figure 1–1), we start by attempting to find an analytic model that fits our assumptions about the system. We first try an analytic model based on a part of queuing theory known as machine interference. (The machine interference problem is reported in Feller [1950, ch. 17] and Cox and Smith [1963, ch. IV].)

a mathematical model of the 2-4 labeling operation

Presenting some of the theoretical derivation behind the queuing-theory solution will enable us to show why the assumptions lead to a closed-form prediction and what happens when these conditions are not met. As we shall see, the most critical assumption in the queuing formulation relates to stability of relationships over time. (Those readers who are familiar with queuing theory or those who wish to skip this theoretical discussion can go directly to Section 2–5 without loss of continuity.)*

Let us begin by examining the statistical implications of the fact that the probability of an operating labeler requiring adjustment in a small interval of time is a constant and independent of the time since it last required adjustment. It will be shown that the probability distribution that describes the chances of a labeler failing exactly t time units after its last repair is a negative exponential distribution, i.e.,

$$\text{Prob. (labeler fails at } t) = \lambda e^{-\lambda t} \qquad (2\text{–}4)$$

where $1/\lambda$ is the mean time between machine failures.

Assume this relationship is true. We should then be able to show that the assumption holds. The probability of a machine that has not failed for t time periods requiring adjustment in a small interval t to $t + \delta$ can be derived as follows:

Prob. (failure in t to $t + \delta \mid$ no failure to t)

$$= \frac{\text{Prob. (fails after } t \text{ and before } t + \delta)}{\text{Prob. (fails after } t)}$$

$$= \frac{\displaystyle\int_{t}^{t+\delta} \lambda e^{-\lambda x}\, dx}{\displaystyle\int_{t}^{\infty} \lambda e^{-\lambda x}\, dx} = \frac{e^{-\lambda t} - e^{-\lambda(t+\delta)}}{e^{-\lambda t}} = 1 - e^{-\lambda \delta}$$

*Material set in different type and with a rule at the left appears at several places in this book. Such mathematical presentations may be skipped without interrupting the continuity of the text.

This result is consistent with our assumption about the characteristics of the labelers; namely, that the probability of a labeler failing in an instant of time is a constant (i.e., λ and δ are fixed) and independent of the time since it last required adjustment (i.e., it is not a function of t).

It is possible to simplify the foregoing probability expression. Using the Taylor series expansion for the exponential expression, this probability becomes

$$1 - \left[1 - \lambda\delta + \frac{(\lambda\delta)^2}{2!} - \frac{(\lambda\delta)^3}{3!} + \cdots + \right]$$

If δ is very small, such that $(\lambda\delta)^i$ is approximately zero for powers greater than 1, then

Prob. (a machine that has not failed for t time periods requires adjustment in t to $t + \delta$) = $\lambda\delta$

Using an argument exactly parallel to that just presented, it can be shown that the probability distribution describing the time when an adjuster will complete repairs on the machine he is currently adjusting is given by

$$\text{Prob. (adjustment completed at } t) = \mu e^{-\mu t} \qquad (2\text{--}5)$$

where $1/\mu$ is the mean time an adjuster required to complete a repair. The probability of a repair being completed in the small interval t to $t + \delta$, given that it is not completed by time t, is $\mu\delta$. Again, we assumed that δ is small enough so that second-order factors can be ignored.

The relevant information needed to describe the behavior of the system is the probability of its being in some state S at time t and the probability of associated state shifts that may occur between t and $t + \delta$. At any instant of time, the state of the system is completely specified by the number of labelers operating. Consider a general system containing M labeling machines and A adjusters. For the case where $m(\geq A)$ labelers are in need of adjustment, all the adjusters are busy and $m - A$ of the machines are down but not being adjusted. If m ($\leq A$) labelers are inoperative, then $A - m$ of the adjusters are idle. Since we do not distinguish between each of the M machines and each of the A adjusters, it makes no difference which machine or adjuster is in which state. Therefore, we can use statistics that describe the system without distinguishing between particular adjusters or labelers.

For a notational description of the state of the labeler system, let $P_i(t)$ = Prob. [i of the labelers are inoperative at time t]. From our previous discussions, we choose a small interval of time, δ, such that there is a constant probability of an operating machine failing or a working repairman completing an adjustment in δ (namely, $\lambda\delta$ and $\mu\delta$, respectively). These probabilities are independent of the state of the system prior to t.

The following analysis could be carried out for our six-labeler problem. However, for purposes of illustration, we derive the model for a four-labeler, two-adjuster problem. Extensions to the six-labeler problem are apparent.

$$P_0(t + \delta) = P_0(t)(1 - 4\lambda\delta) + P_1(t)(\mu\delta) \tag{2-6}$$

$$P_1(t + \delta) = P_0(t)4\lambda\delta + P_1(t)(1 - 3\lambda\delta - \mu\delta) + P_2(t)2\mu\delta \tag{2-7}$$

This equation, for example, means that the probability of just one labeler being down at $t + \delta$ is equal to:

- The probability of no labelers down at t and one of four failing between t and $t + \delta$ (which is $4\lambda\delta$)
- plus the probability of one labeler being down at t and still down at $t + \delta$ with no additional failures between t and $t + \delta$
- plus the probability of two labelers being down at t and one being repaired between t and $t + \delta$ $(2\mu\delta)$

$$P_2(t + \delta) = P_1(t)3\lambda\delta + P_2(t)(1 - 2\lambda\delta - 2\mu\delta) + P_3(t)2\mu\delta \tag{2-8}$$

$$P_3(t + \delta) = P_2(t)2\lambda\delta + P_3(t)(1 - \lambda\delta - 2\mu\delta) + P_4(t)2\mu\delta \tag{2-9}$$

Since there are two adjusters, the probability of one repair is $2\mu\delta$ as long as two or more labelers are down.

$$P_4(t + \delta) = P_3(t)\lambda\delta + P_4(t)(1 - 2\mu\delta) \tag{2-10}$$

These equations are justified only if we choose the size of δ small enough to prohibit multiple events. To show this suppose we were modeling a system with a possibility of zero, one or two events occurring in the interval δ. Under this assumption, Equation 2-6, for example, would have to be rewritten to show all possible multiple event ways of entering $P_0(t + \delta)$ (i.e., all machines operating):

(1) No failures at time t and either (a) no failures in δ or (b) one failure and one repair in δ.
(2) One failure at time t and one repair in δ.
(3) Or, two failures at time t and two repairs in δ.

When we assume δ was small in using the Taylor expansion, we were making a similar assumption.

Equations 2-6 through 2-10 provide a complete mathematical representation of the dynamic behavior of a four-machine, two-adjuster system. Now we are interested in using this model to estimate the cost of operating this labeler system, and so we must estimate the *steady-state* expectation of each down configuration. That is, we will predict the proportion of time the system will spend in each state after conditions have stabilized following the start-up of the system.

We can determine steady-state conditions directly from Equations 2-6 through 2-10. First, convert the expressions to finite differences representing the *change* in probability of being in each of the five states.

By rearranging the equations, we obtain

$$\frac{P_0(t + \delta) - P_0(t)}{\delta} = -4\lambda P_0(t) + \mu P_1(t) \tag{2-11}$$

$$\frac{P_1(t + \delta) - P_1(t)}{\delta} = -(3\lambda + \mu)P_1(t) + 4\lambda P_0(t) + 2\mu P_2(t) \tag{2-12}$$

$$\frac{P_2(t + \delta) - P_2(t)}{\delta} = -(2\lambda + 2\mu)P_2(t) + 3\lambda P_1(t) + 2\mu P_3(t) \tag{2-13}$$

$$\frac{P_3(t + \delta) - P_3(t)}{\delta} = -(\lambda + 2\mu)P_3(t) + 2\lambda P_2(t) + 2\mu P_4(t) \tag{2-14}$$

$$\frac{P_4(t + \delta) - P_4(t)}{\delta} = -2\mu P_4(t) + \lambda P_3(t) \tag{2-15}$$

The time-independent, steady-state solution is obtained by setting the difference equations equal to zero and solving the resulting equations. (Setting the differences equal to zero assumes that the system is in steady-state; the probabilities at $t + \delta$ are the same as at t). Removing the time subscript (which is irrelevant for steady-state analysis) we thus obtain

$$4\lambda P_0 = \mu P_1 \tag{2-16}$$

$$(3\lambda + \mu)P_1 = 4\lambda P_0 + 2\mu P_2 \tag{2-17}$$

$$(2\lambda + 2\mu)P_2 = 3\lambda P_1 + 2\mu P_3 \tag{2-18}$$

$$(\lambda + 2\mu)P_3 = 2\lambda P_2 + 2\mu P_4 \tag{2-19}$$

$$2\mu P_4 = \lambda P_3 \tag{2-20}$$

These equations can be solved recursively for P_i $(i \geq 1)$ in terms of P_0; P_0 can then be determined using the fact that

$$\sum_{i=0}^{4} P_i = 1.0$$

For the foregoing example these calculations yield

$$P_0 = \frac{1}{1 + 4\left(\frac{\lambda}{\mu}\right) + \frac{4 \cdot 3}{2}\left(\frac{\lambda}{\mu}\right)^2 + \frac{4 \cdot 3 \cdot 2}{2^2}\left(\frac{\lambda}{\mu}\right)^3 + \frac{4 \cdot 3 \cdot 2}{2^3}\left(\frac{\lambda}{\mu}\right)^4} \tag{2-21}$$

$$P_1 = 4\left(\frac{\lambda}{\mu}\right) \tag{2-22}$$

$$P_2 = 6\left(\frac{\lambda}{\mu}\right)^2 \tag{2-23}$$

$$P_3 = 6\left(\frac{\lambda}{\mu}\right)^3 \tag{2-24}$$

$$P_4 = 3\left(\frac{\lambda}{\mu}\right)^4 \tag{2-25}$$

Feller [1950, ch. 17] shows that for the general case of M machines and A adjusters, the steady-state probabilities can be obtained using the fact that

$$\sum_{m=1}^{M} P_m = 1.0$$

and the following recursive relationships

$$(m + 1)\mu P_{m+1} = (M - m)\lambda P_m \qquad \text{when } m < A \qquad (2\text{--}26)$$

$$A\mu P_{m+1} = (M - m)\lambda P_m \qquad \text{when } m \geq A \qquad (2\text{--}27)$$

solution to the analytic model with a fixed **2-5** number of adjusters scheduled

The results of queuing theory applied to the basic labeling problem give the following rule for computing the down times. (This summarizes the results of Section 2–4 in the problem terminology.)

All of the $E(D_A(j))$ can be expressed in terms of $E(D_A(0))$, the probability of no labelers down, by the following rules. (M is the number of labelers.)

For $j < A$:

$$E(D_A(j + 1)) = \frac{(M - j)\lambda}{(j + 1)\mu} E(D_A(j)) \qquad (2\text{--}26a)$$

For $j \geq A$:

$$E(D_A(j + 1)) = \frac{(M - j)\lambda}{A\mu} E(D_A(j)) \qquad (2\text{--}27a)$$

The numerical values can be obtained by using the fact that the sum of all probabilities adds to one.

$$\sum_{i=1}^{M} P_i = 1.0$$

Substituting the values for this problem, we obtain the expected down times given in Table 2–2, using the problem parameters:

$$M = 6 \qquad A = 1, 2, 3 \qquad \mu = 0.2 \qquad \lambda = 0.067$$

Number of Adjusters	P_0	P_i = Probability of i machines not operating					
		P_1	P_2	P_3	P_4	P_5	P_6
1	0.054	0.106	0.176	0.232	0.230	0.152	0.050
2	0.155	0.308	0.254	0.168	0.083	0.027	0.004
3	0.178	0.352	0.292	0.128	0.042	0.009	0.001

Table 2–2. Steady-State Probabilities of Number of Labelers Requiring Adjustment

The total cost is then given by Equation 2–2.

$$TC(A) = \sum_{j=1}^{6} C(j) \cdot E(D_A(j)) + A \cdot L$$

where $TC(A)$ is the expected hourly cost to the system when A adjusters are hired, L is the labor cost per hour (i.e., \$8), $E(D_A(j))$ is the probability that j labelers will be inoperative when A adjusters are tending them (from Table 2–2), and C_j is the cost per hour to the system when j machines are inoperative (from Table 2–1). These computations are shown in Table 2–3.

Table 2–3. Cost to the System as a Function of the Number of Adjusters

Number of Adjusters, (A)	Labor Cost per Hour of Operation	Down-time Cost per Hour of Operation	Total Cost per Hour of Operation
1	$ 8	$11.74	$19.74
2	16	3.11	19.11
3	24	1.86	25.86

2-6 more complicated alternatives and an attempt at an analytic solution

Table 2–3 shows that, although there is little economic difference between the effect of hiring one versus two adjusters, either of these alternatives will be superior to hiring three or more of them. Although the total cost of one versus two adjusters is nearly equivalent, the effects on the system are quite different. Hiring only one adjuster produces efficient utilization of labor; however, there is a high incidence of machine down time. On the other hand, hiring two adjusters creates better utilization of machines; but this is achieved only through higher labor costs.

By interpolating the foregoing results, we might conjecture that the system could be operated even more economically if each production line could be assigned the equivalent of one and one-half adjusters. Although it is difficult to hire half a man, the economic effects of such a system can be approximated by hiring two types of adjusters with different functional responsibilities.

(1) Fixed adjusters who are responsible for the adjustment of the six labelers on only one of the production lines.

(2) Rotating adjusters who have a specifically scheduled cycle of responsibility between two or more of the production lines.

For example, the effect of one and a quarter adjusters on each production line can be approximated by assigning one fixed operator to each of the four production lines and one rotating operator who spends fifteen minutes adjusting labelers on each production line (i.e., he has a cycle time of one hour). It is worth examining the efficiency of the total system with rotating adjusters if it can be done inexpensively. If rotating adjusters yield a large reduction in total expenses, management might decide to adopt rotating assignments.

If rotating adjusters are introduced into the labeler repair system, the mathematical queuing theory model derived previously and summarized by Equations 2–26 and 2–27 cannot be used to represent the state of the system. Previously, the only relevant time variable was the expected state of the system at time $t + \delta$ conditional upon its state at time t. Since the factors in the system depended only on the number of labelers and the number of adjusters—factors that do not change over time, we are able to predict steady-state conditions (i.e., without explicit representation of time).

In order to describe mathematically the failure and repair of the labelers when rotating adjusters are employed, we must explicitly include time as a variable in the model. The factors affecting the state of the system are no longer time independent; the number of adjusters available *is* a function of time. This means the methods by which steady-state solutions were obtained for the fixed adjuster system are not valid. The rotating adjuster system has a cyclical oscillation between the steady-state solutions previously predicted for one and two fixed adjusters. Figure 2–2 shows the transient conditions for a schedule of one fixed adjuster and one rotating adjuster who spends one-half hour at this production line and one-half hour away from it.

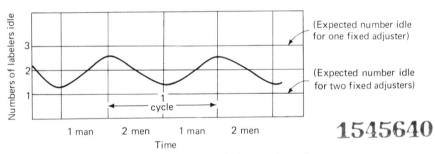

1545640

Figure 2–2 Transient conditions using fixed plus rotating adjusters.

We can describe the state of the labeler system in which one rotating and one fixed adjuster are employed by considering a double-time subscripted state probability.

$P_n(t, C)$ = Prob. [n labelers are inoperative after C complete cycles of the rotating adjuster and t through the C + 1st cycle.]

A cycle begins the first instant that both the fixed and rotating adjusters are tending the machines and ends the last instant that only the fixed adjuster is working. Thus, if a complete cycle lasts T and the rotating adjuster is available for T_A during a cycle,

$$A = 2 \quad \text{if } 0 < t \leq T_A$$
$$A = 1 \quad \text{if } T_A < t \leq T \qquad (2\text{–}28)$$

For any t and C we can define the state of the system at $(t + \delta, C)$ in terms of the possible states at (t, C) and the transitions in δ. Our ability to formulate these equations shows that the mathematical difficulty arising

35

from introducing a rotating adjuster is not one of describing how changes occur in the system. We *can* formulate the symbolic model. The problem is to deduce from the model an expression for the expected down time behavior $E(D_A(j))$ from which operating costs can be derived.

We can partially simplify the problem of time variation because we can show that after the start-up transient disappears, each cycle is indistinguishable from the next. After a great many cycles, the expected state of the system at time (t, C) will be equal to the expected state at $(t, C + 1)$. Thus we can make the following notational change

$$\lim_{C \to \infty} P_n(t, C) = P_n(t) \tag{2-29}$$

For the rotating- plus fixed-adjuster system, we can obtain expressions for $\Delta P_n(t)/\Delta t$ in a fashion similar to Equations 2–11 through 2–15. However, we cannot define a time-independent steady-state solution by setting this difference equation equal to zero. Therefore, the estimate of the cost of operating a system of fixed plus rotating adjusters, we must solve the following set of differential equations (analogous to Equations 2–11 through 2–15).

For $0 < t \leq T_A$ (2 adjusters):

$$\frac{\Delta P_0(t)}{\Delta t} = -6\lambda P_0(t) + \mu P_1(t)$$

$$\frac{\Delta P_1(t)}{\Delta t} = -(5\lambda + \mu)P_1(t) + 6\lambda P_0(t) + 2\mu P_2(t)$$

For $i = 2, 3, 4, 5$:

$$\frac{\Delta P_i(t)}{\Delta t} = -[(6 - i)\lambda + 2\mu]P_i(t)$$
$$+ [6 - (i - 1)]\lambda P_{i-1}(t) + 2\mu P_{i+1}(t)$$

$$\frac{\Delta P_6(t)}{\Delta t} = -2\mu P_6(t) + \lambda P_5(t)$$

For $T_A < t \leq T$ (1 adjuster):

$$\frac{\Delta P_0(t)}{\Delta t} = -6\lambda P_0(t) + \mu P_1(t)$$

For $i = 1, 2, 3, 4, 5$:

$$\frac{\Delta P_i(t)}{\Delta t} = -[(6 - i)\lambda + \mu]P_i(t)$$
$$+ [6 - (i - 1)]\lambda P_{i-1}(t) + \mu P_{i+1}(t)$$

$$\frac{\Delta P_6(t)}{\Delta t} = -\mu P_6(t) + \lambda P_5(t)$$

Present mathematical analysis is unable to provide a solution to this set of equations in the form of formulae (as Equations 2–21 through 2–25), primarily because the probabilities are a function of t.

Briefly, with a rotating-adjuster assignment the mathematical formulation cannot be solved to give a concise formula (as Equations 2–26 and 2–27) for determining the down time.

As we discussed in Chapter 1, research effort can follow any of three directions when unsolveable systems of equations, such as the one just given, arise. One procedure involves searching for other approximation models to the complete problem until a solvable mathematical model can be constructed. If the approximations involve only second-order errors, this procedure can yield the quickest and least expensive solution to the problem, but the probability of finding a useful approximation to a time-dependent system is low. A second (and usually economically infeasible) approach is to *develop* appropriate mathematical techniques. The third approach, simulation, offers a means of utilizing knowledge of the event-to-event transitions that permit explicit treatment of time variation. The labeler problem is typical of situations amenable to simulation because

(1) We are able to describe what is likely (in a probabilistic sense) to happen to the system over a small period of time.

(2) We cannot make mathematical predictions of how the system will behave in the long run.

(3) We need these long-run predictions in order to make policy recommendations.

a simulation model of the rotating adjuster 2-7
problem

The first step in developing the simulation is to translate the descriptions of the adjustment process into a form suitable for a simulation model. This requires a way of describing

(1) The state of the system at any point in time.

(2) How the system is likely to change in the next instant of time.

A set of variable values describes the state of the system. The technique commonly used to provide the second part of such a description is a flow chart. A flow chart is nothing more than an orderly representation of the sequence of events that may occur in each simulated time period. A simulation model of the system is developed by replacing the flow chart's partially qualitative description of what will occur by a precise, quantitative specification in the form of a computer program.

In developing this simulation it is necessary to represent probabilistic events: a labeler failure or the completion of an adjustment. The techniques for simulating probabilistic processes in general are discussed in Chapter 7; here we will describe the technique only to the extent needed for this example. As is shown next, we can model the failure-adjustment process if we can find a method to generate a set of *random numbers* that are independent of each other and that are equally likely to take on any value in the interval $0.0 \leq x \leq 1.0$. Considerable research has been devoted to finding a physical process or computer algorithm (procedure) that efficiently generates random numbers (see Chapter 7). Here assume that such random numbers are available.

Now suppose that at some instant of time a labeler is operating. The probability of that labeler failing in the interval t to $t + \delta$ is $\lambda\delta$, and the probability of its continuing to operate is $1 - \lambda\delta$. We can model this by generating a random number X and using the deterministic decision rule: "Machine fails if $X \leq \lambda\delta$ and continues to operate otherwise." In an analogous fashion we can describe the probability of a working repairman completing his repair in $\mu\delta$. (This process may be visualized in the following way. The random number generator is like a deck of, say, 1000 cards numbered from 0.0 to 0.999. Suppose the time interval δ is one and λ is $1/15 = 0.067$. A card is selected at random. If it is 0.067 or less, the machine is assumed to have failed, otherwise it has not. It seems clear that, after many drawings, failures will occur on the average of one in fifteen times.)

The important output of the simulation for our analysis is the length of time the system remains in each possible machine-failure condition. The flow chart can now be prepared to show the steps that simulate the failures and adjustments and records this desired output data. For convenience in introducing simulation methods we have chosen to advance time in this simulation on a unit-by-unit basis.

Figure 2–3 is a flow chart of the simulation model. It shows the procedure used to determine what, if any, changes have occurred in the simulated time interval t to $t + 1$. The status of the system is updated to reflect these changes and the relevant statistics are summarized. Time is then advanced and the process is repeated. Figure 2A–1, at the end of this chapter, is the corresponding FORTRAN program.

Although the flow chart enables us to specify how the simulation operates, three important problems remain to be solved before the simulator becomes operational. First, we must determine alternative operating conditions that are to be evaluated using the simulation model. This problem requires the specification of cycle lengths and the division of the adjuster's time within a cycle. The second problem is to decide what output we need from the simulator in order to analyze the cost of the system under alternative configurations. Third, we must determine the size of a unit of time in the simulator and the length of time the simulator must be run to obtain results that do not depend on the starting values used in the model. We will examine each of these problems.

Alternative Adjuster Schedules to Be Evaluated in the Simulation Model

The efficiency of the adjuster-labeler system is affected both by the total length of a rotation cycle and by the percentage of the cycle when rotating adjusters are tending a group of labelers. It is possible to analyze a large number of alternative combinations of these variables and to optimize the system with respect to both factors. There are several reasons why such optimization studies are unlikely to be carried out. One reason is that many of the recommendations would not be accepted by management because they involve infeasible implementation problems. For example, an optimum cycle of thirty-seven minutes duration is unlikely to be implemented. Second, the dollar savings created by unusual combinations of cycle schedules are not likely to justify the effort in obtaining them. Therefore, we will assume that management has provided three specific alternatives to be evaluated initially by the simulator.

(1) A cycle of time of one hour, with one adjuster tending the six labelers for one quarter of an hour and two adjusters tending them for three quarters of an hour.

(2) A cycle time of one hour with one-half hour having only one adjuster and one-half hour having two.

(3) A cycle time of one hour with three quarters of an hour using one adjuster and one quarter using two.

Form of Simulation Output

We have already mentioned that in the limit, the distribution of labeler down time repeats from cycle to cycle; but is transient within the cycle. To evaluate the cost of specific fixed–rotating adjuster combinations, however, we need to estimate expected down time over the complete cycle. We can obtain this by averaging the distribution over a large number of cycles. We can now obtain the information needed to estimate the cost of operating the labeler system by running the simulator for an appropriate length of time (how long will be made explicit in the next section) and determining the percentage of time when $0, 1, 2, \ldots, 6$ labelers are inoperative.

The Time Dimension

In the symbolic model we assumed the time increment, δ, was small enough so that the probability of multiple events occurring in δ was approximately zero. We must choose a δ that also permits this assumption for the simulator; that is, the time advance must be small relative to the likelihood of events occurring. Unfortunately, the smaller we make δ, the more simulation running time is required to obtain stable estimates of down-time distributions. Therefore, the analyst must balance the economics of computer running time with the requirements of model representability. No fixed rules exist to evaluate this trade-off; it will be examined further in Chapter 7.

Since the mean failure time is fifteen minutes and the mean adjustment time is five minutes, the probability of a machine under repair having the repair completed in one minute is 0.2, and the probability of an operating labeler failing in any minute is 0.067. If δ is one quarter of a minute, the

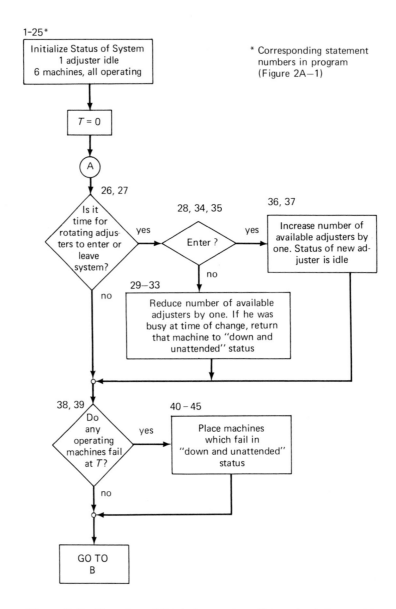

Figure 2–3 Flow chart of fixed plus rotating adjuster simulation model.

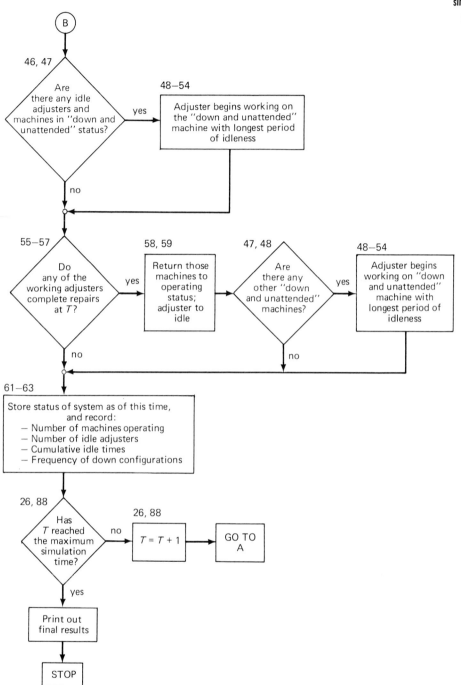

Figure 2-3 (continued)

41

probabilities drop to 0.05 and 0.016, respectively. Let us explore briefly the implications of these alternative time increments.

Two types of errors result from selecting a time unit that is too large. We illustrate these errors by comparing the predictions from particular time units (i.e., one minute and one-quarter minute) with those that would have been achieved had time advanced in a continuous fashion (which implies the time advance is dt as defined in differential calculus). One error is in the estimation of the probability that an event will occur in a time-advance interval. If the time unit is δ, we know (from Equation 2–5) that the probability of a repair being completed in δ is

$$\int_0^\delta 0.2e^{-0.2t} \, dt = 1 - e^{-0.2\delta}$$

Our finite approximation of this is 0.2δ. The errors in the approximation for δ of one-quarter minute and one minute are presented in Table 2–4.

Table 2–4.   Errors in Event Occurrence Probabilities as a Function of Size of Time Unit

Unit of Time Advance	Correct Probability	Model's Approximation	Error per Simulated Minute of Operation
1 minute	0.181	0.2	0.019
$\frac{1}{4}$ minute	0.049	0.05	0.004

The second error involves the occurrence of multiple events in δ. The likelihood of such occurrences can be computed directly from the probabilities of machines failing or repairs being completed. The labeler configuration in which multiple events are most likely to occur is: two machines under repair and the other four operating (because the likelihood of an adjuster completing a repair in δ is greater than the probability of a machine's failing). The chances of multiple events occurring under these conditions for $\delta = 1$ minute and $\delta = \frac{1}{4}$ minute are presented in Table 2–5.

Table 2–5.   Likelihood of Multiple Events Within a Simulation Time Unit

Unit of Time Advance	Probability of More Than One Event in Time Interval
1 minute	0.134
$\frac{1}{4}$ minute	0.055

The analyst must utilize information of the type presented in Tables 2–4 and 2–5 along with estimated computer running costs for various advance intervals to determine the appropriate one. Suppose the analyst decided that $\delta = \frac{1}{4}$ minute was best. In order to test the error in this approximation and also to estimate the number of simulation time periods required to achieve stability, the simulator was run for the case of only two *fixed* adjusters. Since, when the simulation is run long enough, the starting conditions do not affect the final predictions, we arbitrarily assume that all machines are running at the start of the simulation. The cumulative average of the probabilities for more than 200 simulated hours of operation are presented in Figure 2–4.

When compared with the results of the analytic model, the simulation solution deviates by less than one percent. From this we conclude that a simulation step size of one-quarter minute accurately represents the analytic requirements. With respect to the transient conditions, "eyeball estimate" suggests simulation runs of between 10,000 and 20,000 time units (i.e., between forty-two and eighty-four working hours) in order to obtain valid results. For convenience, we choose to run the simulation for 19,200 time units, which is equivalent to ten shifts of eight hours each. The choice of simulator run time is sometimes more complicated; we will return to the problem in Chapter 8.

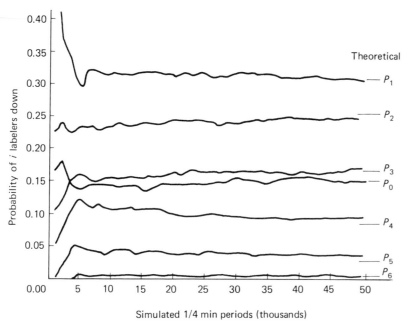

Figure 2–4 Simulation results for 50,000 $\frac{1}{4}$-minute time periods when two fixed repairmen tend the system.

simulation results 2-8

In Table 2–6 we present the average number of time units when zero through six labelers are inoperative as a function of the rotating adjusters' work schedule. These data are derived from the simulation runs.

We compute the total cost for these combinations of fixed plus rotating adjusters using Equation 2–2. The results are presented in Table 2–7. (For completeness we repeat the analytic solution to the one and two fixed adjuster systems.

43

Portion of Hour When Rotating Adjuster is Tending Labeler Line	P_m = Probability of m machines not operating						
	P_0	P_1	P_2	P_3	P_4	P_5	P_6
$\frac{1}{4}$	0.067	0.155	0.201	0.225	0.212	0.106	0.034
$\frac{1}{2}$	0.096	0.215	0.243	0.211	0.146	0.076	0.012
$\frac{3}{4}$	0.111	0.241	0.251	0.219	0.126	0.044	0.009

Table 2–6. Average Fraction of Time When m Machines Are Not Operating

If the cost figures are correctly estimated, the use of a rotating adjuster with a one-half hour cycle plus one fixed adjuster on each of the four production lines saves over $28,000 per year. Now management can decide whether such savings justify implementation of the program.

Table 2–7.
Cost as a
Function of
Number of
Equivalent
Adjusters

Number of Adjusters	Labor Cost per Hour of Operation	Down Time per Hour of Operation	Total Cost per Hour of Operation
1	$ 8	$11.74	$19.74
$1\frac{1}{4}$	10	9.05	19.05
$1\frac{1}{2}$	12	5.93	17.93
$1\frac{3}{4}$	14	4.61	18.61
2	16	3.11	19.11

2-9 conclusion

The adjuster-labeler problem illustrates the way that a simulation can be quickly prepared and used. It should be noted, however, that the simulator was run under fairly restricted alternative systems. Only the one hour rotating adjuster cycle was examined. The fact that the first simulation indicates possible savings may lead management to remove these restrictions and simulate the system under other alternative cycle lengths.

With this chapter as an introduction, we turn to the specifics of simulation construction. In the next chapter we will examine the steps in the development and use of a simulation model.

exercises

2–1 Draw the flow chart for a simulation of the following single-server queue.

Mean time between arrivals = 10 minutes

Mean service time = 7 minutes

Both times are distributed exponentially so that the probability of the event in a small time $\delta = 1/\text{mean}$.

Arrivals do not join the queue if the queue is longer than three. Units in the queue leave if they have been waiting longer than eleven minutes.

2–2 Is the situation in Exercise 2–1 amenable to analytic solution [Cox and Smith, 1963, Ch. IV]. Why or why not?

references

Cox, D. R., and W. L. Smith, *Queues*, Wiley, New York, 1963.

Feller, W., *An Introduction to Probability Theory and Its Applications*, Wiley, New York, 1950.

appendix 2A

Machine Adjustment Simulator

Variable Dictionary for Program in Figure 2A–1

ITM	number of time units to be simulated
M	number of labelers
DUMMY	initial value for random number generator
A	probability of failure in one time unit
R	probability of repair in one time unit
N	number of adjusters
NUM	number of time units after start of hour when rotating repairman enters
ICON	time when first printouts are required
ITCON	time at end of next 3-minute period*
NHR	time in hours
JHR	number of time units in an hour
IC	number of units past last hour
NDW	number of labelers down and unattended
JQ(J)	number of time units J labelers down (frequency table)
IM(J)	status of labeler J; 1 = up; 0 = down.
IDTM(J)	cumulative idle time on labeler J
IQP(K)	queue identifier of the kth labeler to be down and un-attended
IR(J)	status of adjuster J; 0 = idle; 1–6 is labeler identifier for current activity
IDTR(J)	adjuster J's cumulative idle time
IT	time (simulated time in unts)
KC	temporarily holds number of labelers down
AM(I)	fraction labeler I is idle so far
AR(I)	fraction adjuster I is idle so far
AQ(J)	fraction of time system had J labelers down

Time Units Used

Time unit = $\frac{1}{4}$ minute	1 shift = 8 hours = 1920 units
1 hour = 240 units	5 shifts = 9600 units

* Printouts are made every 3 minutes for the last hour in each 5-shift period.

```
C   MACHINE ADJUSTMENT MODEL
C
0001          DIMENSION IM(10),IQP(10),IR(10),IDTM(1000),IDTR(1000),AR(10),
             1AM(10),AQ(10),JQ(10)
0002          ITM=50000
0003          M=6                      Six labeling machines
0004          DUMMY=356523.0           Starting basis for random numbers
0005          A=0.0
0006          R=0.0
0007          N=2                      Two adjusters
0008          DO 160 III=1,2           Two runs
0009          A=A+0.05
0010          R=R+0.15
0011          ICCN=1000
0012          IC=5
0013          NDW=0
0014          DO 1 J=1,M
0015          JQ(J)=0
0016          IM(J)=1
0017          IDTM(J)=0
0018          IQP(J)=0
0019    1     CONTINUE
0020          JQ(M+1)=0
0021          DO 2 J=1,2
0022          IR(J)=0
0023          IDTR(J)=0
0024    2     CONTINUE
0025          DO 150 IT=1,ITM        "Do" loop advance time, unit by unit
0026    4     DO 10 J=1,M
0027          IF (IM(J).EQ.0) GO TO 10
0028          YFL=RANNOS(DUMMY)           RANNOS creates a random number
0029          IF (YFL.GE.A) GO TO 10      between 0 and 1
0030          IM(J)=0                  Failure
0031          NDW=NDW+1
0032          IQP(NDW)=J               Queue awaiting adjustment
0033    10    CONTINUE
0034          DO 100 J=1,N
0035          IF (IR(J).NE.0) GO TO 30
0036          IF (NDW.EQ.0) GO TO 100
0037          IR(J)=IQP(1)
0038          NDW=NDW-1
0039          IF (NDW.EQ.0) GO TO 100
0040          DO 20 K=1,NDW
0041    20    IQP(K)=IQP(K+1)
0042          GO TO 100
0043    30    YFL=RANNOS(DUMMY)
0044          IF (YFL.GE.R) GO TO 100
0045          K=IR(J)                  Adjustment complete
0046          IM(K)=1
0047          IR(J)=0
0048    100   CONTINUE
0049          DO 110 J=1,M
0050          IF (IM(J).EQ.0) IDTM(J)=IDTM(J)+1
0051    110   CONTINUE
0052          KC=1
0053          DO 120 J=1,N
0054          IF (IR(J).EQ.0) IDTR(J)=IDTR(J)+1
0055          IF (IR(J).NE.0) KC=KC+1
0056    120   CONTINUE
0057          KC=KC+NDW
0058          JQ(KC)=JQ(KC)+1
0059          IC=IT-ICON
0060          IF (IC.NE.0) GO TO 150
0061          ICCN=ICON+1000         Output process
0062          DO 130 I=1,M
0063    130   AM(I)=FLOAT(IDTM(I))/FLOAT(IT)
0064          DO 140 I=1,N
0065    140   AR(I)=FLOAT(IDTR(I))/FLOAT(IT)
0066          PRINT 901,IT                   Print time
0067          PRINT 900,(AM(I),I=1,M)   Print labeler utilization
0068          PRINT 900,(AR(I),I=1,N)   Print adjuster utilization
0069          MMM=M+1
0070          DO 142 J=1,MMM
0071    142   AQ(J)=FLOAT(JQ(J))/FLOAT(IT)
0072          PRINT 900,(AQ(I),I=1,MMM)   Print fraction of time in
0073    150   CONTINUE                             each state
0074    160   CONTINUE
0075    900   FORMAT (1X,10F8.3)
0076    901   FORMAT (1X,7HTIME = ,I5)
```

	Prob. of failure	Prob. of adjustment
Run 1	.05	.15
Run 2	.1	.3

Figure 2A–1 Program for simulation of machine adjustment process.

```
0077            CALL EXIT
0078            END
```

Output Follows

1st Run   Probability of failure in unit of time = .05
                 Probability of repair in unit of time = .15

```
TIME =   1000
     0.356    0.280    0.331    0.351    0.343    0.247
     0.274    0.411
     0.143    0.297    0.239    0.190    0.102    0.019    0.010
TIME =   2000
     0.332    0.351    0.335    0.365    0.334    0.319
     0.256    0.365
     0.121    0.280    0.245    0.205    0.101    0.038    0.009
TIME =   3000
     0.343    0.321    0.328    0.369    0.313    0.349
     0.254    0.362
     0.123    0.270    0.259    0.202    0.105    0.034    0.006
TIME =   4000
     0.333    0.301    0.318    0.353    0.308    0.339
     0.267    0.382
     0.139    0.277    0.255    0.194    0.097    0.033    0.005
TIME =   5000
     0.333    0.317    0.326    0.345    0.311    0.332
     0.271    0.374
     0.134    0.278    0.255    0.197    0.102    0.030    0.004
TIME =   6000
     0.333    0.313    0.330    0.338    0.313    0.336
     0.269    0.373
     0.131    0.279    0.255    0.199    0.102    0.030    0.003
TIME =   7000
     0.330    0.309    0.332    0.337    0.308    0.342
     0.271    0.374
     0.132    0.280    0.260    0.194    0.098    0.032    0.004
TIME =   8000
     0.330    0.316    0.335    0.337    0.314    0.349
     0.271    0.363
     0.130    0.271    0.264    0.199    0.096    0.033    0.005
TIME =   9000
     0.333    0.323    0.337    0.338    0.322    0.338
     0.266    0.360
     0.127    0.271    0.264    0.202    0.098    0.033    0.005
TIME =  10000
     0.338    0.326    0.346    0.338    0.325    0.341
     0.271    0.356
     0.130    0.265    0.262    0.199    0.102    0.036    0.007
```

Machine utilizations.
Adjuster utilizations
Cumulative time with zero through
six machines down

Printouts continue every
1000 time units.

```
TIME =  48000
     0.330    0.319    0.339    0.328    0.330    0.339
     0.272    0.356
     0.127    0.273    0.269    0.194    0.099    0.033    0.005
TIME =  49000
     0.327    0.318    0.337    0.328    0.330    0.337
     0.274    0.358
     0.128    0.274    0.269    0.192    0.099    0.032    0.005
TIME =  50000
     0.328    0.317    0.337    0.328    0.329    0.337
     0.274    0.359
     0.128    0.275    0.269    0.192    0.098    0.032    0.005
```

End of first run

Figure 2A–1 (continued)

2nd Run   Probability of failure = 0.1
                 Probability of repair = 0.3

TIME = 1000
    0.318   0.356   0.389   0.371   0.343   0.330
    0.296   0.373
    0.094   0.259   0.294   0.214   0.085   0.046   0.008
TIME = 2000
    0.300   0.341   0.392   0.363   0.348   0.348
    0.293   0.381
    0.102   0.254   0.292   0.208   0.092   0.044   0.007
TIME = 3000
    0.318   0.351   0.380   0.358   0.357   0.342
    0.302   0.375
    0.101   0.252   0.284   0.216   0.102   0.039   0.006
TIME = 4000
    0.318   0.357   0.379   0.361   0.354   0.350
    0.305   0.373
    0.102   0.250   0.275   0.222   0.106   0.036   0.007
TIME = 5000
    0.324   0.361   0.371   0.367   0.349   0.350
    0.305   0.371
    0.104   0.246   0.280   0.219   0.109   0.037   0.007

So on each 1000 time units

TIME = 48000
    0.333   0.341   0.346   0.353   0.350   0.362
    0.314   0.384
    0.114   0.248   0.275   0.214   0.109   0.036   0.005
TIME = 49000
    0.332   0.340   0.346   0.354   0.350   0.362
    0.315   0.385
    0.114   0.248   0.275   0.214   0.109   0.036   0.005
TIME = 50000
    0.333   0.340   0.347   0.355   0.350   0.363
    0.314   0.385
    0.113   0.248   0.274   0.214   0.109   0.036   0.005

Figure 2A–1 (continued)

simulation methodology

introduction 3-1

The previous chapter presented a problem solved through simulation. In that chapter the primary emphasis was on the details of a specific simulation model with no reference to general procedures and techniques. In this chapter we look at the gestalt of simulation. Our purpose is to identify the steps that are commonly followed in developing and using simulation models. The number of identifiable steps and the order in which they are carried out is highly dependent upon the particular situation. Nevertheless, there is a common set of processes and a general sequence that is discussed here. In succeeding chapters each of the simulation steps is analyzed in detail.

Figure 3–1 is a flow chart of the major steps in analysis and the sequence in which they are commonly undertaken in industrial simulation projects. Notice that at a number of points the process may return to a previous step. This illustrates one of the important characteristics of successful problem solution: the earlier steps are always subject to revision as additional information is obtained. For example, a review of data often causes some reformulation of the problem. The reformulation may involve only a change in problem emphasis, or it may result in complete restructuring. In dealing with complicated systems, analysts sometimes find that the first definition of the problem needs later revisions because it included too many (or sometimes too few) factors to adequately represent the dynamics. Actual runs of the simulation almost always suggest new alternatives and, therefore, a return to experimental design.

Model building is as much an art as it is a science. One of the difficulties in using a flow diagram to represent the model-building process is that

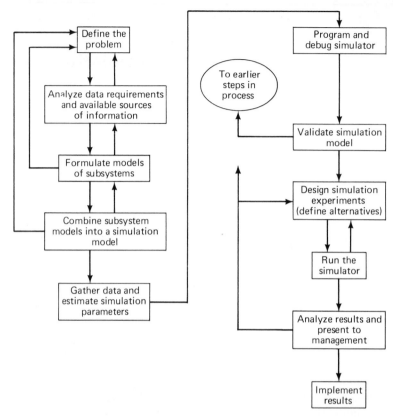

Figure 3–1
Flow chart of steps in the use of simulation.

the process looks more scientific than it really is. The flow chart in Figure 3–1 is only a guide and should not be interpreted as a method that automatically produces the creative leaps required to translate a complicated, real-world system into a more compact and manipulatable simulation model.

In the remainder of this chapter we describe each of the major steps in the flow chart. Our intent is to provide, in some orderly fashion, an exposure to the many problems, questions, and decisions that face an analyst who is developing a computer model of a complicated system.

3-2 defining the problem

Successful problem formulation is the most critical step in developing a model of a system. This is indicated by the number of times the modeling process re-enters this phase of research. An analyst's success in accomplishing other research objectives depends on correct problem formulation.

The first step in problem formulation is to specify the objectives to be achieved through the analysis. These objectives will generally be stated by management after they recognize that some aspect of the system is not functioning to their satisfaction. The problem, as management sees it, is likely to be defined vaguely (from the analyst's point of view), and the objectives stated in qualitative terms. It is the analyst's job to translate these qualitative objectives into operational terms that can be related to a performance index within the system. When multiple objectives are specified, additional complications occur. The analyst may try to resolve these complications by assigning weights to the objectives according to their importance to management. Such a function is commonly known as an *objective function.* A good review of procedures for deriving objective functions is presented in Chapter 3 of Ackoff [1962].

Along with specifying the objective function, the analyst tries to identify *relevant variables* in the system; that is, variables that affect the performance as measured by the objective function. He then (as we noted in Chapter 1) separates the relevant variables into two classes; those having values that can be controlled by the decision maker and those with values that cannot be so manipulated. The objective from the analyst's point is to predict the behavior of the uncontrollable variables and choose the levels of the controllable variables in a manner that maximizes the stated objective function.

The distinction between controllable and uncontrollable variables is not always clear. Depending on the scope of the study, variables are sometimes treated as uncontrollable, although the decision maker has (or has potentially) some control over them. In the example in Chapter 2 we treated the failure rate of the labelers as if it were an uncontrollable factor. However, this variable can probably be altered by decisions about controllables, such as the preventive maintenance timing or machine overhaul and replacement schedules.

We will return to a more detailed examination of the problem-formulation phase of the research in Chapter 4.

analysis of data requirements and 3-3
availability of sources

The problem-formulation phase of the research provides us with an objective function to compute a measure of performance for evaluating alternative solutions to the problem. All parameters and variables that affect this measure of performance are identified. In this step we determine whether data is available to estimate the values of parameters and of historical values of variables. (This step does not necessarily precede the subsystem modeling to be discussed in Section 3–4.) For use in the simulation, data are needed to:

- estimate values of constants and parameters
- provide starting values for all variables
- provide data with which simulation outputs can be compared for validation.

To ensure that this data will be available when needed, sources of data are located and their adequacy is evaluated.

Analysis of the data requirements is expedited by recognizing the kinds of variables encountered in modeling large-scale systems. A *relevant variable* is a characteristic or attribute of the system that is observed to take on different values and that in some way affects the measure of performance of the system over this range of values. A *parameter* is a characteristic or attribute of the system that has only one value over all foreseeable ranges of operation (but may change as different alternatives are studied). A parameter or variable having a value that affects, but is itself unaffected by, the system is an *exogenous factor.* It represents a factor in the environment of the system under study. A parameter or variable having a value determined by other variables in the system is an *endogenous factor.* These distinctions become precise as the model is determined.

Figure 3–2 summarizes this classification and relates these data types to requirements for data collection and analysis. The controllable variables are those to be set by the decision maker (who is exogenous to the system under study). During analysis these would be set according to some experimental design or search procedure. If the system (or one like it) is operating, data may be obtained on historical values of the controllables in order to help validate the model; that is, in order to test whether the model produces the same outputs as the actual system under the same conditions.

Exogeneous, uncontrollable variables must be input to the model to represent the relevant parts of the world assumed to be external to the

| | Controllable | | Uncontrollable | |
	Static	Dynamic	Static	Dynamic
Exogenous	Set by search procedure Historical data may be used to validate	(Policies change with time)	Must estimate to determine starting values and changes over time	
Endogenous	Do not exist		Parameter Must estimate to provide starting values	(Includes performance measures) Historical data may be used to validate

Figure 3–2 Classification of data types and their use in simulation models.

system. A specific value of each of these variables is required as a starting condition for the model. Some basis for estimating the dynamic values of the exogenous, uncontrollable variables is needed as input to the model over the time it is to be run. The representation of these exogenous values might be a time series or a distribution from which specific values can be drawn. The estimate of dynamic, exogenous, values can come from some theoretical considerations or from the collection and statistical analysis of historical data. (If the computation of an exogenous variable is done by a formula or procedure, then, in effect, this variable has been made endogenous, and the model has been extended. Models are often extended in just this way.)

The dynamic, endogenous variables are, of course, those to be predicted by the model. Estimates of their values at some point in time (for example, from historical data) would be needed to set the initial values for starting the simulation. Data for a series of times might be needed to test validity. Values must be estimated for all the parameters, also, either from theory or from past data.

In Figure 3–3 this classification is applied to the variables and parameters in the machine-adjustment problem of Chapter 2.

An analyst *must* be able to collect data on (or estimate in some other way) the behavior of exogenous, uncontrollable variables and parameters. Besides using historical data to estimate variable values, other ways of obtaining estimates of exogenous variables are to derive them from theoretical grounds or to use subjective estimates of probability distributions. Theory can usually be applied where the variable is the result of a physical or chemical process; subjective estimates are used where either the person's estimate is a direct part of the simulation (i.e., a game) or where there is no other way of obtaining an estimate. If no estimates can be obtained, the problem must be reformulated. Lack of data for the other types in the classification is not as critical, especially if the analyst can test the validity of his model other than by using it to reproduce historical conditions.

Availability of historical data for endogenous, uncontrollable variables is especially desirable for validating complicated systems that have been segmented into subsystems. The endogenous data permit the analyst to test his subsystem models individually before integrating them into a model of the entire system. General rules cannot be given for segmenting a large problem into subsystems; this is almost entirely dependent upon the structures of the system being analyzed. Subsystems should be as independent of each other as is possible (i.e., have few common endogenous variables). The size of a subsystem necessary to meet this requirement depends on the amount of interaction between variables in the total system.

Once the overall problem has been segmented into subsystems, and the sources of data have been analyzed to provide the necessary information to construct—and, possibly, validate—such subsystem models, the construction of subsystem models can start. In the next section we consider methods for such model construction.

| | Controllable | | Uncontrollable | |
	Static	Dynamic	Static	Dynamic
Exogenous	Number of fixed repairmen	Number of rotating repairmen and their schedule of work	Mean labeler failure rate Mean repair rate Number of labelers	None
Endogenous	Do not exist		Mean down time per labeler Repairmen utilization	Labeler down times Probability distribution of number of labelers down

Figure 3–3   Application of data classification to labeler problem.

3-4 formulation of models of the subsystems

Subsystems of large problems can be identified by analyzing the system in one of three ways. The first method of analysis is the *flow approach.* This method is often used for a system having dynamic properties determined by the flow of physical or information entities through the system. The flow approach would be used to analyze material processing. The subsystems are identified by examining the aspects of the system that produce a physical or information change in the flowing entity. To be relevant to the study, such change must, of course, affect the measure of performance in the objective function. The flow approach was used to analyze the labeler system in Chapter 2.

A second method of identifying and modeling subsystems is the *functional approach.* This method of analysis is commonly used when there are no directly observable flowing elements in the system, but when there is a reasonably clear sequence of functions to be performed. For example, the functional approach might be used to analyze a production control process.

The third method of identifying the subsystems is known as the *state-change approach.* This approach is useful for a system that has a large number of interdependent relationships for which no specific subgrouping can be observed. The method of analysis requires examination of the state of the system at points of time. At each time interval the entire system is examined to determine if any change has occurred. A subsystem identified by this method is a subprocedure used to compute a class of state changes.

Subsystems may, in turn, be modeled by the same approaches. Since the subsystems are less complex than the total system, it is sometimes possible to obtain mathematical relationships that describe the dynamics of a subsystem even though this is not possible for the entire complex. For example, in the labeler-adjustment problem we were able to describe the failure properties of the labeler system using specific mathematical probability distributions.

If subsystems cannot be identified and models developed to describe their behavior, the model-building process becomes much more complicated. Without submodels the entire simulation model must be formulated and validated at once; this is difficult to do when a large number of assumptions about variable interactions have been built into the simulation. In a later chapter we shall examine attempts to model human thought processes by simulation. Much of the model-building difficulty in this case arises because it is currently impossible to separate thought processes into subsystems that can be tested as separate units.

Wherever possible the decision maker for whom the study is being undertaken should participate directly in the overall and submodel formulations, both to further his own knowledge and so that he will better understand the results.

combining the subsystem models into 3-5 a simulation model of the system

At this stage we must select the most appropriate language in which to write the simulation. This decision involves the following considerations:

- the efficiency of alternative languages in computer translation and running speed,
- the difficulty of translating the description of the subsystems and their interrelations into the simulation language,
- the output desired from the simulation and the ease of obtaining the output.

The analyst translates the subsystem concepts into a flow chart that describes the logical sequence of activities in the system. (This is illustrated in detail in Chapter 5.) This may be analogous to a set of difference equations or it may be a state-change model. The flow-chart logic is then programmed in the selected language.

estimating simulation variables 3-6 and parameters

It is beyond the scope of this book to provide a detailed treatment of the procedures for summarizing real-world data as manageable statistical descriptions of system characteristics. The most common data process is to collect the values of a variable over time and to compute a frequency distribution from which such values are assumed to derive. There are many references to procedures for this basic statistical process (see, for example, Miller [1965], Wine [1964], or Moroney [1956]). The main problems here are economic and those that are related to the imperfect nature of the world. The economic problems stem from the expense in observing, recording, and collecting data. The existence of a good information system, of course, helps reduce these costs. Other problems result from the fact that the data is incomplete (missing observations) or inaccurate owing to observation or reporting errors. Statistical texts discuss techniques for handling these problems so that the resulting representation of the variable is as accurate as possible.

In some cases values must be represented as a time series. When the variable is known to have cyclical (seasonal) or growth trends or some other dynamic properties, more complex data analysis methods are needed [Brown 1963]. The most difficult kind of complication to handle in regard to data is the one resulting from the interaction of several variables that are exogenous to the model but which are related in the external world. Sometimes these variables tend to vary together and cause *multicollinearity.* Often exogenous variables are represented as a value plus a normally distributed error term or disturbance. Another difficulty occurs when there is a relationship between the variance in the error terms of these variables (heterosedasticity). The econometricians have had to deal with these problems for many years, and their literature provides discussion of techniques for compensating for these problems [Johnston, 1963; Goldberger, 1964].

Although statistical procedures have been developed to account for many of the factors that complicate the analysis of real-world data, the analyst must first recognize that *his* data may contain these complicating factors. Failure to recognize and identify complications can cause simulation output to mispredict the behavior of the system. These mispredictions might lead the analyst to conclude that the simulation model is itself not satisfactory when the problem really lies in the method of representing the exogenous parameters and variables. It is important to translate accurately real-world data into the input forms required by the simulation model.

3-7 debugging the simulator

Submodels are chosen in a way so that they are nearly independent of other submodels. This condition can usually be used to advantage in debugging the complete simulation program, for it implies that each submodel can be written and tested independently. The submodels are tested by comparing their endogenous output with corresponding historical data. When the outputs match, the subroutines are included in the total simulation model. In this way the debugging proceeds on a component basis. The overall model must also be tested for potential programming and logical errors.

validating the model 3-8

Problems of validation are not unique to simulation models. However, some literature, which is addressed specifically to tests of the validity of simulation models, is discussed in detail in Chapter 8. A common method for validating is to compare the output of the simulation model to historical data under similar environmental conditions (i.e., under similar exogenous and control values). If the output of the simulation model is close to the historical data, the simulation is accepted as a realistic representation of the system. However, the ultimate validation of any model is how well it predicts the future; a simulation model must at some point undergo such a test.

design of simulation experiments 3-9

The important aspects of the design and analysis of experiments have been treated extensively. (Three excellent sources of this literature are Davies [1963], Wilde [1964], and Kempthorne [1952].) Although most experimental design work was originally developed for physical processes (such as experimentation on agricultural or chemical processes) the literature is directly relevant to the use of a simulation.

An experimental design requires observation of the system under specific combinations of those variables capable of being manipulated. The simulation model is operated under these control conditions and inferences are drawn about the relationship between the controllable variables and the measure of performance. The decision as to the extent of experimentation is influenced by several considerations: the cost of the computer time required to estimate performance for a combination of controllable variables, the sensitivity of the measure of performance to specific variables, and the extent of interdependence between control variables. We will examine features of experimental designs (including search procedures) in detail in a later chapter.

running the simulation 3-10

The simulation model is now tested and can now be run according to the experimental design. Although conceptually simple, this step becomes crucial because observation of the output during the runs indicates need for further work: uncovering further bugs, changing the experimental design to explore interesting relationships, even reformulation of the model or the problem. If management can become involved in this ongoing examination of run outputs, they will gain the insights to guide reformulation of the model so that it answers *their* questions.

3-11 analysis of results and presentation to management

Seldom are the results of a simulation experiment completely consistent with the preconceptions of the outcome; the output of a study will provide some new insight into the interrelations between the components of the system. Therefore, it is critical that the presentation to management of the simulation results are in a form that maximizes this insight. Ideally, management will be involved *throughout* the process. That way managerial expertise can be used to build richer models and they can benefit from the insights.

A correctly designed experiment makes data analysis straightforward. The *interpretation* of the results of the analysis, however, is not necessarily straightforward. How the analyst interprets the results and the implications he draws from them can be the determining factor in whether management judges the simulation research to have been successful. One important strategy for the analyst to employ in presenting results is to be sure the language used is the terminology familiar to management. One of the greatest reasons for lack of implementation is that management does not understand what is being proposed.

Since it is unlikely that the analyst has been able to make a perfect translation of the manager's objectives into an objective function, it is wise to provide the decision maker with a range of solutions deduced from the simulation model. The analyst can thus obtain additional information on the correct objective function by interacting directly with management on the relative value of the alternative solutions.

In Chapter 4 we consider more extensively the process of effective interaction between the researcher and the manager. The importance of this phase of a study (whether it uses simulation or not) can not be over-emphasized. No matter how good a research study is, it is of little pragmatic value unless some recommendations are accepted and implemented. Many studies are not implemented because the researcher either ignores this phase of the study altogether or does not effectively carry out a dialogue with the manager [Churchman, 1964].

3-12 effective implementation of simulation results

As we have just indicated, the likelihood of implementation is directly tied to the effectiveness with which the analyst reports the results of the study to the manager. One of the common misconceptions about simulation studies is that they are one-shot affairs; that is, that the manager asks the question and the researcher answers it through his simulation. This happens only in unsuccessful cases. Systems are not static and, as a result, the simulation model should be constantly updated and improved to reflect changes in the system. If periodic updating of the model takes place, the dynamic aspects of the system are less likely to surprise management in the future.

Often a research project will generate a number of unanswered questions. Additional analysis may be recommended to examine these aspects in more detail. Thus the process of conducting operations research is a continuous one. Previous research results should be effectively utilized in the current and future analysis efforts. Therefore, implementation of any analysis should be looked at from two points of view. First, it should be examined for specific operational recommendations which can be made as a result of the study. Second, it should provide management with additional knowledge and understanding of the organization as an entity. This knowledge may uncover important, but currently unrecognized, problems that require analysis.

The major steps in conducting and implementing simulation research have been presented. We have tried to emphasize the ongoing, inter-related aspects of these steps. The next chapter goes into more detail about several steps. Our emphasis will be on those phases that are commonly encountered in all types of model building.

exercise

3–1 A banking association wishes to provide its members with a simulation program as well as with related precedures that will permit the member banks to assign tellers on the banking floor most effectively.

(a) Propose a design and implementation program to the association to carry out this objective.
(b) Outline the instruction manual that would be provided to a bank wishing to use this package.

references

Ackoff, R. L., *Scientific Method: Optimizing Applied Research Decisions*, Wiley, New York, 1962.

Brown, R., *Smoothing, Forecasting and Prediction of Discrete Time Series*, Prentice-Hall, Englewood Cliffs, N. J., 1963.

Churchman, C., "Managerial Acceptance of Scientific Recommendations," *California Management Review*, Vol. 7, No. 1, Fall 1964, pp. 31–38.

Davies, O. (ed.), *The Design and Analysis of Industrial Experiments,* 2nd ed., Hafner, New York, 1963.

Goldberger, A. S., *Econometric Theory*, Wiley, New York, 1964.*

Johnston, J., *Econometric Methods,* McGraw-Hill, New York, 1963.*

Kempthorne, O., *The Design and Analysis of Experiments*, Wiley, New York, 1952.*

Miller, I., and J. Freund, *Probability and Statistics for Engineers,* Prentice-Hall, Englewood Cliffs, N. J., 1965.

Moroney, M., *Facts from Figures*, Penguin, Baltimore, 1956.

Wilde, D. J., *Optimum Seeking Methods,* Prentice-Hall, Englewood Cliffs, N. J., 1964.

Wine, R., *Statistics for Scientists and Engineers*, Prentice-Hall, Englewood Cliffs, N. J., 1964.

*Requires mathematical sophistication.

model building and use

introduction 4-1

Several of the model-building steps identified in Chapter 3 must be completed regardless of the type of model used. Any decision-aiding study based on the use of formal models must:

- formulate the problem in workable terms.
- identify the relevant variables in the system and separate their interactions by analysis of subsystems.
- utilize the results and conclusions drawn from the model to aid the decision maker.
- assist in the implementation of decisions.

These four steps are part of the art of model building; there are no standard procedures for their execution. An art must be learned by apprenticeship, and in this chapter we will try to make our approach to each of these steps explicit. Our language and examples will be in terms of simulation-model construction; however, the content of this chapter would not be much different had the book been addressed to the construction of analog or symbolic models.

The reader can speed the process of learning problem formulation by synthesizing the recommendations of practitioners in various fields. Therefore, we suggest reading the pertinent chapters in books listed at the end of this chapter. Ultimately, however, mastering problem formulation requires real-world experience. Some lessons can only be learned by getting your hands dirty.

61

4-2 problem formulation

An analyst is virtually never in a position to judge whether the problem he formulated was *the* correct one. It is true that he can show some formulations to be incorrect by examining them syntactically (i.e., on the basis of internal consistency). However, formulations that are syntactically sound are not necessarily correct on more pragmatic grounds and correctness using pragmatic criteria is not very easy to measure.

Ideally, we would like to judge the value of formulations by measuring their usefulness to the decision maker. Such a criterion is impossible to quantify since it requires both an objective definition of usefulness and a method of summarizing the expected consequences of alternative formulations. Because of these problems we usually rely on experience and intuition in deciding when the formulation phase can be (at least tentatively) accepted and other phases of analysis begun.

We will concentrate on what is known about or characteristic of the problem-formulation phase by answering three questions:

- What information is contained in a successfully defined problem?
- What is the typical environment in which the formulation occurs?
- What types of aids does an analyst use in such formulation?

Operations-research problem statements have a common form. Using notions developed in *Scientific Method* [Ackoff, 1962] a problem can be represented as

$$V_i = g(P_i)$$
$$P_i = f(C_i; U)$$

(4–1)

where V_i = the *value* to the decision maker of implementing proposed alternative i

P_i = m-element vector; that is, a set of m *performance measures* (e.g., profits, inventory levels, capital investment) affected by implementing alternative i

$g(P)$ = *objective function* which translates the m-performance measures into a single-dimensional value function

C_i = n-element vector; that is, n values showing the level of each of the n relevant *controllable variables* associated with i (e.g., price of product, advertising levels, choice of distribution channels)

U = a set of values for each of the *uncontrollable variables* which affect the performance (e.g., conditions of the economy, competitor activity)

$f(C_i; U)$ = the *model*; a functional relationship or procedure that predicts the performance measures P_i which would be observed in the real system if i were implemented.

The problem-formulation phase is completed when we have

(1) Identified the set of controllable variables $c_1, c_2, \ldots, c_n$.

(2) Identified the set of uncontrollable variables $u_1, u_2, \ldots, u_k$ that make up U.

(3) Identified the set of performance measures $p_1, p_2, \ldots, p_m$.

(4) Defined the objective function $g(P)$.

The beginning of the problem-formulation process is not as clearly defined. Practically, the process begins when the analyst knows a task is before him.

Sometimes an analyst will recognize from his other activities within the organization that research is needed on a particular problem. Analysis often begins as a result of specific management directives. When the problem-formulation phase is initiated through management's actions, the assignment may be vague or quite specific; if it is specific it may be right or wrong. The analyst might be told to "see if we can get more production out of the drill press room," or he might be specifically told that "we need another drill press; prepare a justification for it." The second directive might actually be wrong, since a detailed study could show that better scheduling rules would increase production as much as adding a new drill press and would do so more cheaply. When the analyst receives very specific directives, he is under some political pressure to carry them out. However, he should be aware that doing this may be a suboptimal solution. If preliminary analysis indicates that this is the case, the analyst should be sure the decision maker is willing to forego the chance of a better solution.

In the maintenance example in Chapter 2, the problem might have been initiated by recognition on the part of line management that production rates were lower than they should be. An awareness that some change might benefit the organization is often the start of a study. Since the purpose of the maintenance example was to introduce simulation concepts, we minimized the formulation phase and simply stated the objective —to minimize expected costs. In most real-world situations the translation of the performance measures into an operating objective function is very difficult. Even in reasonably well understood problems, such as inventory control, analysts have great difficulty finding common measures for production effort and for being out-of-stock.

We further simplified the maintenance example by assuming that the only controllable variables of interest were the time and number of adjusters assigned to labelers on each production line. In fact, many other important controllable variables could have been considered, such as machine capacity, employee skill improvement training, job scheduling, or preventive maintenance schedules. How many and which of these would have been included in a larger study is a decision the analyst must face in real-world problem formulation. Such a decision depends in part on the likelihood of successfully constructing and solving a model of the more complex problem. One of the reasons for using simulation models is that real-world complexities can often be added to an existing model without a large increase in analysis time. This means that the model can itself be used to determine which of the potentially controllable factors yields the greatest change in the performance of the system (i.e., it can be used to determine what the problem really is).

We have treated problem formulation as the first step in the model-building process and as if there were a clear-cut sequence in which the analysis occurs: problem formulation, model formulation, model use, and so forth. As we pointed out in Chapter 3, however, these steps are really entwined. Knowledge of models and theories is an important source of guidance for problem formulation. (Philosophically, is it even possible to describe any problem precisely without some model in mind?) For example, most analysts who are faced with an allocation problem use the ideas of linear programming to initially organize the variable relationships, constraints, and system objectives in their minds. This thought process greatly influences the way the problem will be formulated, even when the actual situation does not satisfy linear-programming requirements.

We will see in Chapter 6 that simulation languages, which have been developed principally to reduce the cost of constructing simulation models, also serve as guides to problem formulation. Each simulation language contains an implicit view of the world, which, when learned by the analyst, may be very useful in making sense out of a situation. For this reason a good grounding in existing theories, models, and simulation languages can be extremely useful to the analyst in the problem-formulation phase. (This is part of the experience factor we referred to earlier.) For the purposes of this book, however, it will not be necessary to be highly conversant with any special theories, models, or simulation languages. We will review any background information necessary for the problems we use as examples.

When the analyst has successfully met the four conditions of problem formulation, he begins the task of model construction (i.e., defining the $f(C, U)$ in Equation 4–1). Model construction is discussed in the next chapter; however, the transitional stage between problem formulation and model construction is covered here. This transition is the identification of subsystems and variables in the system.

4-3 methods of identifying subsystems and variables

When a person first encounters a situation foreign to him, he generally sees it as a mass of confusion. It usually does not take too long before he begins to make sense out of the confusion. An analyst may have some related experience that provides useful guidelines for making sense of the process. He may have worked with this part of the organization before, or with systems that have similar characteristics.

The extent to which observation and previous experience assist in gaining understanding varies. An analyst with experience in manufacturing will have little trouble in beginning to formulate structural relations, or even specific model ideas, about operations in a machine shop. However, even an experienced market analyst could have trouble formulating variable relations that predict the market for, say, home stereo units. One reason for this is that such market predictions require an understanding of consumer behavior, and less is known about representing behavioral processes than about representing manufacturing processes. In addition, the marketing problem is greatly affected by information flows within the system (e.g., advertising campaigns), which are much harder to observe than the material flows in a manufacturing system.

Perhaps the most important point about problem formulation is that the analyst should be intimate with the situation and its theoretical basis, either from previous experience or by intensive study. The analyst's function at this stage is to translate the situation into a model. A predictive model can result only if the analyst is aware of the factors and relationships causing the behavior in the system. This means not only having a grasp of how the system works by observing it, but also a good understanding of theories of why it behaves in the way it does. To successfully simulate a petrochemical plant it is necessary to understand chemistry, thermo-dynamics, and mechanics. To simulate the behavior in a particular con-sumer market, it is necessary to understand what is known about relevant psychological and sociological theories of behavior as well as to know how the product is distributed.

In this section we assume that the analyst is completely new to the problem situation. We will illustrate several approaches that we have found useful for making sense of an unfamiliar situation.

Flow Approach

The most common method of grasping a situation is to follow the flow of the major items being processed. In the example in Chapter 2, use of this approach would lead to tracing the flow of the product. We would start with the basic raw materials and show the entry of other materials and components as the product passes through the manufacturing and assembly processes. It becomes clear (after some observation) that the sequence of steps in the system can be viewed as an alternation of *processing* (changing the product) and *movement* (to the next process). The flow approach quickly reveals where processing delays may occur and the effects of such delays on subsequent processing.

It is natural for groups of processes to be treated as a basic subsystem when flow analysis is used. A process is a point in the operation where products undergo some change; it usually involves a facility for making the change, an operator, materials, and a processing procedure (e.g., manufacturing instructions). Further details about the processing opera-tion unfold through observation and questioning. For example, unusual complications required to keep the facilities in operating condition may come to the analyst's attention. After the subsystems are identified, preliminary economic studies can be made to indicate where improvements will give a high payoff.

After the analyst has made some sense of the overall system using the flow approach, he may apply it to one of the subsystems originally identified. For example, if the flow approach had been used to identify the labeler operation as a subsystem in the packaging operation, the analyst could begin to look at the labeler subsystem as a flow problem, even though no item actually flows. It is possible to imagine a flow of machines (operating) that "leave" the production process when they fail and go to a repair process. After repair, the machines "flow" back to the production line. The conceptualization of imaginary flows is sometimes very useful in problem formulation.

In most systems there are two physical flows: products and people. There are also other kinds of flows, the two most important of which are information and money. (It might be argued that financial flows are just a special form of information flow—that information which denotes value; this philosophical point will not be pursued here.)

Information flow is more difficult to trace than physical flow because most information is invisible, being communicated or processed by people or inside computers. An analyst can obtain a good idea of information flows by studying such documents as orders, advertising messages, reports of action (e.g., receiving reports, production reports), confirmations of action, technical procedures, manufacturing procedures, inquiries, status reports, policy statements, and so forth. Amstutz [1967, ch. 3] has presented an excellent discussion of the development of a system (the marketing subsystem of a business) on the flow basis.

In some organizations the major flow is information. Insurance companies provide a typical example. In tracing information flow we find a pattern of alternating communication and information processing steps. Thus, again we tend to focus on groups of processing steps as subsystems.

In most situations all the major flow elements should be traced before subsystems are identified. Subsystems defined after examining just physical flows may not be as rich as those defined by examining the interaction between physical, information and financial flows.

One of the authors was faced with the case of defining the data processing problem in a hospital. (The original question was, "How can we use computers to improve patient care?") Progress really began in problem formulation when the flow of patients through the system was charted. Figure 4–1 is a simplified chart of this flow. The flow approach helped pinpoint key processes where computers might help, for example, bed assignment and retrieval of patient records. More important, it helped identify key decisions. Chapters 4 and 5 in *Industrial Dynamics* [Forrester, 1961] present another discussion of the development of flow models.

Functional Approach

With complex systems (e.g., the social welfare system), the flow approach may not be the best way to identify subsystems, as there may not be an obvious flowing element. In these cases, a commonly used

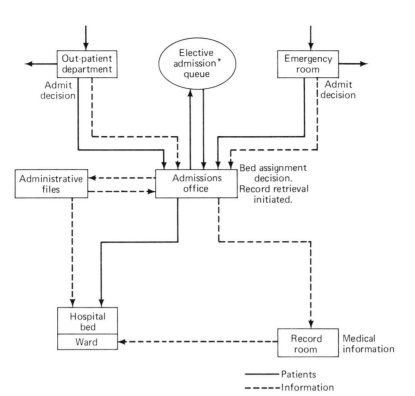

*Patients who can be admitted when room in the appropriate ward is available.

Figure 4–1   Simplified version of hospital flows.

approach is to identify functions in the system and to trace the sequence in which they occur.

Suppose the problem area is production control in a manufacturing plant. It is not clear what flows in this case, but a sequence of specific functions can be identified readily. These functions are triggered by a call from a customer. (In other situations a process starts at a specified time rather than with the arrival of an external input.) Upon receipt of the customer order the following functions might be observed:

- establishing price and delivery date
- engineering the product to customer specifications
- machine loading
- inventory processing
- work scheduling
- dispatching (assigning jobs to facilities)
- shipping
- accounting and invoicing

The analyst can now probe more deeply into each function, determining who does it, what facilities and information must be available, what

67

procedures are followed, and what outputs result. From analysis of each function, subsystems are identified by appropriate grouping of the functions and subfunctions.

There are seven major types of functions that occur in industrial systems:

- material processing
- transportation
- storage
- information processing
- communication
- information storage (filing)
- decision making

In most cases there are two sequences of functions, often proceeding in parallel. One sequence deals with physical movement and involves material processing, transportation, and storage functions. The other deals with organizational control and includes information processing and filing, decision making and communication. A system that consists largely of the control activities is especially suited to a functional rather than to a flow analysis.

After the functions are identified, the system modeling is initiated by describing (often in a flow-chart form) the procedures by which each function is or may be carried out. This provides a start on the development of the necessary models of the subsystems.

In the situation used for an example in Chapter 2 the functions might be

- scheduling the work
- dispatching work to specific production lines
- processing
- transporting jobs between processes (on conveyor belts)
- storing in-process work (temporary back-ups)
- providing operators
- providing materials
- maintaining the facilities
- providing maintenance personnel

It is, of course, these last two functions that came under particular scrutiny in Chapter 2. The analyst finally focused on the decision function of scheduling maintenance personnel as *the* problem.

State-Change Approach

The state-change approach is particularly suited to problems destined for simulation analysis, but it can be used in any situation. This view of the world divides time into a series of instants or points. At each instance we can imagine taking a snapshot of the system. The snapshot is the *state of the system*. Formally, the state is represented by specifying the values of the relevant exogenous and endogenous variables [Zemach, 1968].

A first task in making sense of a situation using state-change analysis is to identify the relevant variables. The next, and most difficult, step is to define the relationships that describe how the state (each of the variables) changes as time moves from one instant to the next. Since every variable does not necessarily change at each advance in time, the time-dependent relationships can be conditional on the present (and past) states; that is, a particular variable may change only when the present state has certain characteristics. The relationships for state change therefore involve two parts.

(1) A procedure for determining whether a variable or group of variables *should* change.

(2) The computational procedure that makes these changes updates the variables.

Subsystems are defined in a way that minimizes the effects of changes in one subsystem on the behavior of the others. In state-change models, subsystems are subprocedures.

In the example of Chapter 2, some of the state variables would be

- whether a labeling machine was operative or down
- down time (cumulative)
- whether a repairman was busy or not
- adjustment time
- whether a machine was processing material or was operative but idle
- labeler processing rates (through-put)

(The last two state variables were not used in the model in Chapter 2 because that Chapter dealt solely with maintenance problems.)

Examples of change-of-state procedures will be illustrated throughout this book. A simulation model is usually a state-change model, and hence much of this book is devoted to state-change models and their use.

documenting the problem 4-4

Documentation is a vital part of the process of developing a simulator or any other type of model. Documentation serves as the basis for communication between the various people who must be involved in the modeling effort if it is to be successful. Such communication paths must be created between

- decision maker and analyst
- analyst and computer programmer
- analyst and other personnel affected by the study

In some cases there is also communication from the analyst to the profession in general (i.e., through journal articles, professional meetings, and so forth) so that others may improve research practices as a result of individual experience.

One thing that must be documented is the definition of the problem. Often this is done after the model is defined, rather than immediately after the problem-formulation phase. Such a delay permits the problem to be stated by reference to the model and how it will be used. Nevertheless, it is desirable to have the most complete statement of the problem possible as early in the study as possible. This statement should include

- a description of the organization in which the problem exists
- a statement of the decision that is to be made and the range of alternatives possible (to the extent that they are presently recognized)
- a list of the constraints and guidelines, considered to be outside the problem area, which form the set of assumptions under which the analysis is being done
- a statement of the basic nature of the processes in the system as complete as possible before the model is formulated

It is important to document the details of the subsystems just as it is important to document the overall formulation. The flow approach provides a natural basis for documentation. Flow diagrams (like Figures 2–1 and 4–1) show the movement of items or information through a sequence of processes, activities, communication channels, and decision-making steps. Such diagrams are extremely useful in communicating formulations and findings. Indeed, flow diagrams often help in clarifying the problem for the analyst himself. In early versions of the flow diagrams the processes are usually described by brief English language statements, although some generally recognized symbolism may be used. Later flow charts may become more formal.

Functional and state-change approaches are a little more difficult to document. The functional approach is often documented by means of a flow chart, which has a format similar to a flow diagram but the arrows and boxes have different interpretations. The arrows represent the sequence in which functions are performed (not the paths by which items flow). The boxes contain descriptions of the procedures by which the functions are performed.

Documentation of state-change models usually begins with a listing and description of the variables that represent the state. Next, it is necessary to describe the procedures by which the state changes from time period to time period. This can be done by computer-like flow charts.

With the representation in flow-chart form, the analyst can interact with other people involved in the modeling effort to review the assumptions implicit in the representation. We have concentrated here on the documentation of the technical aspects of the problem. Complete documentation would include information for the management of the study itself; progress and expenditure data. This documentation is that required for any well-run engineering or management study as discussed in texts on project management [Cleland and King, 1968].

implementing results 4-5

Having reviewed the very early phases of an analyst's effort, let us now skip to the end of the process. Imagine that the study has been made using a model. Quantitative results are available that indicate (within the validity of the model) what the decision should be—what is the best course of action. How are these results to be used? The use of model results, like formulating the problem, does not depend upon the type of model used. Also, as with problem formulation, the methods by which results are successfully implemented are more a function of the managerial abilities of the analyst than his scientific expertise. Methods for implementing solutions are best learned by practice. In addition to gaining actual experience, the reader is advised to review the several discussions of implementation by leading operations research authors listed at the end of this chapter [Amstutz, 1967, ch. 15; Churchman, 1964; Cleland and King, 1968; King, 1968; McKenney, 1968]. In this section we will try to give the guidelines for use of model results.

The use of models and their results is not a straight-line sequence. A particular modeling effort will often provide the decision maker with new insights into his own systems. These insights are likely to create new aspects to old problems, or even completely new problems that should be studied. Thus, a decision maker may not implement actions on the basis of a particular modeling effort; the result may be to request the analysts to perform further work under new guidelines. Obviously, these circumstances require that the decision maker and the analyst work on the problem almost as a team. They evolve a model together which at any time represents the situation as best it can be understood and which is used as required to assist in on-going decision making.

The analyst must also recognize that his model will never contain all of the factors in the decision maker's mind. For example, it is sometimes difficult to know the real objective function by which the decision maker operates. An approximation to this objective function is especially difficult to obtain when the decision-making process is carried out by a group in which each individual operates under different political pressures. Because the model is only an approximation, the analyst usually presents the results of the analysis to the decision maker for his guidance and

71

further interpretation in addition to making specific recommendations himself. The more the decision maker understands about the model, its assumptions, and the objective function, the better he will be able to use it to improve his decision-making capabilities.

To take the most difficult case, assume the decision maker has not been very involved in the analytic process. Some guidelines to successful implementation in this circumstance are:

- Plan to present the results, if possible, in a series of presentations rather than in one brief (or extended) report. (It takes time for most people to absorb new viewpoints.)

- In the initial presentations carefully review the assumptions and constraints in the study so objections to them can be taken into account in subsequent analysis.

- Review the model used and explain in nontechnical terms the principal relationships and variables. Use visual aids if at all possible.

- State carefully the objective function being used; that is, what is it that the analyst assumed was being optimized: costs, profits, growth rate, or some combination of these.

- Indicate as many of the details of the models as possible. Pay special attention to exceptional cases, since these are often of great interest to a manager.

- Summarize the alternative solutions being considered. Specify the results predicted (including confidence in each prediction) for each alternative.

After the manager has absorbed and internalized the results, presumably a decision will be forthcoming.

The model itself should become a device for monitoring the progress of the implementation phase. As data become available from early implementation, the model can be used to make better forecasts of what is likely to happen at later stages. The decision maker can adjust timing and specific recommendations based on this further analysis. Of course, it is also possible that the model will be found to be incomplete in some respects and this can be improved as implementation proceeds.

A report should be prepared on the analytic effort. Where a continuously evolving model is used, it is sometimes difficult to determine at what stage to stop analysis and produce this documentation. An arbitrary decision may have to be made by the project leader to document the model as of a certain date even though its evolution continues. The purpose of this documentation is several-fold:

(1) It permits the project to continue with a minimum of added costs in the case of personnel changes.

(2) It provides a source of information for analysts who may wish to return to the problem at some future date (after a lapse in the study).

(3) It provides a basis for internal reports and professional papers that disseminate the knowledge gained.

(4) It forces the analysts to examine logically all phases of the project and thus serves as a tool for improved analysis.

(5) It provides a partial basis for judging the validity of the analysis and the resulting recommendations.

A good manager or analysis team leader, for the fourth reason alone, should insist on documentation at appropriate times. A team that cannot document its work has not done much. The amount of documentation required will vary with the particular form of model used; however, a rule of thumb is that documentation should be sufficient to permit another qualified analyst to pick up and continue the project with little searching for additional information.

Finally, the analyst should devise a way to check on the implemented decisions. Periodic, if not continuous, monitoring is desirable to determine when parameters change or when some of the assumptions upon which the decision was made might change. These changes would signal the need for further study and a review of the decision. Such monitoring is especially important when the decision is made frequently and automatically; for example, if it were carried out clerically or on a computer, as would be the case with an inventory reorder rule.

Perhaps the most important point about implementation is that the recommendations from the study are instituted only when there is mutual trust between the decision maker and the analyst. Where this does not exist, the work of the analyst will probably be fruitless, even though he is technically very capable.

exercises

4–1 Try to apply the three problem formulation approaches—flow, functional, and state change—to the floor operations of a bank. (A local banker will probably cooperate in providing a description of the process and some data.) Prepare a report describing

(a) the key decisions
(b) the problem, the decision requiring most attention
(c) a representation of the situation as a flow, a sequence of functions, state changes
(d) which representation appears to be most suitable and why

(Where this book is used in a class, it is suggested that each member of the class give a presentation describing the recommendations derived from, and the results of, a simulation study.)

4–2 Describe the state and state-change processes for a multiproduct inventory situation. Include the accounting processes. Assume

(1) There are ten products.
(2) Demand for the products is expressed as orders giving the product and a quantity. Distributions of order interarrival times and of quantities are known. Some products have seasonal trends.

73

(3) Orders arrive from fifteen different customers, any of whom order any product from time to time.
(4) Reorders are placed by standard inventory procedures.
(5) Unit costs and prices are constant.
(6) Substitutions are permissible (but not desired by the customers) in the following cases:
  product 1 for product 4
  product 6 for product 10
(7) Back orders are held until they can be filled.

references

Ackoff, R. L., *Scientific Method: Optimizing Applied Research Decisions,* Wiley, New York, 1962.

Amstutz, A. E., *Computer Simulation of Competitive Market Response,* M.I.T. Press, Cambridge, Mass., 1967.

Churchman, C., "Managerial Acceptance of Scientific Recommendations," *California Management Review,* Vol. 7, No. 1, Fall 1964, pp. 31–38.

Cleland, D. I., and W. R. King, *Systems Analysis and Project Management,* McGraw-Hill, New York, 1968.

Forrester, J. W., *Industrial Dynamics,* M.I.T. Press, Cambridge, Mass., 1961.

King, Paul E., "Simulation: Management Planning Tool," *IEEE Transactions on Systems Science and Cybernetics,* Vol. SSC–4, No. 4, November 1968, pp. 373–76.

McKenney, James L., "An Approach to Simulation Model Development for Improved Planning," Working Paper No. 140, Graduate School of Business, Stanford University, Palo Alto, Calif., June 1968.

Zemach, R., "A State Space Model for Resource Allocation in Higher Education," *IEEE Transactions on Systems Science and Cybernetics,* Vol. SSC–4, No. 2, July 1968, p. 108.

5

developing the simulation model and program

introduction 5-1

In Chapter 2 we used a machine adjustment problem to illustrate the nature of simulation and to distinguish it from analytic model-building methods. The flow chart for that problem was written in a fashion that made it easy for the reader to grasp simulation concepts. The simplest way of describing the behavior of the machine repair system was used, regardless of its computational efficiency. For such a small system, computer running time is not greatly affected by the way the flow chart or computer program is organized. Normally, however, this is not the case. Therefore, this chapter describes a procedure for representing the behavior of systems in an organized fashion that leads to computationally efficient computer programs.

We begin this chapter by describing the basic form of simulation procedures. Then we show how this form of representation is realized in a specific example.

a basic form for organizing 5-2
simulation models*

Formulating simulation models is, in one respect, more difficult than formulating other quantitative models. If, for example, a system can be described in a way that meets the assumptions of linear programming

---

* Adapted with permission from Chapter 2, "Simulation: Uses," *Progress in Operations Research*, Vol. III (ed. by Julius Aronofsky), Wiley, New York, 1969.

(i.e., all variables are linearly related in the objective and constraint functions), the theory of linear programming itself forms a guide to subsequent model building. It defines the organization of the data and the way the data are used to solve the problem. On the other hand, if no standard model appears to fit and the analyst builds a simulation model, he will find very few guidelines for representing the system because there is no well developed situation-independent theory of simulation analogous to that of linear programming. As simulation techniques have become more refined, however, the beginnings of a theory of simulation are starting to appear. For example, systems that have discrete units (such as job lots or customers) flowing through a sequence of processing stations (such as machine tool centers or bank tellers) have a common form (Figure 5–1).

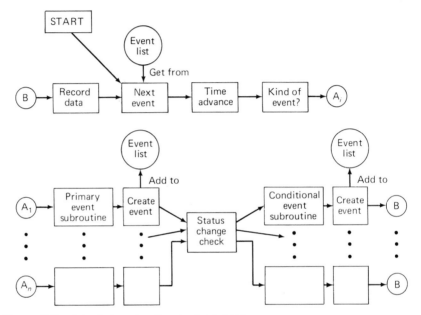

Figure 5–1 A basic form for discrete simulations.

The key to simulation of discrete entity systems (discrete simulation) is the procedure for representing processes. A *process* is an activity that proceeds over time. Its initiation, alteration, or conclusion is called an *event*. If, and only if, an event occurs, the state of the system changes. In a discrete simulation, processes are not modeled explicitly; they are represented by the modeling of the events that affect the status of the process. Sometimes the status change in one process will affect the status of another. These *conditional process changes* are treated as if they all occurred at the completion event time. For example, a truck can be simulated as being at its origination point, then being in transit, and, finally, being at its destination. When the trip ends, the cargo also is suddenly at the destination.

The first task in building a simulator is to specify an event list (or event file). This list contains descriptions of events computed to occur at some future time in the simulation. At any time in the course of the simulator, the event list specifies the time at which predictable future events will occur. The event list is constantly augmented as other events are predicted and the system state changes. The event list is the bookkeeping device to facilitate predicting the time and conditions when events occur. In most large systems, subroutines are developed that make the predictions of when each type of event (e.g., the time when a labeling machine will fail) will occur.

The event-time prediction subroutines are the central part of a simulation model because they represent the analyst's hypotheses of how the system and environment determine process duration. In some cases this may be deterministic; for example, the duration that a machine will operate is equal to a set-up time plus a multiple of the number of units to be processed. In other cases the process duration (or other event time) may be probabilistic. Each event is an observation from the probability distribution hypothesized to represent the duration. For example, in the machine repair problem in Chapter 2 we used the exponential distribution to represent machine failures. (We defer any general discussion of methods for generating variates from particular distributions until Chapter 7.)

When the analyst has specified an event list and an exhaustive set of event prediction subroutines, the basic form of the simulation can be represented as in Figure 5–1. The simulation sequence begins when the event list is searched to find the *next* event—the one with the lowest event time. The simulated clock is then advanced to that time; that is, we advance the simulator on an *event-to-event* basis. As the flow chart shows, the next step is to determine the kind of event that has occurred; for example, is it the arrival of a job in the shop or the completion of a job on a machine? The kind of event will have been stored in the event list. The *primary* subroutines then change in the system status. For example, the arrival of a job would require that a job record be created with variables representing the priorities and processing time for the job at machines where processing must take place. A primary event may directly cause the creation of a new future event regardless of the status of the system. For example, the arrival time of the next job can be determined on the basis of the time of a current arrival. The appropriate event prediction subroutine is used to determine when the next arrival will occur.

As a result of the primary event, the state of the system has changed. The *conditional* event routines are used to trigger future events that are caused by the new system status. For example, if a machine is idle and a job has just arrived in the queue, it is possible to put the job on the machine. Now the conditions are such that an event representing the end of the processing time can be created. When all the conditional events have been added to the event list, the whole process repeats itself. This repetition moves the simulated system through time and the dynamic performance of this system is summarized by recording appropriate data.

The basic simulation form just described provides a guide to model-building activity in a number of complex environments. It is also the basis of many special simulation languages. We will use this form as a guide to solving the example problem that follows.

5-3 the example situation*

The environment for this problem is a shop that produces plastic subassemblies. The shop has three processing stations that we will refer to as *machines* (Figure 5–2). At the first processing station, the plastic raw material is molded into the proper shapes using special dies on the molding machine. At the second station, the plastic parts are separated, trimmed, and buffed. At the last station, the parts are assembled into the

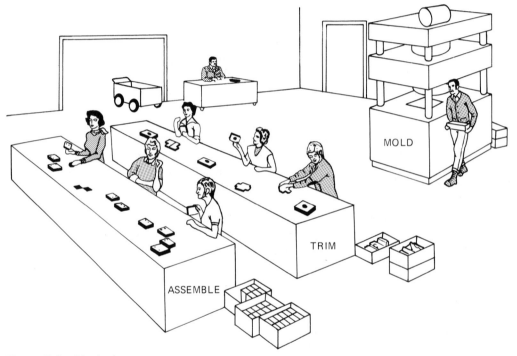

MOLD

TRIM

ASSEMBLE

Figure 5–2 Plastic shop.

final product. All jobs pass through each of these three processes, and we assume that each station can process only one job at a time. Since the process time varies from job to job, the shop cannot be scheduled perfectly, and waiting lines or queues of jobs to be processed will build up in front of the various processing stations.

When a job arrives, the materials and dies needed for its completion are always available. The job order that accompanies each job gives

* Adapted and reprinted by permission from *An Introduction to Simulation*, Audio Education Package, Western Region, © 1967 by International Business Machines Corporation.

the processing times required at each station; these times are assumed (for now) to be predictable, constant values for any job. Figure 5–3 is a typical job order. All processing times are given in hours, and all due times are given in working hours from an initial start time.

The principal features of the shop are incoming jobs, the three processes (mold, trim, and assemble), and queues or waiting lines of jobs before each machine. There are many aspects of shop operation that are ignored in this example. For instance, we do not distinguish the set-up time from the running time on the molding operation, nor do we recognize machine downtime. Assume that these and other details are not required to develop a model appropriate to this study.

Job No. 37	Due Time 33
Process	Process Time Required
Mold	4 hours
Trim	3
Assembly	5

Figure 5–3 Typical job order.

Problem Formulation

The objective of management in this shop is to *minimize the total lateness; the number of hours that jobs are completed late.* The decision or control variable is the rule, called a *dispatch* rule, for scheduling jobs. Currently this is first come, first served. It has been suggested that the rule "each processing station should take the job from those waiting that has the shortest processing time" would be better. Another suggested rule is "each station should take the job waiting that has the nearest due time."

It is difficult to predict by judgment which of these alternative rules will minimize lateness hours. Lateness depends on the complex interaction of the three processing times. It also turns out there is no good mathematical theory for predicting the lateness under these conditions. The simulator about to be designed will assist in choosing the best dispatch policy.

In this example the problem is best understood using the flow approach described in the previous chapter. The flow is of jobs through the shop. Figure 5–4 illustrates this first abstraction of the system. The problem formulation includes listing variables (and range of their values) that would be altered by alternative dispatch rules as well as a description of the job data arrival patterns, the process times, and the due dates. These factors will be presented as we proceed with model formulation.

Model Formulation

As discussed in Chapter 2, it is not hard to find real waiting-line situations for which queuing theory is unable to predict the behavior of the system. This example cannot be solved using queuing theory because

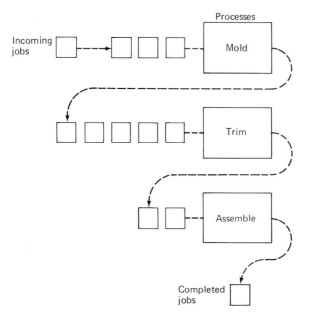

Figure 5–4 Flow analysis of the plastic shop.

the arrival and process times are not manageable statistical distributions. The fact that dispatch rules other than first come, first served are being considered further complicates the problem. (The problem involves priority queues for which there is little mathematical theory.) Thus, simulation appears to be the best technique.

To develop a simulator we must study this shop by observing and predicting changes of state; that is, by representing the dynamics of the system. If we were asked to represent the dynamics of the real shop, we might well start by trying to take a snapshot of the shop at frequent intervals of time. Since the smallest processing time is one hour, we could obtain a fairly complete description by taking a snapshot of the shop every hour starting at the beginning of the period to be studied. If we did this, we might get pictures for a typical day as shown in Figure 5–5. At the start of observation (Figure 5–5a), Job 10 is in the molding process, Job 7 in the trim, and Job 9 in the assembly process. Jobs 5 and 6 are waiting to be assembled, and Job 8 is waiting for the trim processing. After one hour of operation (Figure 5–5b), we see that Job 11 has arrived and entered the waiting line for the first process. After two hours have passed (Figure 5–5c), a number of changes have occurred. Job 12 has arrived and is waiting for the first process. Job 9 finished processing in the assembly operation and has departed from the shop. Therefore, Job 5, which had been waiting for assembly, is now in the assembly process. Similar changes of status occur during the rest of the day (see Figure 5–5d through i).

We present this detailed description of the shop's operation because it is typical of the way the analyst will receive information from observation of the shop and from discussions with personnel who know the operations. There are several factors to notice in this particular sequence

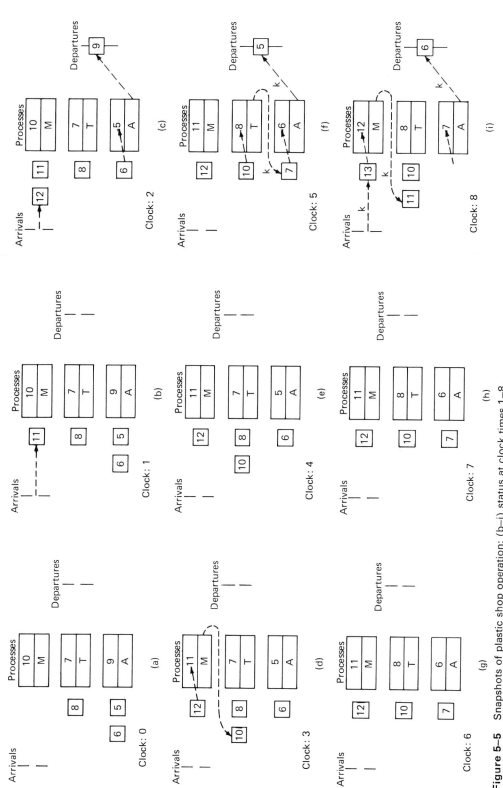

Figure 5-5 Snapshots of plastic shop operation; (b–i) status at clock times 1–8.

of events. First, we are examining the snapshot of the system at the *end* of each time period. We do not look in detail at what goes on between the hourly snapshots. (We must choose a unit of time that will provide an accurate description of the system. In Chapter 7 we discuss how the time unit should be selected.) Second, system changes occur in two different ways: either events initiate some action at a specific time (primary or predictable events), or events are consequences of other activity (conditional events). For example, at hour 5 the primary events are the completion of Job 7 in trim (which then goes to wait for assembly), and the completion of Job 5 in assembly. A resulting conditional event is Job 8's movement from the waiting line into the trim process. This conditional event involves two steps: the decision as to which job in the waiting line to take (8 or 10) and the movement of that job from a waiting to a processing status. Finally, note that there are time periods when there are no status changes in the shop (i.e., time periods 4, 6, and 7).

The fact that some time periods go by without changes means that we can obtain a complete representation of what actually happened by taking a picture *only when changes occur.* Imagine, for example, that a bell rings and a photograph is taken every time some change in status occurs. The sequence of pictures we would take would be b, c, d, f, i. The problem now is to describe this sequence of events in a concise and general way so that the dynamics of this particular shop are represented *independently of the particular time period being observed.* We want to be able to describe the snapshot—the state—every time a change occurs. This snapshot, along with the event list, is used to predict when the next snapshot should be taken. Then we compute what the state will look like at that time. These prediction procedures are the basis for the simulation model.

The first step toward a simulation model is to obtain a concise representation of the state of the shop. This is best done by defining numerical quantities (variables) to represent the various parts of the shop. Table 5–1 summarizes the starting conditions numerically—it is an abstract of the

Table 5–1.
Summary of Conditions at the Start of the Shift

Job	Processing Time			Status*	Arrival Time	Due Time
	Mold	Trim	Assemble			
5			3	Wait A	↑	5
6			3	Wait A	(In	6
7		5†	1	T	process)	3
8		4	2	Wait T		10
9			2†	A		2
10	3†	1	1	M	↓	2
11	5	4	3		1	27
12	6	2	3		2	10
13	2	2	2		7	8

* Wait = waiting in queue for process noted; M = mold; T = trim; A = assemble.
† Remaining processing time.

initial snapshot. Table 5–2 is a numerical representation of the remaining snapshots—in even more concise form. In this table the numbers under the arrival column are the numbers of the jobs entering the shop. The numbers under the processes column are the jobs being processed at each station during the time unit. The queues column shows which jobs are in the three waiting lines. For example, in the first row, Jobs 5 and 6 (in that order) are waiting for assembly. Finally, we show the jobs that have been completed in the depart column. To show the dynamics we have indicated the status at the beginning and at the end of each time period. This is done only to facilitate reading; the status at the end of one time period is exactly the same as the status at the beginning of the next period.

Simulated Clock	Arrivals	Processes			Queues			Depart
		Mold	Trim	Assemble	Wait M	Wait T	Wait A	
(Beginning)	(11)	10	7	9		8	5, 6	
1 (End)		10	7	9	11	8	5, 6	
2	(12)	10	7	(9)	11	8	5, 6	
		10	7	5	11, 12	8	6	9
3		(10)	7	5	11, 12	8	6	
		11	7	5	12	8, 10	6	
4		11	7	5	12	8, 10	6	
		11	7	5	12	8, 10	6	
5		11	(7)	(5)	12	8, 10	6	
		11	8	6	12	10	7	5
6		11	8	6	12	10	7	
		11	8	6	12	10	7	
7		11	8	6	12	10	7	
		11	8	6	12	10	7	
8	(13)	(11)	8	(6)	12	10	7	
		(12)	8	7	13	10, 11		6

Table 5–2. Concise Description of the State of System at Time Instances (Coded "Snapshots")

The circled items in the table show which jobs change during the period. It is these changes that must be represented by the dynamics of the simulator. Let us examine how we can represent such changes in a model. Recall that the *state* of the system is the complete numerical description of its status at any point in time (a row in Table 5–2). An *event* is a change in the state of the system and occurs at an instant of time. The model represents the dynamics by predicting the time when an event occurs and by examining the event's effect on the state of the system. To make the simulation general, the state is represented by variables that can take on different values. These variables tend to fall into groups that we will call *tables* or *arrays.* (They will become, in fact, data arrays in the program.)

Six tables are needed to describe the *state* of the plastic shop operations. A brief description of the characteristics of each table is now given; examples follow.

JOB TABLE

The purpose of the shop is to process the jobs into final products. Therefore, it is necessary to keep track of the status of each job, and a table is needed to do so. Data from this table will be accumulated for a statistical analysis of the characteristics of jobs that enter the shop, where delays occur, lateness, and so forth. (We have put future job arrivals on the job table as a convenient way of introducing a backlog of jobs.)

ROUTING TABLE

This table defines the sequence of processing stations for each job. (The routing table is trivial in this example because all jobs have the same sequence, but it can become complex in other cases.)

EVENT TABLE

This table keeps track of what should happen at future time periods. In other words, it retains the forecasts of primary events.

MACHINE TABLE

To insure that jobs from queues are put on idle machines, and that the proper job is removed from a machine and placed in the next queue, it is necessary to maintain records on the status of each processing station. This data is also needed to obtain summary information about each machine's processing record (in this example, machine utilization).

QUEUES

The focus of this study is on how to remove jobs from queues (i.e., waiting lines) when a machine is idle. It is necessary to keep track of the specific jobs in each queue and the sequence in which they arrive (for use in representing FIFO or LIFO dispatch rules).

OUTPUT TABLE

One output from the system could be a complete list of activities such as the one in Table 5–2. Generally, however, the analyst is interested in summary data. For scheduling problems, interest centers around output such as total throughput (jobs per day), machine utilization, and job lateness. As the simulation operates, it is necessary to accumulate the data that can produce these statistics. The data is accumulated in output arrays. In this example the output array accumulates a frequency count of hours late. Output may be visualized as the data that a record keeper would gather if he were standing in the shop examining key events occurring during the day's activity.

We begin our detailed discussion of the plastic shop by analyzing the event table, since this table plays a central role in simulation models. The initial event table for the shop is shown in Figure 5–6a. In it are all future events that are known at the start. For example, we know from Table 5–2 that Job 7 is at the trim process and will be completed five periods later. We record this in line 5 of Figure 5–6a. Since we are starting at time zero, the completion of Job 7's trim occurs at time 5. This is a prediction that we can make because we can determine the exact processing times required for each job. (Later we will see that we can determine future simulation events even when we cannot make exact estimates of the processing time.) In the initial events table, we list all future job arrivals and the times when each of the processing centers will complete their *current* jobs.

Time	Type of Event	Machine or Job
1	Arrival (A)	11
2	A	12
8	A	13
2	Completion (C)	A
5	C	T
3	C	M

Figure 5–6a Initial condition event table.

At time 2, there is a change in status of the assembly process; Job 9 is completed and Job 5 replaces it (see Table 5–2). We know from the job description data (Table 5–1) that it will take three hours to complete the assembly of Job 5. Thus, we predict that there will be a completion in assembly at time 5. The event list is thus augmented (Figure 5–6b) to include this predicted completion. Figure 5–6c shows the event list as of the end of time period 8.

Time	Type of Event	Machine or Job	
1	Arrival (A)	11	
2	A	12	
8	A	13	*Starting*
2	Completion (C)	A	*status*
5	C	T	
3	C	M	
5	C	A	

Figure 5–6b Event table at a later time.

The event list can be kept quite small by restricting the list to include only the *next* event to occur at each process. When an event occurs to change the status of a process, the event table is altered to determine when the status of *that* process will change again. This procedure has the advantage that the queue, machine, routing, and job tables are referenced only to obtain the specific information needed to predict correctly when the next event will occur and what the event will be. In the plastic shop problem, the event table would indicate the time when the next job is to arrive in the shop and the completion times for the current jobs in the mold, trim, and assembly processes. The next change in the system must be caused by one of these four events. For example,

85

if we know that Job 8 will be completed at the mold station at time 14, we do not put any information about its completion on trim. (In fact, we do not have a submodel to predict that completion.)

This event table permits us to advance the simulator and to examine when future events will occur. The clock in the simulator can be advanced directly from the event table. We can skip the time units where no change occurs and so advance from event to event. If we scan the event list and pick out the event with the lowest number in the first column (time), we determine the next event. For example, if we do this assuming we were starting to analyze time 8 (see Figure 5–6c), we obtain three events: completions on mold and assembly and the arrival of Job 13. (Fewer multiple events would occur if we chose a very small time unit. In the machine repair problem in Chapter 2, multiple events were avoided in this manner. Another way to handle multiple events is to use a special rule to sequence them. An example of such a. rule occurs later in this case study.)

Figure 5–6c Event table at end of time 8.

Time	Type of Event	Machine or Job	
1	Arrival (A)	11*	
2	A	12*	
8	A	13*	Starting
2	Completion (C)	A*	status
5	C	T*	
3	C	M*	
5	C	A*	
8	C	M*	
9	C	T	
8	C	A*	
14	C	M	
9	C	A	

* Completed events—these entries would be removed from the table to make room for new events.

Figure 5–7 is a summary of all the table elements that would be required for the model. (The specific data in the tables are hypothetical and do not relate to the example.) The information contained in each table is fairly self-explanatory; however, a few comments may be helpful. The second column in the job table (status) is a code indicating where the job is in the system. The fourth item in the machine table records the time at which the machine last became idle. This information is necessary to compute cumulative idle time on the machines. The output table for the model gathers simulation statistics needed to generate a frequency distribution of job lateness.

The Simulation Procedure

We now have a set of tables to represent the complete status of the shop at any time. The next step is to create a procedure (in the form of a flow chart) that will tell how to update the status of the system when something does change and how to maintain the events list so the simulation can continue to generate new events. That is, we need the logical

Figure 5-7 Summary of table elements.

Table Name	1	2	3	4	5	6	7	8
Event table	Time (112) (117) ...	Type of event (Completion—C) (Arrival—A)	Machine/Job (M) (59)	Mold time (4)	Trim time (3)	Assembly (6)		
Job table	Job no. (27) ...	Status (Wait M)	Mold time (8)	Trim time (2)	Assembly time (2)	Arrival time (101)	Due time (130)	Completion time ( )
Machine table	Machine (M) (T) (A)	Job no. (17) (15) (11)	Cumulative idle time (27) (35) (43)	Last completion time (109) (105) (107)				
Queue wait M	Job no. (16)	Job no. (18)	Job no. (27)					
Queue wait T	Job no. (12)							
Queue wait A	Job no. (14)							
Output table	Lateness (≤ 0) (1) (2) ...	Number of jobs 15 5 3						
Clock	Current time (110)							

87

rules for combining and updating the information in the data tables. As a guide we use the basic flow discussed in Section 5–1. The general procedure repeats this cycle:

(1) Find the next event.

(2) Update the clock.

(3) Update the system status.

(4) Create a future event.

Figure 5–8 is a representation of the flow for the procedural model that shows about the same level of detail as the basic flow chart in Figure 5–1. A detailed flow chart of the shop's operation is presented in Figure 5–9. Although the description is fairly self-contained, a few comments may be helpful.

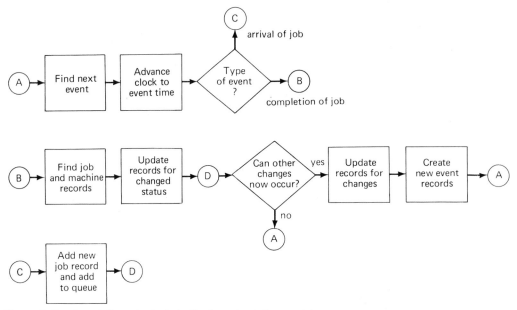

Figure 5–8   Overall flow chart of plastic shop simulation model.

In the first step shown in Figure 5–9, the model is initialized; that is, the conditions in the shop at the beginning of the simulation period are entered in each of the tables. Step 3, a way of determining whether the simulation should be continued, compares current clock time with the total desired simulation time. Step 6 illustrates why it is important to organize the tables so that information is readily available. In this step we take the job number from the arrival event record and use it to create a new job record. Step 9 also requires efficient information retrieval. One of the process machines has completed a job, and we need data about the machine and about the completed job to update statistics on lateness and utilization factors.

Step 12 is required if we wish to compute idle time. Step 16 is required because the last completion from assembly changes the state in a way different from completion of intermediate processes. Step 20 illustrates the computer storage allocation problems that sometimes occur in simulation models. Since a job that has finished the assembly process is no longer in the system, we would like to remove all the data about the job except whatever is required for statistical analysis. This removal leaves more space for records of new jobs entering the system. If no attempt is made to conserve space, the memory requirements for even a simple simulation become extremely large. In Step 21 we ensure that the same event is not processed twice by removing it from the event table when it becomes current.

Notice the implications of Step 22 with respect to multiple events occurring at the same time. In most programs searches through the machine table are made in numerical sequence; thus, if machines 1 and 3 are both idle, we will first put a job on 1 and then on 3. Since the clock does not advance during these computations, no difference in the effects of this ordering bias should result. However, in very complex situations the order in which multiple events are processed may have significant effects. For example, the time to process a job on machine 3 might take longer if an operator is put on machine 1 first because of, say, limited manpower. When there is interaction between the order in which events are processed, the time unit must be made very much smaller to reduce the significance of the interaction, or special procedures must be included.

Step 29 simply changes the code in the status entry to indicate that the job is now in process and not waiting in queue. We will discuss Step 31 at length in a later chapter, to show how to represent situations where probability distributions are used to represent processing times.

The appendices to this chapter present and describe the simulation program. Readers who have not had experience with this type of computer program should study those sections in detail.

Executing the Procedure

A computer is a device for executing procedures. Since we have defined our model in terms of tables of data, and procedures for updating the data entries, we should be able to program a computer to execute the model. Such execution will provide a dynamic representation of the shop's activities. The following are key points in the execution phase:

(1) We must be able to state the entries in the tables in a precise form that the computer can handle. Since modern computer languages enable the analyst to handle virtually any collection of numbers and alphanumeric characters (names), this is no real problem. Furthermore, most computer languages have special facilities for organizing data such as arrays, tables, or lists.

(2) The computer must be able to execute operations defined in the flow chart. These operations include arithmetic manipulations of data, comparisons, finding entries in tables, and accomplishing

appropriate input and output functions. Modern programming languages can perform these operations. The important task in creating the simulation program from the flow chart is to express *accurately* the flow-chart logic in statements that the computer will accept. It is not difficult to approximate the flow-chart description, but it is difficult to avoid building into the program very subtle assumptions that were not included in the original model. Usually these assumptions are not consciously introduced by the programmer and are therefore very difficult to eliminate. These problems lead analysts to write their own programs rather than to try to communicate with a programmer.

When the program has been written and debugged, it (along with initial values in the tables) is entered into the computer. When the computer is started it will execute the program, carrying on the flow-chart procedure for as long as has been designated. This is called one *computer run.* A run is a simulation of the situation under a specified set of conditions for a given period of time—it therefore permits the analyst to predict the performance of the shop under those operating conditions. By running the simulation under different operating conditions (in this case, different dispatch rules), the analyst can determine which provide the best performance.

5-4 conclusions

We have used the plastic shop situation to show how an unstructured problem is converted into a simulation model in the form of a computer program. The scheduling problem was not completely analyzed in this chapter. For example, we ignored problems of validating the model, designing experiments to determine the best scheduling rule, and specifying an objective function. These problems are discussed elsewhere.

We have gone exhaustively through a model construction procedure to develop this simulator. The problem environment would not normally warrant such detail; for a simulation of this size many short-cuts could be taken. However, this simple example illustrates a general way of structuring simulation models. It can be used on complex problems and it also makes it easier to show why special simulation languages (like GPSS and Simscript) take the form they do. In the next chapter we will examine the characteristics of these languages.

Those who are familiar with one or more general-purpose programming languages (e.g., FORTRAN) can convert the flow chart in Figure 5–9 into a computer program. In Appendix 5A of this chapter, we describe a method for storing and accessing the data tables used in a simulation. In Appendix 5B there is a FORTRAN computer program for the simulation model. Statements throughout the program relate it to the numbered boxes in the flow chart (Figure 5–9). Additional comments are provided to explain the table arrays and some of the subtle aspects of the program.

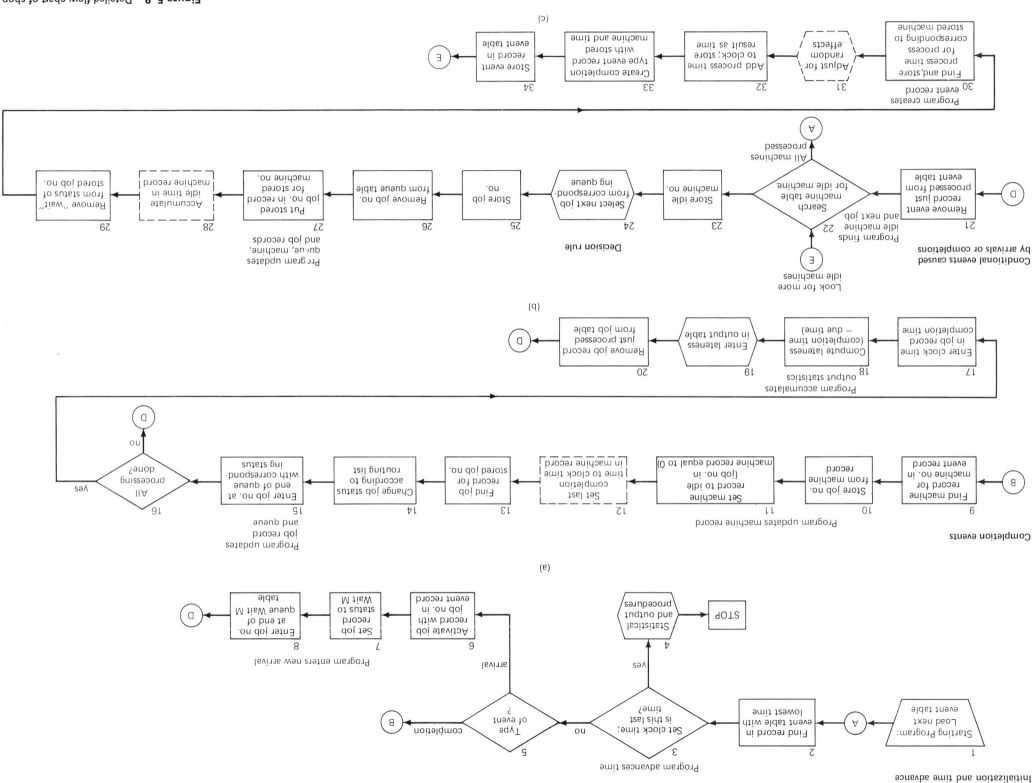

Figure 5-9 Detailed flow chart of shop.

exercises

5–1 Modify the simulation in Figure 5B–1 so that jobs are generated rather than read in from a backlog. Jobs are generated with the following characteristics:

(1) Job interarrival time is *eight times* the following probability density function:

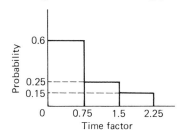

(2) Processing times for all jobs are:

Machine	Time
M	3
T	5
A	4

Hint: Write a routine to be initiated whenever an arrival event occurs. This routine should create the next arrival event list entry (with the appropriate interarrival time) and create the new job data for the job table.

The interarrival time can be generated by first creating a random number between zero and one (most computing centers have a library routine for this) and then choosing a *time factor* according to whether the random number is:

less than 0.6

between 0.6 and 0.85

over 0.85

Interpolation is necessary to obtain the final interarrival factor. Note that variables considered as integers in Figure 5B–1 will not have to be considered real (floating).

5–2 Revise the program of Exercise 5–1 so that the estimated process times (created when jobs are generated) are probabilistic. The process times are found by multiplying the times given in Exercise 5–1 (now considered as expected times) by the following discrete probability distribution:

Multiplier	Probability
0.75	0.25
1.0	0.50
1.25	0.25

5–3 Modify the version of the simulator resulting from Exercises 5–1 and 5–2 so that the *actual* processing times are derived by multiplying the estimated times (given by the job generation process) by the following uniform distribution:

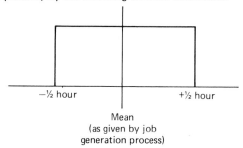

5–4 Modify the simulator so that:

(a) The process can be stopped after a given number of jobs have been completed (rather than after a specified clock time).

(b) The simulator can be run until a number of jobs have been completed; then all statistical data can be cleared and the simulator restarted and run for another specified number of job completions.

5–5 Modify the program so that new jobs are read in at the appropriate point using externally provided data, rather than generated as in 5–1.

5–6 For the situation and the required output data described below:
(a) Prepare a flow chart for a simulator.
(b) Program the simulator in FORTRAN and run it.
(c) Present the output data requested.

Situation: A shop has three machines that fail from time to time. The serviceman repairs the machines on a first-fail, first-serviced basis. Time is measured in units of 15 minutes each. Assume one shift operation. It has been found that the machines fail completely at random with a probability of failure in any unit of time of 0.1. A study of repair times indicates that they are distributed as follows:

Repair Time Units	Percent of Cases
1	30
2	20
3	20
4	10
5	20

Required output data:

(1) Frequency distribution of machine downtime durations for each machine and for all machines combined.

(2) Utilization = (usable time)/(total time) for each machine and overall.

appendix 5A

Tables for Information Storage and Retrieval

Before describing the specific data arrays used in the program, the general method of storage is described. This method is a very simplified version of the list-processing methods used in simulation language systems and other more sophisticated programs. Assume we have to store some data variables, which we will call DATA, about objects or *entities* in the system. (In this problem, jobs and machines are entities.) For each entity there are M variables or items of data, including the entity serial or identification number. No more than N entities are expected to be in the system at one time. (In more sophisticated programs the arrays can be open ended and the limitation on the number of items that can be stored is total available core.)

The storage arrangement is shown in Figure 5A–1. The data variables have a double subscript (two indices), I and J. The J index identifies which of the M variables associated with an entity is to be stored or retrieved. This is shown as columns in the figure. The I index identifies arbitrary lines or rows down the array. The first entry ($J = 1$) is either the entity identification or a code E indicating that this row is empty and can be used for new data. Thus, in the figure, row 2 has the data for entity 5, row 3 for entity 1, row 5 is empty, and so on.

To store new data, we locate an empty row by searching for DATA $(I, 1) = E$ over I (with $J = 1$). When an I meeting this criterion is found, it becomes the line indicator or *pointer* and the variables for this new entity are stored into DATA $(I, 1)$ (usually the entity identifier), DATA $(I, 2)$, DATA $(I, 3)$, and so on.

Data (I, J)

Figure 5A–1 Method of storing tables.

I	1	2	3	M − 1	M
1	E	—	—	—	—
2	5	31	0.2	A	2
3	1	41	0.1	A	3
4	6	32	0.1	B	1
5	E	—	—	—	—
6	E	—	—	—	—
7	3	10	0.8	A	2
8	E	—	—	—	—
9	4	39	0.7	A	6
10	E	—	—	—	—
11	E	—	—	—	—
12	E	—	—	—	—
N	E	—	—	—	—

If a particular entity is to be located, the table is again searched for DATA $(I, 1) = $ *the required entity identifier number.* The I found again becomes the pointer. The variable DATA $(I, 4)$ would then be the fourth item of data for this entity.

An entity with a particular characteristic can be found and changed, if required. If (using the data in Figure 5A–1) we want to find an entity with the Mth data item $= 1$, we search over DATA (I, M), testing each item as I varies from 1 to N until the desired match DATA $(I, M) = 1$ is found. In this case we would get a match at $I = 4$. DATA $(4, 1) = 6$, so that the entity with this characteristic is number 6.

To remove the data for an entity (as when a job is no longer in the system), the proper row is found by searching, and then DATA $(I, 1)$ is set $= E$. Although the rest of the data remains, it is written over when new data is entered.

This procedure removes the entity location of the data from the core identification (the line number) and so permits some dynamic storage reallocation.

appendix 5B

FORTRAN Program of Plastic Shop Simulator (Using Shortest-Processing-Time-First Decision Rule)

Tables

In the actual program that follows, the event, job, and machine tables are handled in the way described in Appendix 5A.

The search for a specific job number in the job table, which must be made several times, is set up as a FUNCTION subprogram. Error messages result if the table is completely searched and the desired entry is not found.

The FORTRAN arrays used in the program coincide directly with the data layout in Figure 5–7. These array designations are:

Event table: JEVENT (I, J)
I is a line pointer. (The first index of the event, job, and machine arrays is the arbitrary line indicator.)
J is used to select the following variables:
$J = 1$: event time (i.e., JEVENT $(I, 1)$ = event time in line I)
2: type of event (JEVENT $(I, 2)$ = 1 if event was an arrival, = 2 if event was a completion)
3: machine number for completion events, job number for arrival events

Job table: JOB (I, J)
I is the line pointer.
J is used as follows:
1 = job number
2 = job status (1 = mold, 2 = trim, 3 = assembly); if this number is 10 higher it means job is waiting in the preceding queue
3 = mold-processing time, i.e., JOB $(I, 3)$ is the mold-processing time of job whose number is the value of JOB $(I, 1)$
4 = trim-processing time
5 = assembly-processing time
6 = arrival time
7 = due time
8 = completion time (filled in during the simulation)

Machine table: JMACH (I, J)
I is the line pointer.
J is used as follows:
1 = machine identifier
2 = identifier of the job on the machine
3 = cumulative idle time
4 = last completion time

Queues: KUE (*I, J*)

    I is the queue number (1 = mold queue, 2 = trim queue, 3 = assembly queue).

    J is used to indicate the sequence of jobs; KUE (*I, J*) holds the job number of the *J*th job in queue *I*.

Output table: JOUT (*I*)

    I is the amount of lateness; JOUT (*I*) is the number of jobs *I* units late.

Routing: JRT (*I*)

    JRT (*I*) gives the queue number to which a job should go when it leaves machine *I*.

```
      C    PLSATIC SHOP MODEL - BASIC VERSION
      C
      C***STEP 1
      C    THIS IS NOT THE MOST EFFICIENT WAY TO ENTER DATA, IT IS THE
      C EASIEST TO USE AND FOLLOW.
      C
      C
0001          DIMENSION JEVENT(100,8),          JMACH(3,4),KUE(3,10),JOUT(11),
             1JRT(3),XMU(3)
0002          COMMON JOB(50,9)
0003          KEND=20
0004          DO 20 I=1,50
0005          DO 20 J = 1,9
0006    20    JOB(I,J)=0
0007    100   JOB(1,1)=5
0008          JOB(1,2)=13
      C    A STATUS OVER 10 MEANS WAITING.   1=M, 2=T, 3=A.
0009          JOB(1,5)=3
0010          JOB(1,6)=-5
0011          JOB(1,7)=5
0012          JOB(2,1)=6
0013          JOB(2,2)=13
0014          JOB(2,5)=3
0015          JOB(2,6)=-3
0016          JOB(2,7)=6
0017          JOB(3,1)=7
0018          JOB(3,2)=2
0019          JOB(3,4)=5
0020          JOB(3,5)=1
0021          JOB(3,6)=-10
0022          JOB(3,7)=3
0023          JOB(4,1)=8
0024          JOB(4,2)=12
0025          JOB(4,4)=4
0026          JOB(4,5)=2
0027          JOB(4,6)=-11
0028          JOB(4,7)=10
0029          JOB(5,1)=9
0030          JOB(5,2)=3
0031          JOB(5,5)=2
0032          JOB(5,6)=-12
0033          JOB(5,7)=2
0034          JOB(6,1)=10
0035          JOB(6,2)=1
0036          JOB(6,3)=3
0037          JOB(6,4)=1
0038          JOB(6,5)=1
0039          JOB(6,6)=-1
0040          JOB(6,7)=2
0041          JOB(50,1)=11
      C STATUS OF 0 MEANS NOT ARRIVED YET
0042          JOB(50,2)=0
0043          JOB(50,3)=5
0044          JOB(50,4)=4
0045          JOB(50,5)=3
0046          JOB(50,6)=1
0047          JOB(50,7)=27
0048          JOB(49,1)=12
0049          JOB(49,2)=0
0050          JOB(49,3)=6
0051          JOB(49,4)=2
0052          JOB(49,5)=3
0053          JOB(49,6)=2
0054          JOB(49,7)=10
0055          JOB(48,1)=13
0056          JOB(48,2)=0
0057          JOB(48,3)=2
0058          JOB(48,4)=2
0059          JOB(48,5)=2
0060          JOB(48,6)=7
0061          JOB(48,7)=8
0062          DO 102 I=1,100
0063          DO 104 J=2,8
0064    104   JEVENT(I,J)=0
0065    102   JEVENT(I,1)=KEND+20
0066          JEVENT(1,1)=1
0067          JEVENT(1,2)=1
      C    TYPE CF EVENT,  1= ARRIVAL ,   2= COMPLETION
0068          JEVENT(1,3)=11
0069          JEVENT(2,1)=2
```

Figure 5B-1   Program for simulation of the plastic shop—deterministic model.

```
0070                  JEVENT(2,2)=1
0071                  JEVENT(2,3)=12
0072                  JEVENT(3,1)=8
0073                  JEVENT(3,2)=1
0074                  JEVENT(3,3)=13
0075                  JEVENT(4,1)=2
0076                  JEVENT(4,2)=2
0077                  JEVENT(4,3)=3
0078                  JEVENT(5,1)=5
0079                  JEVENT(5,2)=2
0080                  JEVENT(5,3)=2
0081                  JEVENT(6,1)=3
0082                  JEVENT(6,2)=2
0083                  JEVENT(6,3)=1
0084                  JEVENT(7,1)=30
0085                  JEVENT(7,2)=1
0086                  JEVENT(7,3)=14
0087                  JMACH(1,1)=1
0088                  JMACH(1,2)=10
0089                  JMACH(1,3)=0
0090                  JMACH(1,4)=0
0091                  JMACH(2,1)=2
0092                  JMACH(2,2)=7
0093                  JMACH(2,3)=0
0094                  JMACH(2,4)=0
0095                  JMACH(3,1)=3
0096                  JMACH(3,2)=9
0097                  JMACH(3,3)=0
0098                  JMACH(3,4)=0
0099                  DO 101 I=1,3
0100                  DO 101 J=1,10
0101          101     KUE(I,J)=0
0102                  KUE(2,1)=8
0103                  KUE(3,1)=5
0104                  KUE(3,2)=6
0105                  JRT(1)=12
0106                  JRT(2)=13
0107                  JRT(3)=20
             C STATUS OF 20 MEANS JOB FINISHED.
0108                  KLOCK=0
0109                  DO 103 I=1,11
0110          103     JOUT(I)=0
             C *** STEP 2              These STEP numbers correspond to
0111          200     IT=KEND+1          blocks in the flow chart
0112                  DO 201 I=1,100
0113                  IF(JEVENT(I,1).GE.IT) GO TO 201
0114                  J=I
0115                  IT=JEVENT(I,1)
0116          201     CONTINUE
             C   IN CASE OF TIES, EVENTS ARE SELECTED AT RANDOM.
             C
             C   J IS 'LINE' NO. OF NEXT EVENT.
0117                  KLOCK = JEVENT(J,1)
0118                  WRITE(6,202) KLOCK,JEVENT(J,2),JEVENT(J,3)
0119          202     FORMAT(1X,3I4)
             C *** STEP 3
0120                  IF(KLOCK.GE.KEND) GO TO 400
             C *** STEP 5
0121                  IF (JEVENT(J,2).EQ.1) GO TO 600
0122                  GO TO 900
             C *** STEP 6
0123          600     K=JFIND(JEVENT(J,3))
0124                  IF(K.EQ.-1) GO TO 400
             C IF NEW JOBS WERE TO BE READ IN AS THE SIMULATION PROCEEDED,
             C THEY WOULD BE READ IN HERE.
             C
             C
             C    K IS THE 'LINE' NO. OF NEW JOB.
             C *** STEP 7
0125          700     JOB(K,2)=11
             C *** STEP 8
0126                  DO 801 I=1,10
0127                  IF(KUE(1,I).NE.0) GO TO 801
0128                  KUE(1,I)=JOB(K,1)
0129                  GO TO 2100
0130          801     CONTINUE
0131                  WRITE(6,802) JOB(K,1)
0132          802     FORMAT(1X,'QUEUE 1 SPACE EXCEEDED', 'JOB',I4,' LOST')
0133                  GO TO 2100
             C *** STEP 9
0134          900     DO 901 IM=1,3
```

Figure 5B–1 (continued)   97

```
0135                 IF(JMACH(IM,1).EQ.JEVENT(J,3))L=IM
0136         901 CONTINUE
C  L  IS LINE NO. (AND MACH. NO.) OF MACH. ON WHICH COMPLETION OCCURED.
C
C  M WHICH IS JMACH(L,2) IS THE JOB NO.
0137             M=JMACH(L,2)
C *** STEP 11
0138             JMACH(L,2)=0
C *** STEP 12
0139             JMACH(L,4)=KLOCK
C *** STEP 13
0140             K=JFIND(M)
C  K IS LINE NO. OF JOB RECORD
0141             IF(K.EQ.-1) GO TO 400
C *** STEP 14
0142        1400 JOB(K,2)=JRT(L)
C *** STEP 15
0143             IF (JOB(K,2).EQ.20) GO TO 1600
C  KQ IS QUEUE NO.
0144             KQ=JOB(K,2)-10
0145             DO 1501 I=1,10
0146             IF (KUE(KQ,I).NE.0) GO TO 1501
0147             KUE(KQ,I)=JOB(K,1)
0148             GO TO 1600
0149        1501 CONTINUE
0150             WRITE(6,1502) KQ,JOB(K,1)
0151        1502 FORMAT(1X,'QUEUE ',I1,' SPACE EXCEEDED,  JOB', I4, ' LOST')
C *** STEP 16
0152        1600 IF(JOB(K,2).NE.20) GO TO 2100
C IF STATUS IS 20 , JOB FINISHE(D.
C *** STEP 17
0153             JOB(K,8)=KLOCK
C *** STEP 18
0154             LATE=KLOCK-JOB(K,7)
C COULD PRINT OUT FINISHING JOB DATA HERE.
C *** STEP 19
0155             IF (LATE.LE.0) GO TO 2100
0156             DO 1901 I=1,10
0157             IF (LATE.NE.I) GO TO 1901
0158             JOUT(I)=JOUT(I)+1
0159             GO TO 2100
0160        1901 CONTINUE
0161             JOUT(11)=JOUT(11)+1
C *** STEP 21
C EVENT TIME OF KEND+20 MEANS FREE SPACE
0162        2100 JEVENT(J,1)=KEND+20
C *** STEP 22
0163        2200 DO 2201 I=1,3
0164             IF(JMACH(I,2).EQ.0) GO TO 2300
0165             GO TO 2201
C *** STEP 23
0166        2300 L=JMACH(I,1)
C IPT IS SHORTEST PROCESS TIME FOUND SO FAR.
0167             IPT=100
C DISPATCH RULE IS SHORTEST PROCESSING TIME FIRST.
C *** STEP 24
0168        2400 DO 2401 IK=1,10
0169             JJ=KUE(L,IK)
0170             IF(JJ.EQ.0) GO TO 2401
0171             K=JFIND(JJ)
0172             IF(K.EQ.-1) GO TO 400
0173             IF (JOB(K,L+2).GE.IPT) GO TO 2401
0174             IPT=JOB(K,L+2)
0175             KK=K
0176             II=IK
C  II IS QUEUE POSITION.
0177        2401 CONTINUE
0178             IF (IPT.EQ.100) GO TO 2201
C IPT=100 MEANS QUEUE EMPTY
C *** STEP 25
C KK IS JOB LINE NO. OF JOB TO PUT ON IDLE MACHINE.
C *** STEP 26
0179             KUE(L,II)=0
C *** STEP 27
0180             JMACH(L,2)=JOB(KK,1)
C *** STEP 28
0181             JMACH(L,3)=JMACH(L,3)+KLOCK-JMACH(L,4)
C *** STEP 29
0182             JOB(KK,2)=JOB(KK,2)-10
C *** STEPS 30,32
C NO RANDOM EFFECTS ( SO NO STEP 31)
```

Figure 5B–1 (continued)

```
0183                    ITIME=JOB(KK,L+2)+KLOCK
            C *** STEP 33
0184              DO 3301 IQ=1,100
0185              IF(JEVENT(IQ,1).EQ.KEND+20) GO TO 3400
0186         3301 CONTINUE
0187              WRITE(6,3303)
0188         3303 FORMAT(1X,' EVENT LIST FULL, GOING TO OUTPUT PROCESS.')
0189              GO TO 400
            C *** STEP 34
0190         3400 JEVENT(IQ,1)=ITIME
0191              JEVENT(IQ,2)=2
0192              JEVENT(IQ,3)=L
0193         2201 CONTINUE
0194              GO TO 200
            C *** STEP 4
0195          400 A=KEND
0196              WRITE(6,403)
0197          403 FORMAT(1H1,' MACH',T10,' IDLE HRS',T20,'MACH UTIL')
0198              DO 401 I=1,3
0199              X=JMACH(I,3)
0200              XMU(I)=(1.-(X/A))*100.
0201          401 WRITE(6,402) I,JMACH(I,3),XMU(I)
0202          402 FORMAT(1X,I1,T10,I3,T20,F10.5///)
0203              WRITE(6,404)
0204          404 FORMAT(1H1,1X,' LATE HRS',T15,' JOBS',/)
0205              DO 405 I=1,10
0206          405 WRITE(6,410) I, JOUT(I)
0207          410 FORMAT(2X,I2,T15,I3)
0208              WRITE(6,406) JOUT(11)
0209          406 FORMAT (3X,' OVER 10',T15,I3/1H1)
            C  PRINT OUT EVENT TABLE AS A DEBUGGING AID.
0210              WRITE(6,407)((JEVENT(I,J),J=1,8),I=1,100)
0211          407 FORMAT(1X,8I4)
0212              WRITE(6,498)
0213          498 FORMAT(///)                          Outputs job table
0214              WRITE(6,408)((JOB(I,J),J=1,9),I=1,50)  for debugging
0215          408 FORMAT(1X,9I4)
0216              WRITE(6,499) KLOCK
0217          499 FORMAT(1X, 'TIME AT END OF RUN', I10)
0218              STOP
0219              END
```

Subroutine to search Job Table

```
0001              FUNCTION JFIND(JJ)
0002              COMMON JOB(50,9)
0003              DO 50 I=1,50
0004              IF(JOB(I,1).NE.JJ) GO TO 50
0005              JFIND=I
0006              RETURN
0007           50 CONTINUE
0008           51 WRITE(6,52)JJ
0009           52 FORMAT(1X,' JOB NOT FOUND, GOING TO OUTPUT PROCESS.')
0010              JFIND=-1
0011              RETURN
0012              END
```

Data from plastic shop simulation

Event printout
Time type data

```
1    1   11
2    1   12
2    2    3
3    2    1
5    2    3
5    2    2
6    2    2
8    2    3
8    2    1
8    1   13
9    2    3
```

Figure 5B–1 (continued)   99

```
10    2    3
10    2    2
12    2    3
14    2    2
14    2    1
16    2    1
16    2    2
17    2    3
18    2    2
20    2    3
```

```
MACH      IDLE HRS   MACH UTIL
1          0         100.00000


2          0         100.00000


3          2          90.00000
```

```
LATE HRS      JOBS

  1            0
  2            2
  3            0
  4            0
  5            0
  6            1
  7            0
  8            1
  9            0
 10            0
    OVER 10    0
```

Listing of the significant
entries of the Event List
at end of run.

```
20    2    3    0    0    0    0    0
40    2    2    0    0    0    0    0
40    2    2    0    0    0    0    0
40    2    2    0    0    0    0    0
40    2    2    0    0    0    0    0
40    2    1    0    0    0    0    0
30    1   14    0    0    0    0    0
40    0    0    0    0    0    0    0
40    0    0    0    0    0    0    0
40    0    0    0    0    0    0    0
40    0    0    0    0    0    0    0
40    0    0    0    0    0    0    0
```

Listing of significant
entries of Job Table at
end of run.

```
 5   20    0    0    3   -5    5    5    0
 6   20    0    0    3   -3    6    8    0
 7   20    0    5    1  -10    3    9    0
 8   20    0    4    2  -11   10   12    0
 9   20    0    0    2  -12    2    2    0
10   20    3    1    1   -1    2   10    0
 0    0    0    0    0    0    0    0    0
 0    0    0    0    0    0    0    0    0

 0    0    0    0    0    0    0    0    0
 0    0    0    0    0    0    0    0    0
13   13    2    2    2    7    8    0    0
12    3    6    2    3    2   10    0    0
11   20    5    4    3    1   27   17    0
```

```
TIME AT END OF RUN          20
```

Figure 5B–1 (continued)

appendix 5C

Two FORTRAN Simulators

This appendix contains:

(1) A program that is a simulation of the plastic shop model incorporating the requirements of Exercises 5–1 through 5–4.

(2) An answer to Exercise 5–6.*

* Prepared by H. Johri, University of Waterloo, Waterloo, Ontario.

```
C PLASTIC SHOP MODEL WITH GENERATED INPUTS AND STOCHASTIC INTER-
C ARRIVAL TIMES AND PROCESSING TIMES.
C
C
C THIS VERSION INCORPORATES EXERCISES 5.1, 5.2, AND 5.3
C
C EACH STEP OF THE FLOW CHART IS LABELLED AS 'STEP N' ON THE
C LISTING BELOW. THE PROGRAM CAN BE FOLLOWED BY COMPARING WITH
C THE FLOW CHART.
C
C***STEP 1
C
C
0001          DIMENSION XMU(3),PTM(3)
0002          COMMON JOB(50,9)
0003          REAL KLOCK,JOB              Clock time is a real variable
0004          REAL      JEVENT(100,3), JMACH(3,4),KUE(3,20),JOUT(11),
             1JRT(3)
0005          READ (5,1) JOBEND           Defines end of run
0006    1     FORMAT(I4)
0007          KEND=10000
0008          DO 20 I=1,50
0009          DO 20 J = 1,9
0010   20     JOB(I,J)=0
C STATUS OF 0 MEANS NOT ARRIVED YET
0011   100    JOB(50,1)=1                 Work in process data
0012          JOB(50,2)=0
0013          JOB(50,3)=3
0014          JOB(50,4)=5
0015          JOB(50,5)=4
0016          JOB(50,6)=1
0017          JOB(50,7)=27
0018          DO 102 I=1,100
0019          DO 104 J=2,3
0020   104    JEVENT(I,J)=0
0021   102    JEVENT(I,1)=-1
C   SET UP EVENT NOTICE FOR FIRST JOB.
0022          JEVENT(1,1)=1
0023          JEVENT(1,2)=1
C   TYPE OF EVENT, 1= ARRIVAL ,    2= COMPLETION
0024          JEVENT(1,3)=1
0025          DO 105 I=1,3
0026          JMACH(I,1)=I
0027          DO 105 J=2,4
0028   105    JMACH(I,J)=0
0029          DO 101 I=1,3
0030          DO 101 J=1,20
0031   101    KUE(I,J)=0
C   ROUTING TABLE.
0032          JRT(1)=12
0033          JRT(2)=13
0034          JRT(3)=20
C STATUS OF 20 MEANS JOB FINISHED.
0035          PTM(1)=3                    PTM defines expected
0036          PTM(2)=5                    processing times
0037          PTM(3)=4
0038          KLOCK=0
0039          DO 103 I=1,11
0040   103    JOUT(I)=0
C   SET JOB COUNTER TO LAST JOB TO ENTER
0041          JOBNO=1
0042          JOBTOT=0
C SET STARTING RANDOM NUMBER.
0043          IX=100000013
C *** STEP 2
0044   200    T=KEND+1
0045          DO 201 I=1,100
0046          IF(JEVENT(I,1).EQ.-1) GO TO 201
0047          IF(JEVENT(I,1).GE. T) GO TO 201
0048          J=I
0049          T=JEVENT(I,1)
0050   201    CONTINUE
C   IN CASE OF TIES, EVENTS ARE SELECTED AT RANDOM.
C
C   J IS 'LINE' NO. OF NEXT EVENT.
C     THE FOLLOWING WAS OUT IN AS A DEBUG AID.
0051          IF (JEVENT(J,1).GE.KLOCK) GO TO 205
0052          WRITE(6,206)
0053   206    FORMAT(1X,'CLOCK WENT BACKWARDS')
```

Figure 5C–1 Program for simulation of the plastic shop—stochastic model with generated input.

```
0054                STOP
0055        205  KLOCK = JEVENT(J,1)
           C   WRITE OUT EVENTS AS THEY OCCUR UNTIL KLOCK=15.
0056                IF(KLOCK.GT.15) GO TO 300
0057                WRITE(6,202) KLOCK,JEVENT(J,2),JEVENT(J,3)
0058        202  FORMAT(1X,3F6.2)
           C *** STEP 3
0059        300  IF(KLOCK.GE.KEND) GO TO 450        Stop if time exceeds KEND
0060                IF(JOBTOT.GE.JOBEND) GO TO 400    Stop if no. jobs equals JOB END
           C *** STEP 5
0061                IF (JEVENT(J,2).EQ.1) GO TO 600
0062                GO TO 900
           C *** STEP 6
0063        600  JJJ=JEVENT(J,3)
0064                K=JFIND(JJJ)
0065                IF(K.EQ.-1) GO TO 400
           C
           C   CREATE NEW JOB FOR ENTRY  AFTER INTERARRIVAL TIME.
           C
           C *** STEP 6.5                              These steps are
0066        650  NJ=JFIND(0)                           added to generate
           C FINDS A SPACE IN THE JOB TABLE            a new job based
0067                IF(NJ.EQ.-1) GO TO 400             on job characteristic
           C  NJ  IS NO. OF AVAILABLE LINE IN JOB TABLE.  distributions
           C  JOB CHARACTERISTICS ARE NOW SET UP.
0068        652  JOBNO=JOBNO+1
0069                JOB(NJ,1)=JOBNO
0070                JOB(NJ,2)=0
           C   MEAN PROCESSING TIMES ARE ASSIGNED.
0071                DO 653 JJJ=1,3
0072                P=PTM(JJJ)
0073                CALL MODP (IX,IY,P)                MODP is a subroutine
0074        653  JOB(NJ,JJJ+2)=P                       to add random variation
           C NOW INTERARRIVAL TIME IS CALCULATED.      to process times
0075                CALL RANDU(IX,IY,R)
0076                IX=IY
0077                IF(R.GT.0.6) GO TO 655             These steps create the
0078                DT=(R/0.6)*0.75                    next job arrival time
           C  DT IS INTERARRIVAL TIME    MODIFIER.     according to the specified
0079                GO TO 659                          distribution
0080        655  IF(R.GT.0.85) GO TO 656
0081                DT=((R-0.6)/0.25)*0.75+0.75
0082                GO TO 659
0083        656  DT=((R-0.85)/0.15)*0.75+1.5
           C   MEAN INTERARRIVAL TIME IS 8.
0084        659  JOB(NJ,6)=KLOCK+DT*8.
           C DUE TIME SET NEXT.
0085                CALL RANDU(IX,IY,R)
0086                IX=IY
0087                JOB(NJ,7)=JOB(NJ,6)+12+(10.*R)
0088                JOB(NJ,8)=0
           C   NOW EVENT TABLE IS SET-UP FOR THE ARRIVAL OF THIS NEW JOB.
0089                DO 660 NJE=1,100
0090                IF(JEVENT(NJE,1).EQ.-1     ) GO TO 670
0091        660  CONTINUE
0092                WRITE(6,661)
0093        661  FORMAT(1X,'EVENT LIST FULL,GOING TO OUTPUT PROCESS.(NEW JOB)')
0094                GO TO 400
           C NJE IS NO. OF AVILABLE LINE IN EVENT TABLE.
0095        670  JEVENT(NJE,1)=JOB(NJ,6)
0096                JEVENT(NJE,2)=1
0097                JEVENT(NJE,3)=JOB(NJ,1)              New job has
           C  K IS THE LINE NO. OF THE JOB JUST ENTERING THE SHOP.  been created and the simulation returns
           C *** STEP 7                                 to processing the job
0098        700  JOB(K,2)=11                            just arrived
           C *** STEP 8
0099                DO 801 I=1,20
0100                IF(KUE(1,I).NE.0) GO TO 801
0101                KUE(1,I)=JOB(K,1)
0102                GO TO 2100
0103        801  CONTINUE
0104                WRITE(6,802) JOB(K,1)
0105        802  FORMAT(1X,'QUEUE 1 SPACE EXCEEDED', 'JOB',I4,' LOST')
0106                GO TO 2100
           C *** STEP 9
0107        900  DO 901 IM=1,3
0108                IF(JMACH(IM,1).EQ.JEVENT(J,3))L=IM
0109        901  CONTINUE
           C  L  IS LINE NO. (AND MACH. NO.) OF MACH. ON WHICH COMPLETION OCCURRED
           C
           C  M WHICH IS JMACH(L,2) IS THE JOB NO.
```

Figure 5C–1 (continued)

```
0110                M=JMACH(L,2)
         C *** STEP 11
0111                JMACH(L,2)=0
         C *** STEP 12
0112                JMACH(L,4)=KLOCK
         C *** STEP 13
0113                K=JFIND(M)
         C   K IS LINE NO. OF JOB RECORD
0114                IF(K.EQ.-1) GO TO 400
         C *** STEP 14
0115       1400 JOB(K,2)=JRT(L)
         C *** STEP 15
0116                IF (JOB(K,2).EQ.20) GO TO 1600
         C   KQ IS QUEUE NO.
0117                KQ=JOB(K,2)-10
0118                DO 1501 I=1,10
0119                IF (KUE(KQ,I).NE.0) GO TO 1501
0120                KUE(KQ,I)=JOB(K,1)
0121                GO TO 1600
0122       1501 CONTINUE
0123                WRITE(6,1502) KQ,JOB(K,1)
0124       1502 FORMAT(1X,'QUEUE ',I1,' SPACE EXCEEDED,   JOB', I4, ' LOST')
         C *** STEP 16
0125       1600 IF(JOB(K,2).NE.20) GO TO 2100
         C IF STATUS IS 20 , JOB FINISHE(D.
         C *** STEP 17
0126                JOB(K,8)=KLOCK
         C ADD TO NO. OF JOBS FINISHED.
0127                JOBTOT=JOBTOT+1
         C *** STEP 18
0128                LATE=KLOCK-JOB(K,7)
         C COULD PRINT OUT FINISHING JOB DATA HERE.
         C *** STEP 19
0129                IF (LATE.LE.0) GO TO 2000
0130                DO 1901 I=1,10
0131                IF (LATE.NE.I) GO TO 1901
0132                JOUT(I)=JOUT(I)+1
0133                GO TO 2000
0134       1901 CONTINUE
0135                JOUT(11)=JOUT(11)+1
         C   XXX   STEP 20
0136       2000 JOB(K,1)=0
         C   ZERO IN COL. 1 MEANS JOB IS COMPLETED, LINE IN JOB TABLE IS FREE.
         C *** STEP 21
         C   EVENT TIME OF -1  MEANS A FREE LINE.
0137       2100 JEVENT(J,1)=-1
         C *** STEP 22
0138       2200 DO 2201 I=1,3
0139                IF(JMACH(I,2).EQ.0) GO TO 2300
0140                GO TO 2201
         C *** STEP 23
0141       2300 L=JMACH(I,1)
         C IPT IS SHORTEST PROCESS TIME FOUND SO FAR.
0142                IPT=100
         C DISPATCH RULE IS SHORTEST PROCESSING TIME FIRST.
         C *** STEP 24
0143       2400 DO 2401 IK=1,20
0144                JJ=KUE(L,IK)
0145                IF(JJ.EQ.0) GO TO 2401
0146                K=JFIND(JJ)
0147                IF(K.EQ.-1) GO TO 400
0148                IF (JOB(K,L+2).GE.IPT) GO TO 2401
0149                IPT=JOB(K,L+2)
0150                KK=K
0151                II=IK
         C   II IS QUEUE POSITION.
0152       2401 CONTINUE
0153                IF (IPT.EQ.100) GO TO 2201
         C IPT=100 MEANS QUEUE EMPTY
         C *** STEP 25
         C KK IS JOB LINE NO. OF JOB TO PUT ON IDLE MACHINE.
         C *** STEP 26
0154                KUE(L,II)=0
         C *** STEP 27
0155                JMACH(L,2)=JOB(KK,1)
         C *** STEP 28
0156                JMACH(L,3)=JMACH(L,3)+KLOCK-JMACH(L,4)
         C *** STEP 29
0157                JOB(KK,2)=JOB(KK,2)-10
         C *** STEP 30 (KK IS JOB LINE AND I IS MACHINE.)
         C *** STEPS 31 AND 32.
```

104   Figure 5C–1 (continued)

```
0158         3100 CALL RANDU(IX,IY,R)
0159              IX=IY
0160              TIME=JOB(KK,L+2)+R-.5+KLOCK
           C *** STEP 33
0161         3300 DO 3301 IQ=1,100
0162              IF(JEVENT(IQ,1).EQ.-1      ) GO TO 3400
0163         3301 CONTINUE
0164              WRITE(6,3303)
0165         3303 FORMAT(1X,' EVENT LIST FULL, GOING TO OUTPUT PROCESS.')
0166              GO TO 400
           C *** STEP 34
0167         3400 JEVENT(IQ,1)= TIME
0168              JEVENT(IQ,2)=2
0169              JEVENT(IQ,3)=L
0170         2201 CONTINUE
0171              GO TO 200
           C *** STEP 4                        End-of-run process
0172          400 A=KLOCK
0173              WRITE(6,403)
0174          403 FORMAT(1H1,' MACH',T10,' IDLE HRS',T20,'MACH UTIL')
0175              DO 401 I=1,3
0176              X=JMACH(I,3)
0177              XMU(I)=(1.-(X/A))*100.
0178          401 WRITE(6,402) I,JMACH(I,3),XMU(I)
0179          402 FORMAT(1X,I1,T10,F7.1,T20,F6.2///)
           C COUNT NO. LATE JOBS
0180              JOBLAT=0
0181              DO 412 I=1,11
0182          412 JOBLAT=JOBLAT+JOUT(I)
0183              WRITE(6,411) JOBTOT,JOBLAT
0184          411 FORMAT(1H1, 'JOBS FINISHED ',I5/'0JOBS LATE',I5///'0DISTRIBUTION
                 1OF LATENESS'///)
0185              WRITE(6,404)
0186          404 FORMAT(1X,' LATE HRS',T15,' JOBS'/)
0187              DO 405 I=1,10
0188          405 WRITE(6,410) I, JOUT(I)
0189          410 FORMAT(2X,I2,T15,F4.1)
0190              WRITE(6,406) JOUT(11)
0191          406 FORMAT(3X,' OVER 10',T15,F6.1/1H1,'EVENT TABLE'//)
           C   PRINT OUT FIRST TEN LINES OF EVENT TABLE.
0192              WRITE(6,407)((JEVENT(I,J),J=1,3),I=1,10)
0193          407 FORMAT(1X,3F9.2)
           C   PRINT OUT FIRST TEN ENTRIES OF JOB TABLE.
0194              WRITE (6,409)
0195          409 FORMAT(//1X,' JOB TABLE'/)
0196              WRITE(6,408)((JOB(I,J),J=1,8),I=1,10)
0197          408 FORMAT(  1X,8F9.2)
0198              WRITE (6,431) KLOCK
0199          431 FORMAT('0STOPPED AT ',F7.1///)
           C *** STEP 4.3                         This step added to
0200              READ(5,430) ISTOP                cause run to clear
0201          430 FORMAT (I4)                       statistics and
0202              IF(ISTOP.EQ.-1.OR.KLOCK.GT.KEND) STOP   restart
0203              JOBEND=ISTOP
0204              DO 420 J=1,11
0205          420 JOUT(J)=0                         Clear statistics
0206              DO 421 J=1,3
0207              JMACH(J,4)=KLOCK
0208          421 JMACH(J,3)=0
0209              JOBTOT=0
0210              GO TO 200                         Restart
0211          450 WRITE(6,460) KLOCK
0212          460 FORMAT(1H0,'EXCEEDED MAX. TIME,  CLOCK IS ',I6///)
0213              GO TO 400
0214              END




0001              FUNCTION JFIND(JJ)
           C
           C SUBROUTINE TO FIND A SPECIFIED JOB IN THE JOB TABLE
           C
0002              COMMON JOB(50,9)
0003              REAL JOB
0004              DO 50 I=1,50
0005              KK=JOB(I,1)
0006              IF(KK.NE.JJ) GO TO 50
0007              JFIND=I
0008              RETURN
0009           50 CONTINUE
```

Figure 5C–1 (continued)   105

```
0010          51    WRITE(6,52)JJ
0011          52    FORMAT(1X,'JOB ',I4,' NOT FOUND. GOING TO OUTPUT PROCESS.')
0012                JFIND=-1
0013                RETURN
0014                END



0001                SUBROUTINE RANDU(IX,IY,YFL)
             C
             C RANDOM NUMBER GENERATING SUBROUTINE
             C
0002                IY=IX*65539
0003                IF(IY) 5,6,6
0004          5     IY=IY+2147483647+1
0005          6     YFL=IY
0006                YFL=YFL*.4656613E-9
0007                RETURN
0008                END



0001                SUBROUTINE MODP (IX,IY,P)
             C
             C SUBROUNTINE TO CHOOSE PROCESS TIME FROM DISTRIBUTION
             C
0002                CALL RANDU(IX,IY,R)
0003                IX=IY
0004                IF(R.LE.0.25) GO TO 1
0005                IF(R.LE.0.75) RETURN
0006                P=P*1.5
0007                RETURN
0008          1     P=P*0.5
0009                RETURN
0010                END



             C
             C THE DATA CARDS (NOT PRINTED OUT) ARE-
             C 0010,1000,-001
             C
             01) IEY032I NULL PROGRAM
```

Data after transient period.
List of event entries as processed
up to time 15.

Time	Type	Data
1.00	1.00	1.00
3.92	2.00	1.00
8.40	1.00	2.00
9.40	2.00	2.00
12.98	2.00	1.00
13.04	2.00	3.00
13.55	1.00	3.00

MACH	IDLE HRS	MACH UTIL
1	17.3	72.51
2	9.6	84.79
3	32.6	48.18

Figure 5C–1 (continued)

JOBS FINISHED   10

JOBS LATE   2

DISTRIBUTION OF LATENESS

LATE HRS	JOBS
1	0.0
2	0.0
3	0.0
4	0.0
5	2.0
6	0.0
7	0.0
8	0.0
9	0.0
10	0.0
OVER 10	0.0

EVENT TABLE

62.89	2.00	2.00
-1.00	2.00	3.00
-1.00	2.00	1.00
-1.00	2.00	1.00
63.73	1.00	14.00
-1.00	0.0	0.0
-1.00	0.0	C.0
-1.00	0.0	C.0
-1.00	0.0	C.0
-1.00	0.0	0.0

JOB TABLE

12.00	2.00	3.00	5.00	4.00	51.42	64.57	0.0
0.0	20.00	4.50	5.00	6.00	33.23	47.82	53.54
8.00	12.00	1.50	5.00	2.00	36.57	50.11	0.0
0.0	20.00	3.00	2.50	2.00	44.65	63.14	57.57
0.0	20.00	3.00	5.00	2.00	38.03	59.61	55.19
0.0	20.00	3.00	2.50	4.00	46.45	67.37	62.19
13.00	12.00	1.50	5.00	2.00	52.09	66.16	0.0
14.00	0.0	1.50	5.00	4.00	63.73	82.87	0.0
0.0	0.0	C.0	0.0	0.0	0.0	0.0	0.0
0.0	0.0	0.0	0.0	0.0	0.0	0.0	0.0

STOPPED AT   62.9

Data from main run.

MACH	IDLE HRS	MACH UTIL
1	3143.7	49.57
2	1149.1	81.57
3	2145.8	65.58

JOBS FINISHED   1000

JOBS LATE   412

Figure 5C–1 (continued)

DISTRIBUTION OF LATENESS

```
LATE HRS      JOBS

  1           56.0
  2           55.0
  3           48.0
  4           34.0
  5           27.0
  6           25.0
  7           21.0
  8           19.0
  9           13.0
 10           14.0
   OVER 10   100.0
```

EVENT TABLE

```
6234.80      2.00      2.00
  -1.00      2.00      3.00
6233.93      2.00      1.00
  -1.00      1.00   1016.00
6236.43      1.00   1017.00
  -1.00      0.0       0.0
  -1.00      0.0       0.0
  -1.00      0.0       0.0
  -1.00      0.0       0.0
  -1.00      0.0       0.0
```

JOB TABLE

```
1015.00    12.00     1.50     2.50     6.00   6231.66   6247.11      0.0
   0.0     20.00     3.00     5.00     4.00   6219.05   6235.23   6233.62
1012.00     2.00     1.50     5.00     6.00   6223.43   6235.86      0.0
1013.00    12.00     1.50     5.00     2.00   6223.88   6238.54      0.0
1008.00    12.00     1.50     7.50     6.00   6201.80   6218.71      0.0
1014.00    12.00     4.50     7.50     2.00   6226.53   6243.80      0.0
1016.00     1.00     1.50     7.50     4.00   6231.69   6247.21      0.0
1017.00     0.0      3.00     5.00     4.00   6236.43   6250.82      0.0
   0.0     20.00     1.50     7.50     4.00   5715.89   5730.34   5738.75
   0.0     20.00     4.50     2.50     4.00   5704.10   5716.82   5724.27
```

STOPPED AT   6233.9

Figure 5C–1 (continued)

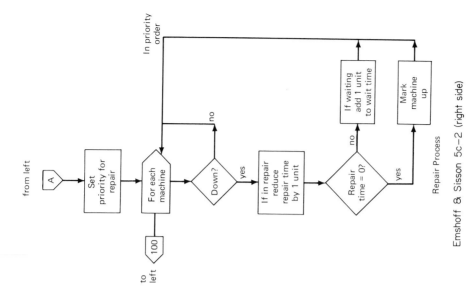

Emshoff & Sisson 5c–2 (right side)

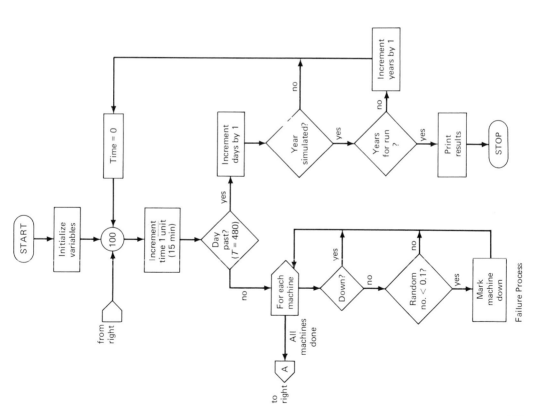

Figure 5C–2   Flow chart for Exercise 5–6.

109

```
      C SIMULATION OF MACHINE REPAIR PROCESS.
      C
      C     ***** LIST  OF  SYMBOLS  *****
      C     T   TIME IN MINUTES SINCE SIMULATION STARTED
      C     MR  CURRENT REPAIR TIME
      C     INTDAY  SIMULATION DAY(480  MINS.)
      C     YEAR  TOTAL PERIOD OF SIMULATION
      C     MAN   STATUS OF REPAIRMAN  1- IF FREE,0 IF BUSY.
      C     KA   INDICATOR OF HOW MANY MACHINES ARE VROKEN DOWN
      C     MACH  INDICATOR OF WHICH MACHINE IS BEING REPAIRED
      C     K(I)  =1 IF MACHINE I BREAKS DOWN OTHERWISEK(I)=0
      C     I1,I2,I3 STATUS INDICATOR OF MACHINES ONE,TWO &THREE
      C     1   IF RUNNING  0 IF BROKEN DOWN
      C     IS  INDEX FOR MACHINE TWO BROKEN DOWN  IS=0 IF TRUE
      C     IT  INDEX FOR MACHINE THREE BROKEN DOEN    IT=0 IF TRUE
      C     IA  INDEX FOR NUMBER OF MACHINES BROKEN DOWN
      C     IB,KB,LB,ID,II,JJ,KK,J ARE THE SUBSCRIPTS
      C     ************************************************************
      C     INITIALISING DATA
0001        INTEGER YEAR
0002        INTEGER T,TR,MR
0003        INTEGER*2 K(3),IPRI(1000),LWT1(1000),LWT2(1000),LWT3(1000)
0004        DIMENSION LDT1(1000),LDT2(1000),LDT3(1000)
0005        DIMENSION RRN(2000)
0006        DIMENSION IFREN1(15),IFREN2(15),IFREN3(15),IFRENO(15)
0007        DATA IFREN1,IFREN2,IFREN3,IFRENO/15*0,15*0,15*0,15*0/
0008        DATA LWT1/1000*0/,LWT2/1000*0/,LWT3/1000*0/,LDT1/1000*0/,LDT2/1000
           .*0/,LDT3/1000*0/
0009        DATA TDT1,TDT2,TDT3/3*0./
0010        DATA INTDAY,MB,K(1),K(2),K(3),KB,KA/7*0/
0011        DATA I1,I2,I3,JDT1,JDT2,JDT3/6*0/
0012        YEAR=30
0013        DATA II,JJ,KK,IA,IXX/5*1/
0014        DATA A,B,IV,N/0.,1.,321457,2000/
0015        CDP=0.
0016        CLT=5.
0017        DATA P,Q,R,S/.3,.5,.7,.8/
0018        FJ=0.100000
0019        CALL RNGEN(IV,RRN,N,A,B)
0020        PRINT 1
0021      1 FORMAT(1H1,/// 19X,'SAMPLE OF RANDOM NUMBERS')
0022        PRINT 300
0023    300 FORMAT(19X,24H*********************** //)
0024        PRINT 2,(RRN(J),J=1,200)
0025      2 FORMAT(1H ,5X,5F10.6)
0026        PRINT 300
0027        MACH=0
0028        JVAL=0
0029        J=15
0030        MR=15
      C     SETTING UP CLOCK TIME
0031     99 T=0
0032    100 T=T+15
0033        IF(J.GT.1900) GO TO 999
0034     98 IF(T.LT.480) GO TO 200
0035        INTDAY=INTDAY+1
0036        IF(INTDAY.LT.YEAR) GO TO 99
0037        GO TO 1000
0038    200 IF(MR.EQ.0) GO TO 201
      C     ACCOUNTING FOR THE REPAIT TIME FOR THE MACHINE CURRENTLY UNDER RPR.
0039        MR=MR-15
0040    201 TR=MR
0041        IF(MR.NE.0) GO TO 104
0042        MAN=1
0043        IF(KA.EQ.0) GO TO 104
0044        IF(MACH-2)101,102,103
0045    101 K(1)=0
0046        I1=1
0047        GO TO 104
0048    102 K(2)=0
0049        I2=1
0050        GO TO 104
0051    103 K(3)=0
0052        I3=1
0053    104 KA=0
0054        CALL BKDN(I1,I2,I3,RRN,J,FJ)
      C     ASSIGNING PRIORITY TO MACHINES REQUIRING REPAIR
0055        DO 10 I=1,3
0056        IF(K(I).EQ.I) GO TO 20
```

Figure 5C–3 Program for simulation of machine repair process (Exercise 5–6).

```
0057                GO TO (11,12,13),I
0058        11      IF(I1.NE.0) GO TO 10
0059                IR=0
0060                GO TO 21
0061        12      IF(I2.NE.0) GO TO 10
0062                IS=0
0063                GO TO 21
0064        13      IF(I3.NE.0) GO TO 10
0065                IT=0
0066        21      IPRI(IA)=I
0067                IA=IA+1
0068                K(I)=I
0069        20      KA=KA+1
0070        10      CONTINUE
0071                IF(KA.NE.0)GO TO 110
0072                GO TO 100
0073        110     IF(MR.EQ.0)GO TO 190
0074                IF(IA.GT.IB)GO TO 160
0075                GO TO 100
0076        190     KB=KB+1
0077                IB=KB
0078                CALL REPAIR(JVAL,MB,RRN,J,P,Q,R,S)
0079                LB=MB
0080                MR=JVAL
0081                TR=JVAL
            C       ACCOUNTING FOR THE WAITING TIME AND DOWN TIME
0082        160     ID=IPRI(IB)
0083                MACH=IPRI(KB)
0084                IF(ID-2)120,130,140
0085        120     IF(MAN.GT.0)GO TO 122
0086                KR=TR
0087                GO TO 121
0088        122     KR=0
0089        121     LWT1(II)=IR+KR
0090                IR=LWT1(II)
0091                IF(MAN.EQ.0)GO TO 123
0092                LDT1(II)=LWT1(II)+TR
0093        123     IF(LB.NE.KB) GO TO 150
0094                JDT1=LDT1(II)
0095                II=II+1
0096                LB=LB+1
0097                MAN=0
0098                GO TO 150
0099        130     IF(MAN.GT.0)GO TO 132
0100                KR=TR
0101                GO TO 131
0102        132     KR=0
0103        131     LWT2(JJ)=IS+KR
0104                IS=LWT2(JJ)
0105                LDT2(JJ)=LWT2(JJ)+TR
0106        133     IF(LB.NE.KB) GO TO 150
0107                JDT2=LDT2(JJ)
0108                JJ=JJ+1
0109                LB=LB+1
0110                MAN=0
0111                GO TO 150
0112        140     IF(MAN.GT.0)GO TO 142
0113                KR=TR
0114                GO TO 141
0115        142     KR=0
0116        141     LWT3(KK)=IT+KR
0117                IT=LWT3(KK)
0118                LDT3(KK)=LWT3(KK)+TR
0119        143     IF(LB.NE.KB) GO TO 150
0120                JDT3=LDT3(KK)
0121                KK=KK+1
0122                LB=LB+1
0123                MAN=0
0124                GO TO 150
0125        150     IB=IB+1
0126                IF(IA.EQ.IB) GO TO 100
0127                GO TO 160
            C       CALCULATE STATISTICS AND PRINT OUT STATEMENTS
0128        1000    NI=II-1
0129                NJ=JJ-1
0130                NK=KK-1
0131                DO 1001 JK=1,NI
0132                TDT1=TDT1+FLOAT(LDT1(JK))
0133                IH=1+LDT1(JK)/15
0134        1001    IFREN1(IH)=IFREN1(IH)+1
0135                DO 1004 JK=1,NJ
```

Figure 5C–3 (continued)

```
0136            TDT2=TDT2+FLOAT(LDT2(JK))
0137            IHT=1+LDT2(JK)/15
0138       1004 IFREN2(IHT)=IFREN2(IHT)+1
0139            DO 1003 JK=1,NK
0140            TDT3=TDT3+FLOAT(LDT3(JK))
0141            IHTT=1+LDT3(JK)/15
0142       1003 IFREN3(IHTT)=IFREN3(IHTT)+1
0143            DO 1002 IXX=1,15
0144       1002 IFRENO(IXX)=IFREN1(IXX)+IFREN2(IXX)+IFREN3(IXX)
0145            TDT=TDT1+TDT2+TDT3
0146            TTJ=FLOAT(YEAR)*480.
0147            UTI1=(1-(TDT1/TTJ))*100.
0148            UTI2=(1-(TDT2/TTJ))*100.
0149            UTI3=(1-(TDT3/TTJ))*100.
0150            UTIO=(1-(TDT/(3.*TTJ)))*100.
0151            TCTL=CLT*(TTJ/15.)
0152            TCTDP=(TTJ/15.)*CDP
0153            TCTDN=(TDT/15.)*12.
0154            TCOST=TCTL+TCTDP+TCTDN
0155            PRINT 1009
0156       1009 FORMAT(1H1,//// 23X,'TABLE OF FREQUENCY DISTRIBUTION',/30X,'MACHINE'
                .EDOWN TIME')
0157            PRINT 305
0158        305 FORMAT(1H ,23X,31H****************************** /////)
0159            PRINT 306
0160        306 FORMAT(10X,'CLASS INTERVAL', 6X,'MACHINE',6X,'MACHINE',7X,'MACHINE'
                .',7X,'COMBINED',/12X,'IN MINUTES',10X,'ONE',9X,'TWO',10X,'THREE'/)
0161            CALL XLINE
0162            ITEM=0
0163            DO 1011 IT=1,15
0164            ITIM1=0+ITEM
0165            ITIM2=ITIM1+14
0166            ITEM=ITIM2+1
0167            PRINT 1012,ITIM1,ITIM2,IFREN1(IT),IFREN2(IT),IFREN3(IT),
                1IFRENO(IT)
0168       1012 FORMAT(1H ,10X,I4,'-',I4,10X,I4,9X,I4,10X,I4,11X,I4,12X,I4,12X,I4,
                .11X,I4)
0169       1011 CONTINUE
0170            CALL XLINE
0171            PRINT 1013,UTI1,UTI2,UTI3,UTIO
0172       1013 FORMAT(//// 23X,'MACHINE-ONE    UTILISATION =',F10.3,2X,'PERCENT'/2
                .3X,'MACHINE-TWO    UTILISATION ='F10.3,2X,'PERCENT'/23X,'MACHINE THREE
                .REE UTILISATION =',F10.3,2X,'PERCENT'/23X,'   COMBINED    UTILISATION =',F1
                .ON =',F10.3,2X,'PERCENT')
0173            PRINT 317
0174        317 FORMAT(1H1,/////////////// 31X,'COST CALCULATIONS'/20X,'BASISO   SIM
                .ULATION PERIOD OF THIRTY DAYS'/20X,41H**************************
                .************ //)
0175            PRINT 312,TCTL,TCTDP,TCTDN,TCOST
0176        312 FORMAT(31X,'COST(LABOUR)  $',F10.3/31X,'COST(DEPRTN)  $',F10.3/31X
                .,'COST(DNTIME)  $',F10.3//33X,'TOTAL COST  $',F10.3/20X,41H*******
                .***************************** ////)
0177            GO TO 1700
0178        999 IV=IV+22000
0179            CALL RNGEN(IV,RRN,N,A,B)
0180            J=15
0181            GO TO 98
0182       1700 CALL EXIT
0183            END



0001            SUBROUTINE REPAIR(ITR,MB,RRN,J,P,Q,R,S)
           C    SUBROUTINE DETERMINES REPAIR TIME FOR THE MACHINE REQUIRINF REPAIR
0002            DIMENSION RRN(2000)
0003            J=J+1
0004            IF(RRN(J).LT.P)ITR=15
0005            IF(RRN(J).GE.P.AND.RRN(J).LT.Q) ITR=30
0006            IF(RRN(J).GE.Q.AND.RRN(J).LT.R)ITR=45
0007            IF(RRN(J).GE.R.AND.RRN(J).LT.S) ITR=60
0008            IF(RRN(J).GE.S) ITR=75
0009            MB=MB+1
0010            RETURN
0011            END



0001            SUBROUTINE BKDN(I1,I2,I3,RRN,J,FJ)
           C    SUBROUTINR DETERMINES STATUS OF DIFFERENT MACHINES
0002            DIMENSION RRN(2000)
```

112   **Figure 5C–3** (continued)

```
0003                 IF(I1.EQ.0) GO TO 2
0004                 J=J+1
0005                 IF(RRN(J).GT.FJ) GO TO 2
0006                 I1=0
0007          2      IF(I2.EQ.0) GO TO 4
0008                 J=J+1
0009                 IF(RRN(J).GT.FJ) GO TO 4
0010                 I2=0
0011          4      IF(I3.EQ.0) GO TO 6
0012                 J=J+1
0013                 IF(RRN(J).GT.FJ) GO TO 6
0014                 I3=0
0015          6      RETURN
0016                 END


0001                 SUBROUTINE XLINE          Subroutine to
0002          100    FORMAT('0',20A4)          print line of
0003                 DIMENSION AST(20)         astericks
0004                 DATA AST/20*'****'/
0005                 PRINT 100,AST
0006                 RETURN
0007                 END


0001                 SUBROUTINE RNGEN(IV,RRN,N,A,B)
0002                 REAL RNEW
0003                 INTEGER PLUS / Z1000000 / , IBIT / Z40000000 / , HEX / Z10003 /
0004                 INTEGER OLD , NEW , SEED
0005                 EQUIVALENCE (NEW, RNEW)
0006                 DIMENSION RRN(N)
0007                 OLD=IABS(IV)
0008                 DO 1 I=1,N
0009          10     OLD = OLD * HEX
0010                 NEW = OLD / 256
0011                 IF( NEW .LT. 0 ) NEW = NEW + PLUS
0012                 NEW = NEW + IBIT
0013          1      RRN(I)=RNEW+0.0
0014                 RETURN
0015                 END
```

Output from Repair Simulation

```
                SAMPLE OF RANDOM NUMBERS
                ************************


     0.905269  0.430941  0.438224  0.750875  0.561232
     0.609524  0.606054  0.150604  0.449142  0.339416
     0.994216  0.910550  0.515356  0.897187  0.744921
     0.394844  0.664771  0.435033  0.627258  0.848250
     0.444179  0.030824  0.187336  0.846601  0.393578
     0.742061  0.910157  0.782397  0.502967  0.976233
     0.330692  0.198053  0.212095  0.490090  0.031688
     0.779313  0.390688  0.330314  0.465689  0.821308
     0.736646  0.028098  0.538778  0.979784  0.029698
     0.360135  0.893531  0.119969  0.678039  0.988508
     0.828699  0.075619  0.995427  0.291991  0.793102
     0.130695  0.646252  0.701253  0.391248  0.036218
     0.696072  0.850468  0.838163  0.374765  0.705120
     0.857837  0.800944  0.085129  0.302279  0.047507
     0.564534  0.959637  0.677023  0.425403  0.459206
     0.926615  0.426833  0.221463  0.487281  0.930518
     0.197574  0.810786  0.086547  0.222212  0.554347
     0.326172  0.967910  0.871916  0.520305  0.274584
     0.964759  0.317295  0.220944  0.470008  0.831547
     0.759213  0.071356  0.595217  0.929099  0.217641
     0.943953  0.704950  0.734129  0.060220  0.754161
     0.982989  0.110481  0.815986  0.901586  0.065645
     0.279591  0.086742  0.004139  0.244151  0.427659
     0.368595  0.362637  0.858464  0.887053  0.596143
     0.593375  0.194965  0.829418  0.221820  0.866159
     0.200574  0.408011  0.642902  0.185314  0.325765
```

Figure 5C–3 (continued)

```
0.286757   0.788663   0.151159   0.808992   0.493518
0.680185   0.639447   0.715018   0.535083   0.775337
0.836281   0.039651   0.711377   0.911397   0.065994
0.193390   0.566390   0.657835   0.849497   0.176466
0.413325   0.891753   0.630598   0.757806   0.871457
0.408484   0.607790   0.970389   0.352224   0.379837
0.109007   0.235515   0.432025   0.472512   0.946847
0.428478   0.049245   0.439161   0.191767   0.198149
0.462991   0.994611   0.800742   0.852956   0.911057
0.789737   0.538902   0.125786   0.904596   0.295498
0.631626   0.130275   0.097017   0.409628   0.584611
0.821018   0.664606   0.598477   0.609412   0.270177
0.136352   0.386519   0.091946   0.073004   0.610507
0.006005   0.541467   0.194759   0.295351   0.019278
          *************************
```

TABLE OF FREQUENCY DISTRIBUTION
MACHINEDOWN TIME
****

CLASS INTERVAL IN MINUTES	MACHINE ONE	MACHINE TWO	MACHINE THREE	COMBINED
0- 14	0	0	0	0
15- 29	10	14	9	33
30- 44	14	12	7	33
45- 59	15	12	15	42
60- 74	7	12	11	30
75- 89	13	11	13	37
90- 104	4	5	8	17
105- 119	7	3	1	11
120- 134	0	3	2	5
135- 149	3	2	2	7
150- 164	0	0	0	0
165- 179	0	0	1	1
180- 194	0	0	0	0
195- 209	0	0	0	0
210- 224	0	0	0	0

```
MACHINE-ONE    UTILISATION =    71.250  PERCENT
MACHINE-TWO    UTILISATION =    71.875  PERCENT
MACHINE THREE  UTILISATION =    71.146  PERCENT
     COMBINED  UTILISATION =    71.424  PERCENT
```

COST CALCULATIONS
BASISO SIMULATION PERIOD OF THIRTY DAYS
****

```
COST(LABOUR)  $   4800.000
COST(DEPRTN)  $      0.0
COST(DNTIME)  $   9876.000

TOTAL COST  $  14676.000
```
****

114   **Figure 5C–3** (continued)

simulation languages

introduction

This chapter discusses ways of deciding on the best simulation language in which to program the model. We presume that the analyst has already studied his problem in detail and is able to describe verbally how the model would operate. Although our discussion will apply to the construction of any simulation, emphasis will be on models of discrete situations; that is, where events occur at discrete points in time.

We devote a full chapter to simulation languages because preparation of the simulator is the heart of the research process. It is the most time-consuming phase, and the use of a suitable simulation language can significantly reduce preparation costs. The economic feasibility of the entire study sometimes depends on the choice of a proper simulation language.

Before comparing the advantages and disadvantages of the available languages, we will show why the selection process is so critical. We do this by relating the language selection to the other phases of the process, with specific emphasis on the communication problems between each phase.

simulation languages—what and why

The advantages of a special simulation language can be explained by a review of the process of translating a problem into a simulation program. At some point the analyst has the problem situation in mind. He has at his command a native language, say English, which is augmented by technical terminology. He first describes the situation as precisely as possible in this language. This description is then used by a programmer (who may be the same person) to prepare a computer program in a multi-purpose language (e.g., FORTRAN). The program must, of course, be debugged. This process looks like this:

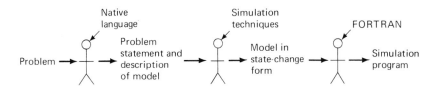

If the analyst knows FORTRAN and does his own programming, the communication problem is reduced; however, this does not eliminate the effort required to prepare and test the simulator program after the situation is understood.

Analysts went through this sequence of steps many times in the early days of simulation (the late 1950s). Many of the situations being simulated could be categorized broadly as systems involving the flow of items through processes. Most of these programs had functionally similar processes (e.g., an item arriving at a processing station). Recognition of these similarities led to the idea of developing special languages in which the operators (commands) would perform the common functions. Parameters used with the operators would specialize the function to represent the particular situation. Several simulation languages were developed almost simultaneously in the early 1960s by groups of researchers who recognized this commonality. In this chapter we will survey the major simulation languages and investigate one of them in some detail.

Almost all simulations require these common functions:

- create random numbers (as in Exercise 5–1, discussed further in Chapter 7)
- create random variates (like service time in the repairman example in Chapter 2 or the interarrival time in Exercise 5–1)
- advance time, either by one unit or to next event
- record data for output
- perform statistical analyses on recorded data
- arrange outputs in specified formats
- detect and report logical inconsistencies and other error conditions

Simulations in which discrete items are processed (or changed) by specific operations have, in addition to the functions just listed, the following common processes:

- determine type of event (after retrieval from an event list)
- call subroutines to adjust the state variables as a result of the event

- identify specific state conditions
- store and retrieve data from lists (tables or arrays), including the event list and those that represent the state

This last group of functions can be deduced from the basic form shown in Figure 5–1. Usually each function is performed by a subroutine. Some, such as storage and retrieval, are handled automatically. Others are called into use by language operators put into a program sequence that represents the particular situation's structure.

The major advantage of using a simulation language is the savings in time required to prepare and debug the simulator. It is not uncommon for this reduction to be a factor of ten, e.g., from six man-months to two man-weeks. (The case study presented in Chapter 10 compares the programming efficiency of a special simulation language to a FORTRAN simulator.) In addition, the resulting simulator is generally easier to modify than one written in a multipurpose language.

Besides obvious savings in time and flexibility, another rather dramatic change occurs as a result of using specially designed simulation languages. Some of these are actually *languages* in the more general sense; that is, they are useful in describing a situation independent of the fact that they can be translated by a computer into machine language. Such a language has a vocabulary and a syntax (grammar) and, if well designed, can be quite descriptive. As with other languages, people who use simulation languages tend to think in them. Thus *the language becomes an aid to problem formulation*. The process begins to look like this:

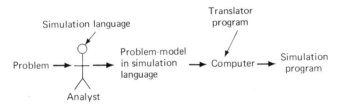

The conceptualization into a state-change model is facilitated, and one manual step, from problem statement to computer program, has been eliminated. Debugging is still required, but if the translator program is a good one it reports errors in simulation language terms and considerably expedites the debugging process. These benefits result because the analyst is thinking in simulation language terms.

an example of a simulation language: GPSS 6-3

The most popular, and, for many types of problems, the most useful, simulation language is GPSS (General Purpose Simulation System, IBM). To illustrate the characteristics of this language, we will show several short examples and, finally the GPSS simulation program for the plastic shop problem described in Chapter 5.

Before describing the GPSS job shop simulator, we should point out some of the design characteristics of the language. One is that GPSS is a *problem*-oriented language; that is, the special features of this language enable the analyst to describe directly the functional flow of the items (jobs) through the system (the shop). In this respect the language is quite different from a multipurpose language such as FORTRAN. In a FORTRAN simulation, the model is usually written in state-change form; a series of procedural steps determine the next state of the system. The required changes are made in the values of variables affected by the stage change. Flows of items are not described directly by the language. The GPSS translator converts the process flow description directly to a machine-usable state-change program. Let us begin to illustrate GPSS properties with a few simple examples.

GENERATE 10,5

is a statement in GPSS that creates new transactions. The *transactions* will have a particular meaning (e.g., jobs entering a shop) in the context of the problem. In the foregoing case, transactions are created with a mean interarrival time of ten units but with an equal chance of being anywhere between five and fifteen units. (The specification "10,5" can be interpreted as 10 ± 5, a uniform probability distribution.) We now may want to simulate this transaction entering a queue (on a first-come, first-served basis), awaiting its turn, and finally being processed. In GPSS this system would be modeled as:

```
GENERATE     10,5
QUEUE        ONE
SEIZE        MACH
DEPART       ONE
ADVANCE      7
RELEASE      MACH
TERMINATE    1
```

QUEUE means enter the queue called ONE. When a transaction reaches the head of the queue it SEIZEs the machine (a facility) called MACH and DEPARTs from the queue. Now this transaction is being processed. The process will continue for an amount of time determined by the ADVANCE operate. (In this case the time is seven units. Further on we will discuss how to make process times stochastic.) When the seven-unit process time is over, the transaction is RELEASEd by the machine, and it finally TERMINATEd (i.e., leaves the system). The GPSS system takes care of time advance within its executive routine. The advance is from event to event.

In GPSS much output is provided automatically. Figure 6–1 shows a computer run for this simple machine problem. We automatically obtain utilization figures for any facility SEIZEd and queue statistics for any QUEUE delays. We might, however, want some other information, such as the frequency distribution of overall processing time. This is obtained by inserting some bookkeeping operators into the end of the program just described.

RELEASE	MACH
TABULATE	**1**
1 TABLE	**M1, 0, 1, 25**
TERMINATE	1

The recording of arrival time is performed automatically in GPSS. TABULATE is a statement requesting information specified in TABLE 1. "M1" is a parameter requesting that flow-time data be accumulated according to classes determined by the other three numbers. Flow time is, of course, departure time minus arrival time. "0,1,25" means to tabulate in the following classes: $-\infty$ to 0, 0 to 1, 1 to 2, ..., 24 to ∞. Figure 6–2 shows this program. Note the additional output table.

With this background let us look at a GPSS formulation of the plastic shop problem in Chapter 5. Figure 6–3 is the GPSS program for the problem with arrivals of jobs and processing times that are probabilistic (that is, incorporating the distributions of Exercises 5–1 through 5–3). Job priorities at each process are handled on a first-come, first-served basis. Figure 6–4 is the complete problem analogous to Figure 5C–1 with Exercises 5–1 through 5–3 and with the shortest-processing-time-first priority rule. The LINK and UNLINK operators* create a special queue that can be handled FIFO (first in, first out), LIFO (last in, first out), or on the basis of the value of any parameter. In this case it is set up to select first the job in the queue with the lowest processing time (represented by the values of the parameters $P1$, $P2$, and $P3$). The correspondence between the GPSS program and the FORTRAN program is instructive and can be found by comparing the flow chart of the problem (Figure 5–9) with the FORTRAN program in the appendix at the end of Chapter 5 (Figure 5C–1) and the GPSS program in Figure 6–4. Compare also the outputs of the two programs.

We have used GPSS as an illustration of the simplification possible through a simulation language. Now we will explore the question of selecting a language.

comparison of existing simulation languages 6-4

The decision of which computer language to use for writing a simulation program arises in two contexts:

- when an analysis group, which is likely to use simulation techniques, is formed

- when an individual analyst is about to prepare a simulator

* Refer to the GPSS manual for detailed descriptions of all operators [IBM, 1967b].

BLOCK NUMBER	*LOC	OPERATION	A,B,C,D,E,F,G	COMMENTS
1		GENERATE	10,5	
2		QUEUE	ONE	
3		SEIZE	MACH	
4		DEPART	ONE	
5		ADVANCE	7	
6		RELEASE	MACH	
7		TERMINATE	1	
		START	100	Causes simulation to run until 100 jobs are terminated.

FACILITY SYMBOLS AND CORRESPONDING NUMBERS

1   MACH

QUEUE SYMBOLS AND CORRESPONDING NUMBERS

1   ONE

Figure 6-1   Very simple GPSS program (one queue, one process).

```
1       GENERATE    10    5
2       QUEUE       1
3       SEIZE       1
4       DEPART      1
5       ADVANCE     7
6       RELEASE     1
7       TERMINATE   1
        START       100
```

This is the same program
after assembly, i.e,
translation of mnemonic
to numberical identifiers

Standard GPSS outputs.

RELATIVE CLOCK   1021   ABSOLUTE CLOCK   1021   Ending clock time.
BLOCK COUNTS

BLOCK CURRENT	TOTAL	BLOCK CURRENT	TOTAL	BLOCK CURRENT	TOTAL	BLOCK CURRENT	TOTAL
1	0	101					
2	1	101					
3	0	100					
4	0	100					
5	0	100					
6	0	100					
7	0	100					

Number of jobs which are in (CURRENT)
and have passed through (TOTAL) each block.
(Blocks are defined in program listing)

FACILITY	AVERAGE UTILIZATION	NUMBER ENTRIES	AVERAGE TIME/TRAN	SEIZING TRANS. NO.	PREEMPTING TRANS. NO.
MACH	.685	100	7.000		

average time each
job was processed

QUEUE	MAXIMUM CONTENTS	AVERAGE CONTENTS	TOTAL ENTRIES	ZERO ENTRIES	PERCENT ZEROS	AVERAGE TIME/TRANS	$AVERAGE TIME/TRANS	TABLE NUMBER	CURRENT CONTENTS
ONE	1	.040	101	79	78.2	.405	1.863		1

$AVERAGE TIME/TRANS = AVERAGE TIME/TRANS EXCLUDING ZERO ENTRIES

121

Figure 6-2 Very simple GPSS program with tabulated output.

```
BLOCK
NUMBER   *LOC   OPERATION   A,B,C,D,E,F,G        COMMENTS

         *      SIMPLE EXAMPLE OF GPSS WITH TABULATED OUTPUT
         *

1               GENERATE    10,5
2               QUEUE       ONE
3               SEIZE       MACH
4               DEPART      ONE
5               ADVANCE     7
6               RELEASE     MACH
7               TABULATE    1               BLOCKS or operations to
                                            produce frequency
8         1     TABLE       M1,0,1,26       distribution output.
                TERMINATE   1               M1 means tabulate overall
                START       100             flow time
                JOB
```

Standard outputs follow for TRANSIENT period of 100 jobs.
(Assembly listing not shown)

RELATIVE CLOCK   1021   ABSOLUTE CLOCK   1021

BLOCK COUNTS

BLOCK	CURRENT	TOTAL	BLOCK	CURRENT	TOTAL	BLOCK	CURRENT	TOTAL	BLOCK	CURRENT	TOTAL
1	0	101									
2	1	101									
3	0	100									
4	0	100									
5	0	100									
6	0	100									
7	0	100									
8	0	100									

FACILITY	AVERAGE UTILIZATION	NUMBER ENTRIES	AVERAGE TIME/TRAN	SEIZING TRANS. NO.	PREEMPTING TRANS. NO.
MACH	.685	100	7.000		

QUEUE	MAXIMUM CONTENTS	AVERAGE CONTENTS	TOTAL ENTRIES	ZERO ENTRIES	PERCENT ZEROS	AVERAGE TIME/TRANS	$AVERAGE TIME/TRANS	TABLE NUMBER	CURRENT CONTENTS
ONE	1	.040	101	79	78.2	.405	1.863		1

$AVERAGE TIME/TRANS = AVERAGE TIME/TRANS EXCLUDING ZERO ENTRIES

The following table tabulates the overall delay
in processing jobs.

TABLE 1 ENTRIES IN TABLE 100	MEAN ARGUMENT* 7.369	STANDARD DEVIATION* .812	SUM OF ARGUMENTS 737.000	NON-WEIGHTED

UPPER LIMIT**	OBSERVED FREQUENCY	PER CENT OF TOTAL	CUMULATIVE PERCENTAGE	CUMULATIVE REMAINDER	MULTIPLE OF MEAN	DEVIATION FROM MEAN
0	0	.00	.0	100.0	-.000	-9.076
1	0	.00	.0	100.0	.135	-7.844
2	0	.00	.0	100.0	.271	-6.613
3	0	.00	.0	100.0	.407	-5.381
4	0	.00	.0	100.0	.542	-4.150
5	0	.00	.0	100.0	.678	-2.918
6	0	.00	.0	100.0	.814	-1.687
7	79	78.99	78.9	21.0	.949	-.455
8	9	8.99	87.9	12.0	1.085	.775
9	9	8.99	96.9	3.0	1.221	2.007
10	2	1.99	98.9	1.0	1.356	3.238
11	1	.99	100.0	.0	1.492	4.470

REMAINING FREQUENCIES ARE ALL ZERO

*Standard statistical data is automatically calculated.

**Process time.

Figure 6–3 Program for simulation of plastic shop in GPSS with first-in, first-out queuing.

BLOCK NUMBER	*LOC	OPERATION	A,B,C,D,E,F,G	COMMENTS
	*	PLASTIC SHOP MODEL IN GPSS – FIFO QUEUES		
	**			1 TIME UNIT = 1/10 HOUR Time in tenths of hours
		1 FUNCTION	RN1,D3	DISTRIBUTION FOR PROCESS TIMES
	.25	.5 .75	1.0 1.0 1.5	
		2 FUNCTION	RN1,C4	DISTRIBUTION FOR INPUT TIMES
	0.	0. .6	.75 .85 1.0 2.25	
1		GENERATE	80,FN2	CREATE NEW ARRIVALS
2		TABULATE	10	
3		ASSIGN	1,K30	ASSIGN MOLD TIME (MEAN), PUT IN P1 (P1 is a parameter associated with a job)
4		ASSIGN	2,K50	TRIM TIME
5		ASSIGN	3,K40	ASSEMBLE TIME
6		ASSIGN	4,V2	ASSIGN ALLOWED FLOW TIME (DUE TIME)
7		QUEUE	MQUE	Queuing is automatically first in — first out
8	PROM	SEIZE	MOLD	
9		DEPART	MQUE	
10		ADVANCE	P1,FN1	MOLDING PROCESS TIME PASSES
11		RELEASE	MOLD	
12		QUEUE	TQUE	
13	PROT	SEIZE	TRIM	
14		DEPART	TQUE	
15		ADVANCE	P2,FN1	TRIM
16		RELEASE	TRIM	
17		QUEUE	AQUE	
18	PROA	SEIZE	ASSM	
19		DEPART	AQUE	
20		ADVANCE	P3,FN1	ASSEMBLE
21		RELEASE	ASSM	
22		UNLINK	AQUE,PROA,1	
23		TABULATE	1	ACCUMULATE LATENESS STATISTICS
24		TABULATE	2	
25		TERMINATE	1	JOB LEAVES SHOP
	1	VARIABLE	M1-P4	COMPUTES LATENESS, M1 IS FLOW TIME (Used in Block 24)
	2	VARIABLE	K120+RN1/K10	COMPUTES DUE TIME AS ALLOWED FLOW (Used in Block 6)
	1	TABLE	V1,0,10,100	HOW TO ACCUM. LATENESS STATISTICS
	2	TABLE	M1,0,10,200	Define what to tabulate and formats for corresponding TABULATE blocks
	10	TABLE	IA,0,5,200	

```
START          10        CLEAR STATISTICAL TABLES
RESET
START        1000
```

RELATIVE CLOCK 775   ABSOLUTE CLOCK 775

BLOCK COUNTS

BLOCK CURRENT	TOTAL	BLOCK CURRENT	TOTAL	BLOCK CURRENT	TOTAL	BLOCK CURRENT	TOTAL	BLOCK CURRENT	TOTAL
1	0	13	11	0	13	21	0	10	
2	0	13	12	2	13	22	0	10	
3	0	13	13	2	11	23	0	10	
4	0	13	14	0	11	24	0	10	
5	0	13	15	1	11	25	0	10	
6	0	13	16	0	10				
7	0	13	17	0	10				
8	0	13	18	0	10				
9	0	13	19	0	10				
10	0	13	20	0	10				

FACILITY	AVERAGE UTILIZATION	NUMBER ENTRIES	AVERAGE TIME/TRAN	SEIZING TRANS. NO.	PREEMPTING TRANS. NO.
MOLD	.541	13	32.307		
TRIM	.670	11	47.272		
ASSM	.619	10	48.000	1	

QUEUE	MAXIMUM CONTENTS	AVERAGE CONTENTS	TOTAL ENTRIES	ZERO ENTRIES	PERCENT ZEROS	AVERAGE TIME/TRANS	$AVERAGE TIME/TRANS	TABLE NUMBER	CURRENT CONTENTS
MQUE	2	.294	13	6	46.1	17.538	32.571		
TQUE	2	.303	13	6	46.1	18.076	33.571		
AQUE	1	.117	10	5	50.0	9.099	18.199	2	

$AVERAGE TIME/TRANS = AVERAGE TIME/TRANS EXCLUDING ZERO ENTRIES

TABLE 1 TABULATES LATENESS

ENTRIES IN TABLE 10   MEAN ARGUMENT 6.599   STANDARD DEVIATION 54.312   SUM OF ARGUMENTS 66.000   NON-WEIGHTED

UPPER LIMIT	OBSERVED FREQUENCY	PER CENT OF TOTAL	CUMULATIVE PERCENTAGE	CUMULATIVE REMAINDER	MULTIPLE OF MEAN	DEVIATION FROM MEAN
0	6	59.99	59.9	40.0	-.000	-.121

Figure 6-3 (continued)

10	0	.00	59.9	1.515	40.0	.062
20	0	.00	59.9	3.030	40.0	.246
30	1	9.99	69.9	4.545	30.0	.430
40	0	.00	69.9	6.060	30.0	.614
50	1	9.99	79.9	7.575	20.0	.799
60	0	.00	79.9	9.090	20.0	.983
70	0	.00	79.9	10.606	20.0	1.167
80	0	.00	79.9	12.121	20.0	1.351
90	1	9.99	89.9	13.636	10.0	1.535
100	1	9.99	100.0	15.151	.0	1.719

REMAINING FREQUENCIES ARE ALL ZERO

TABLE 2 TABULATES OVERALL FLOW TIME
ENTRIES IN TABLE 10

| MEAN ARGUMENT 170.199 | | | STANDARD DEVIATION 40.187 | | SUM OF ARGUMENTS 1702.000 | NON-WEIGHTED |

UPPER LIMIT	OBSERVED FREQUENCY	PER CENT OF TOTAL	CUMULATIVE PERCENTAGE	CUMULATIVE REMAINDER	MULTIPLE OF MEAN	DEVIATION FROM MEAN
0	0	.00	.0	100.0	-.000	-4.235
10	0	.00	.0	100.0	.058	-3.986
20	0	.00	.0	100.0	.117	-3.737
30	0	.00	.0	100.0	.176	-3.488
40	0	.00	.0	100.0	.235	-3.239
50	0	.00	.0	100.0	.293	-2.990
60	0	.00	.0	100.0	.352	-2.742
70	0	.00	.0	100.0	.411	-2.493
80	0	.00	.0	100.0	.470	-2.244
90	0	.00	.0	100.0	.528	-1.995
100	0	.00	.0	100.0	.587	-1.746
110	0	.00	.0	100.0	.646	-1.497
120	0	.00	.0	100.0	.705	-1.249
130	2	19.99	19.9	80.0	.763	-1.000
140	0	.00	19.9	80.0	.822	-.751
150	2	19.99	39.9	60.0	.881	-.502
160	2	19.99	59.9	40.0	.940	-.253
170	0	.00	59.9	40.0	.998	-.004
180	0	.00	59.9	40.0	1.057	.243
190	2	19.99	79.9	20.0	1.116	.492
200	0	.00	79.9	20.0	1.175	.741
210	0	.00	79.9	20.0	1.233	.990
220	0	.00	79.9	20.0	1.292	1.239

Figure 6–3 (continued)

150	0	.00	91.6	8.3	2.542	1.558
155	0	.00	91.6	8.3	2.627	1.644
160	0	.00	91.6	8.3	2.711	1.730
165	0	.00	91.6	8.3	2.796	1.815
170	0	.00	91.6	8.3	2.881	1.901
175	0	.00	91.6	8.3	2.966	1.987
180	1	8.33	100.0	.0	3.050	2.072

REMAINING FREQUENCIES ARE ALL ZERO

RESET

START   1000   Clear accumulated statistics.
Run until 1000 jobs have terminated.

Outputs for main run.

RELATIVE CLOCK   62239   ABSOLUTE CLOCK   63014   Total time (transient + main) =

BLOCK COUNTS

BLOCK	CURRENT	TOTAL	BLOCK	CURRENT	TOTAL	BLOCK	CURRENT	TOTAL
1	0	999	11	0	999	21	0	1000
2	0	999	12	1	999	22	0	1000
3	0	999	13	0	1000	23	0	1000
4	0	999	14	0	1000	24	0	1000
5	0	999	15	1	1000	25	0	1000
6	0	999	16	0	1000			
7	0	999	17	0	1000			
8	0	999	18	0	1000			
9	0	999	19	0	1000			
10	0	999	20	0	1000			

FACILITY	AVERAGE UTILIZATION	NUMBER ENTRIES	AVERAGE TIME/TRAN	SEIZING TRANS. NO.	PREEMPTING TRANS. NO.
MOLD	.477	999	29.729		
TRIM	.815	1001	50.694	3	
ASSM	.643	1000	40.079		

QUEUE	MAXIMUM CONTENTS	AVERAGE CONTENTS	TOTAL ENTRIES	ZERO ENTRIES	PERCENT ZEROS	AVERAGE TIME/TRANS	$AVERAGE TIME/TRANS	TABLE NUMBER	CURRENT CONTENTS
MQUE	5	.209	999	589	58.9	13.072	31.851		
TQUE	9	1.325	1001	231	23.0	82.386	107.102		
AQUE	2	.135	1000	661	66.0	8.426	24.858		1

$AVERAGE TIME/TRANS = AVERAGE TIME/TRANS EXCLUDING ZERO ENTRIES

230	1	9.99	89.9	10.0	1.488
240	0	.00	89.9	10.0	1.736
250	1	9.99	100.0	.0	1.985

REMAINING FREQUENCIES ARE ALL ZERO

TABLE 10 TABULATES INTERARRIVAL TIMES

ENTRIES IN TABLE	MEAN ARGUMENT	STANDARD DEVIATION	SUM OF ARGUMENTS	NON-WEIGHTED
12	59.000	58.375	708.000	

UPPER LIMIT	OBSERVED FREQUENCY	PER CENT OF TOTAL	CUMULATIVE PERCENTAGE	CUMULATIVE REMAINDER	MULTIPLE OF MEAN	DEVIATION FROM MEAN
0	0	.00	.0	100.0	-.000	-1.010
5	1	8.33	8.3	91.6	.084	-.925
10	2	16.66	24.9	75.0	.169	-.839
15	0	.00	24.9	75.0	.254	-.753
20	1	8.33	33.3	66.6	.338	-.668
25	1	8.33	41.6	58.3	.423	-.582
30	0	.00	41.6	58.3	.508	-.496
35	2	16.66	58.3	41.6	.593	-.411
40	0	.00	58.3	41.6	.677	-.325
45	0	.00	58.3	41.6	.762	-.239
50	0	.00	58.3	41.6	.847	-.154
55	0	.00	58.3	41.6	.932	-.068
60	0	.00	58.3	41.6	1.016	.017
65	0	.00	58.3	41.6	1.101	.102
70	1	8.33	66.6	33.3	1.186	.188
75	0	.00	66.6	33.3	1.271	.274
80	0	.00	66.6	33.3	1.355	.359
85	1	8.33	74.9	25.0	1.440	.445
90	0	.00	74.9	25.0	1.525	.531
95	0	.00	74.9	25.0	1.610	.616
100	0	.00	74.9	25.0	1.694	.702
105	0	.00	74.9	25.0	1.779	.788
110	0	.00	74.9	25.0	1.864	.873
115	0	.00	74.9	25.0	1.949	.959
120	0	.00	74.9	25.0	2.033	1.044
125	0	.00	74.9	25.0	2.118	1.130
130	1	8.33	83.3	16.6	2.203	1.216
135	1	8.33	91.6	8.3	2.288	1.301
140	0	.00	91.6	8.3	2.372	1.387
145	0	.00	91.6	8.3	2.457	1.473

1

TABLE 1 LATENESS
ENTRIES IN TABLE 1000

MEAN ARGUMENT 55.439   STANDARD DEVIATION 108.187   SUM OF ARGUMENTS 55440.000   NON-WEIGHTED

UPPER LIMIT	OBSERVED FREQUENCY	PER CENT OF TOTAL	CUMULATIVE PERCENTAGE	CUMULATIVE REMAINDER	MULTIPLE OF MEAN	DEVIATION FROM MEAN
0	367	36.69	36.6	63.3	-.000	-.512
10	36	3.59	40.2	59.7	.180	-.420
20	59	5.89	46.1	53.8	.360	-.327
30	33	3.29	49.4	50.5	.541	-.235
40	38	3.79	53.2	46.7	.721	-.142
50	40	3.99	57.2	42.7	.901	-.050
60	38	3.79	61.0	38.9	1.082	.042
70	30	2.99	64.0	35.9	1.262	.134
80	28	2.79	66.8	33.1	1.443	.227
90	27	2.69	69.5	30.4	1.623	.319
100	25	2.49	72.0	27.9	1.803	.411
110	26	2.59	74.6	25.3	1.984	.504
120	25	2.49	77.1	22.8	2.164	.596
130	22	2.19	79.3	20.6	2.344	.689
140	18	1.79	81.1	18.8	2.525	.781
150	22	2.19	83.3	16.6	2.705	.874
160	9	.89	84.2	15.7	2.886	.966
170	17	1.69	85.9	14.0	3.066	1.058
180	6	.59	86.5	13.4	3.246	1.151
190	10	.99	87.5	12.4	3.427	1.243
200	10	.99	88.5	11.4	3.607	1.336
210	13	1.29	89.8	10.1	3.787	1.428
220	8	.79	90.6	9.3	3.968	1.521
230	3	.29	90.9	9.0	4.148	1.613
240	7	.69	91.6	8.3	4.329	1.705
250	10	.99	92.6	7.3	4.509	1.798
260	8	.79	93.4	6.5	4.689	1.890
270	8	.79	94.2	5.7	4.870	1.983
280	5	.49	94.7	5.2	5.050	2.075
290	10	.99	95.7	4.2	5.230	2.168
300	4	.39	96.1	3.8	5.411	2.260
310	6	.59	96.7	3.2	5.591	2.352
320	3	.29	97.0	2.9	5.772	2.445
330	8	.79	97.8	2.1	5.952	2.537
340	3	.29	98.1	1.8	6.132	2.630
350	3	.29	98.4	1.5	6.313	2.722

Figure 6-3 (continued)

Upper Limit	Observed Freq.	Per Cent of Total	Cumulative Percentage	Cumulative Remainder	Multiple of Mean	Deviation from Mean
360	1	.09	98.5	1.4	6.493	2.815
370	2	.19	98.7	1.2	6.673	2.907
380	4	.39	99.1	.8	6.854	2.999
390	1	.09	99.2	.7	7.034	3.092
400	2	.19	99.4	.5	7.215	3.184
410	1	.09	99.5	.4	7.395	3.277
420	1	.09	99.6	.3	7.575	3.369
430	1	.09	99.7	.2	7.756	3.462
440	0	.00	99.7	.2	7.936	3.554
450	1	.09	99.8	.1	8.116	3.646
460	1	.09	100.0	.0	8.297	3.739

REMAINING FREQUENCIES ARE ALL ZERO

TABLE 2 FLOWTIME

ENTRIES IN TABLE 1000   MEAN ARGUMENT 224.507   STANDARD DEVIATION 104.125   SUM OF ARGUMENTS 224508.000   NON-WEIGHTED

UPPER LIMIT	OBSERVED FREQUENCY	PER CENT OF TOTAL	CUMULATIVE PERCENTAGE	CUMULATIVE REMAINDER	MULTIPLE OF MEAN	DEVIATION FROM MEAN
0	0	.00	.0	100.0	-.000	-2.156
10	0	.00	.0	100.0	.044	-2.060
20	0	.00	.0	100.0	.089	-1.964
30	0	.00	.0	100.0	.133	-1.868
40	0	.00	.0	100.0	.178	-1.771
50	0	.00	.0	100.0	.222	-1.675
60	0	.00	.0	100.0	.267	-1.579
70	0	.00	.0	100.0	.311	-1.483
80	13	1.29	1.2	98.6	.356	-1.387
90	6	.59	1.8	98.0	.400	-1.291
100	22	2.19	4.0	95.8	.445	-1.195
110	26	2.59	6.6	93.2	.489	-1.099
120	38	3.79	10.4	89.5	.534	-1.003
130	39	3.89	14.3	85.5	.579	-.907
140	78	7.79	22.1	77.8	.623	-.811
150	59	5.89	28.0	71.9	.668	-.715
160	48	4.79	32.8	67.1	.712	-.619
170	54	5.39	38.2	61.7	.757	-.523
180	54	5.39	43.6	56.3	.801	-.427
190	44	4.39	48.0	51.9	.846	-.331
200	40	3.99	52.0	47.9	.890	-.235
210	30	2.99	55.0	44.9	.935	-.139
220	35	3.49	58.5	41.4	.979	-.043

230	27	2.69	61.2	38.7	1.024	.052
240	38	3.79	65.0	34.9	1.069	.148
250	37	3.69	68.7	31.2	1.113	.244
260	25	2.49	71.2	28.7	1.158	.340
270	30	2.99	74.2	25.7	1.202	.436
280	20	1.99	76.2	23.7	1.247	.532
290	24	2.39	78.6	21.3	1.291	.628
300	22	2.19	80.8	19.1	1.336	.725
310	14	1.39	82.2	17.7	1.380	.821
320	12	1.19	83.4	16.5	1.425	.917
330	15	1.49	84.9	15.0	1.469	1.013
340	13	1.29	86.2	13.7	1.514	1.109
350	11	1.09	87.3	12.6	1.558	1.205
360	13	1.29	88.6	11.3	1.603	1.301
370	5	.49	89.1	10.8	1.648	1.397
380	8	.79	89.9	10.0	1.692	1.493
390	10	.99	90.9	9.0	1.737	1.589
400	8	.79	91.7	8.2	1.781	1.685
410	8	.79	92.5	7.4	1.826	1.781
420	6	.59	93.1	6.8	1.870	1.877
430	10	.99	94.1	5.8	1.915	1.973
440	3	.29	94.4	5.5	1.959	2.069
450	6	.59	95.0	4.9	2.004	2.165
460	7	.69	95.7	4.2	2.048	2.261
470	8	.79	96.5	3.4	2.093	2.357
480	4	.39	96.9	3.0	2.138	2.453
490	2	.19	97.1	2.8	2.182	2.549
500	4	.39	97.5	2.4	2.227	2.645
510	3	.29	97.8	2.1	2.271	2.741
520	5	.49	98.3	1.6	2.316	2.837
530	3	.29	98.6	1.3	2.360	2.933
540	2	.19	98.8	1.1	2.405	3.029
550	4	.39	99.2	.7	2.449	3.125
560	1	.09	99.3	.6	2.494	3.222
570	1	.09	99.4	.5	2.538	3.318
580	2	.19	99.6	.3	2.583	3.414
590	1	.09	99.7	.2	2.627	3.510
600	1	.09	99.8	.1	2.672	3.606
610	0	.00	99.8	.1	2.717	3.702
620	0	.00	99.8	.1	2.761	3.798
630	0	.00	99.8	.1	2.806	3.894
640	1	.09	100.0	.0	2.850	3.990

REMAINING FREQUENCIES ARE ALL ZERO

Figure 6-3 (continued)

TABLE 10 INTERARRIVAL TIMES
ENTRIES IN TABLE
999

MEAN ARGUMENT
62.267

STANDARD DEVIATION
49.187

SUM OF ARGUMENTS
62205.000

NON-WEIGHTED

UPPER LIMIT	OBSERVED FREQUENCY	PER CENT OF TOTAL	CUMULATIVE PERCENTAGE	CUMULATIVE REMAINDER	MULTIPLE OF MEAN	DEVIATION FROM MEAN
0	11	1.10	1.1	98.8	-.000	-1.265
5	72	7.20	8.3	91.6	.080	-1.164
10	57	5.70	14.0	85.9	.160	-1.062
15	55	5.50	19.5	80.4	.240	-.960
20	54	5.40	24.9	75.0	.321	-.859
25	42	4.20	29.1	70.8	.401	-.757
30	35	3.50	32.6	67.3	.481	-.656
35	37	3.70	36.3	63.6	.562	-.554
40	51	5.10	41.4	58.5	.642	-.452
45	54	5.40	46.8	53.1	.722	-.351
50	52	5.20	52.0	47.9	.802	-.249
55	48	4.80	56.8	43.1	.883	-.147
60	36	3.60	60.4	39.5	.963	-.046
65	15	1.50	61.9	38.0	1.043	.055
70	16	1.60	63.5	36.4	1.124	.157
75	21	2.10	65.6	34.3	1.204	.258
80	17	1.70	67.3	32.6	1.284	.360
85	15	1.50	68.8	31.1	1.365	.462
90	16	1.60	70.4	29.5	1.445	.563
95	28	2.80	73.2	26.7	1.525	.665
100	20	2.00	75.2	24.7	1.605	.767
105	29	2.90	78.1	21.8	1.686	.868
110	21	2.10	80.2	19.7	1.766	.970
115	25	2.50	82.7	17.2	1.846	1.072
120	21	2.10	84.8	15.1	1.927	1.173
125	12	1.20	86.0	13.9	2.007	1.275
130	10	1.00	87.0	12.9	2.087	1.377
135	13	1.30	88.3	11.6	2.168	1.478
140	15	1.50	89.8	10.1	2.248	1.580
145	14	1.40	91.2	8.7	2.328	1.681
150	13	1.30	92.5	7.4	2.408	1.783
155	15	1.50	94.0	5.9	2.489	1.885
160	17	1.70	95.7	4.2	2.569	1.986
165	7	.70	96.4	3.5	2.649	2.088
170	10	1.00	97.4	2.5	2.730	2.190
175	13	1.30	98.7	1.2	2.810	2.291
180	12	1.20	100.0	.0	2.890	2.393

REMAINING FREQUENCIES ARE ALL ZERO

```
BLOCK
NUMBER  *LOC    OPERATION  A,B,C,D,E,F,G                    COMMENTS


         *    PLASTIC SHOP MODEL IN GPSS - SHORTEST JOB FIRST DISPATCHING
         *
         *                                  1 TIME UNIT = 1/10 HOUR
              1 FUNCTION    RN2,D3           DISTRIBUTION FOR PROCESS TIMES
         .25    .5     .75   1.0    1.0    1.5
              2 FUNCTION    RN2,C4           DISTRIBUTION FOR INPUT TIMES
         0.     0.     .6    .75    .85    1.5    1.0    2.25
1               GENERATE   80,FN2            CREATE NEW ARRIVALS
2               ASSIGN     1,K30,1           ASSIGN MOLD TIME (MEAN), PUT IN P1
3               ASSIGN     2,K50,1           TRIM TIME
4               ASSIGN     3,K40,1           ASSEMBLE TIME
5               ASSIGN     4,V2              ASSIGN ALLOWED FLOW TIME (DUE TIME)
6               LINK       MQUE,P1,PROM         LINK permits analysts to create non-FIFO queues.
7      PROM     SEIZE      MOLD                  Jobs are entered on to queue with lowest value of PI first
8               ADVANCE    P1,5              MOLDING PROCESS      TIME PASSES
9               RELEASE    MOLD
10              UNLINK     MQUE,PROM,1          Jobs removed from queue
11              LINK       TQUE,P2,PROT
12     PROT     SEIZE      TRIM
13              ADVANCE    P2,5              TRIM
14              RELEASE    TRIM
15              UNLINK     TQUE,PROT,1
16              LINK       AQUE,P3,PROA
17     PROA     SEIZE      ASSM
18              ADVANCE    P3,5              ASSEMBLE
19              RELEASE    ASSM
20              UNLINK     AQUE,PROA,1
21              TABULATE   1                 ACCUMULATE LATENESS STATISTICS
22              TABULATE   2
23              TERMINATE  1                 JOB LEAVES SHOP
              1 VARIABLE    M1-P4            COMPUTES LATENESS, M1 IS FLOW TIME
              2 VARIABLE    K120+RN2/K10     COMPUTES DUE TIME AS ALLOWED FLOW
              1 TABLE       V1,0,10,30       HOW TO ACCUM. LATENESS STATISTICS
              2 TABLE       M1,0,10,30       TABULATES FLOW TIMES.
                START      10
                RESET                        CLEAR STATISTICAL TABLES
                START      1000
                REPORT
                GRAPH      FR,MOLD,ASSM         These operations cause output to
                ORIGIN     55,10                be plotted as well as tabulated
                X          SYM,3,10
                Y          0,.2,5,10
         40     STATEMENT  10,10,FAC. UTIL.
                ENDGRAPH
                GRAPH      TP,1
                ORIGIN     55,10
                X          ,3,5,0,,10
                Y          0,10,10,5
         60     STATEMENT  10,14,LATENESS PERC.
                ENDGRAPH
                OUTPUT
                END        END OF MODEL
```

Figure 6–4 Program for simulation of plastic shop in GPSS with shortest-processing-time-first queue discipline (comparable to Figure 5C–1).

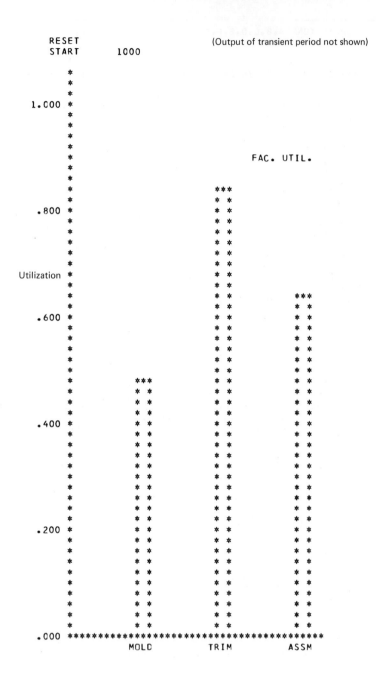

Figure 6–4 (continued)

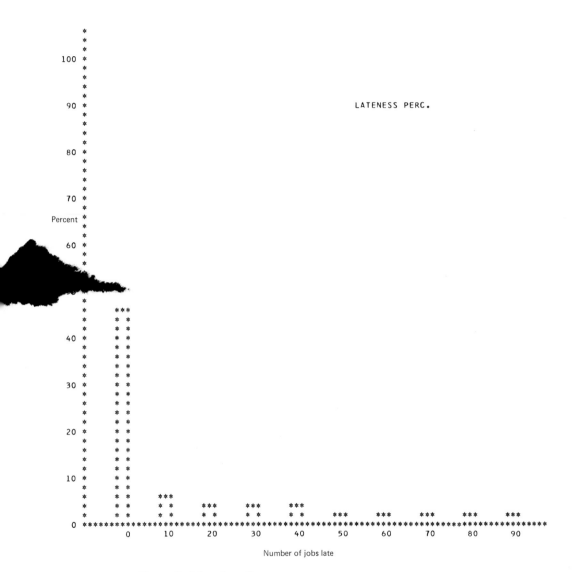

Figure 6–4 (continued)

Tabular Output

Figure 6–4 (continued)

RELATIVE CLOCK   60606   ABSOLUTE CLOCK   61326

BLOCK COUNTS

BLOCK	CURRENT	TOTAL	BLOCK	CURRENT	TOTAL	BLOCK	CURRENT	TOTAL
1	0	1001	11	0	1001	21	0	1000
2	0	1001	12	0	1001	22	0	1000
3	0	1001	13	1	1001	23	0	1000
4	0	1001	14	0	1000			
5	0	1001	15	0	1000			
6	0	1001	16	0	1000			
7	0	1001	17	0	1000			
8	0	1001	18	0	1000			
9	0	1001	19	0	1000			
10	0	1001	20	1	1000			

FACILITY	AVERAGE UTILIZATION	NUMBER ENTRIES	AVERAGE TIME/TRAN	SEIZING TRANS. NO.	PREEMPTING TRANS. NO.
MCLD	.495	1001	30.004		
TRIM	.850	1001	51.476	7	
ASSM	.648	1000	39.314		

USER CHAIN*	TOTAL ENTRIES	AVERAGE TIME/TRANS	CURRENT CONTENTS	AVERAGE CONTENTS	MAXIMUM CONTENTS
MQUE	454	26.354		.197	5
TQUE	797	103.086		1.355	10
AQUE	352	21.454		.124	3

*User defined queues.

136

TABLE 1 LATENESS
ENTRIES IN TABLE
1000

MEAN ARGUMENT 50.981

STANDARD DEVIATION 173.625

SUM OF ARGUMENTS 50982.000

NON-WEIGHTED

UPPER LIMIT	OBSERVED FREQUENCY	PER CENT OF TOTAL	CUMULATIVE PERCENTAGE	CUMULATIVE REMAINDER	MULTIPLE OF MEAN	DEVIATION FROM MEAN
0	464	46.39	46.3	53.6	-.000	-.293
10	74	7.39	53.7	46.2	.196	-.236
20	53	5.29	59.0	40.9	.392	-.178
30	45	4.49	63.5	36.4	.588	-.120
40	42	4.19	67.7	32.2	.784	-.063
50	37	3.69	71.4	28.5	.980	-.005
60	37	3.69	75.1	24.8	1.176	.051
70	22	2.19	77.3	22.6	1.373	.109
80	23	2.29	79.6	20.3	1.569	.167
90	22	2.19	81.8	18.1	1.765	.224
100	20	1.99	83.8	16.1	1.961	.282
110	14	1.39	85.2	14.7	2.157	.339
120	7	.69	85.9	14.0	2.353	.397
130	8	.79	86.7	13.2	2.549	.455
140	7	.69	87.4	12.5	2.746	.512
150	3	.29	87.7	12.2	2.942	.570
160	6	.59	88.3	11.6	3.138	.627
170	8	.79	89.1	10.8	3.334	.685
180	5	.49	89.6	10.3	3.530	.743
190	7	.69	90.3	9.6	3.726	.800
200	8	.79	91.1	8.8	3.922	.858
210	5	.49	91.6	8.3	4.119	.915
220	4	.39	92.0	7.9	4.315	.973
230	3	.29	92.3	7.6	4.511	1.031
240	3	.29	92.6	7.3	4.707	1.088
250	1	.09	92.7	7.2	4.903	1.146
260	1	.09	92.8	7.1	5.099	1.203
270	5	.49	93.3	6.6	5.295	1.261
280	3	.29	93.6	6.3	5.492	1.319
OVERFLOW	63	6.29	100.0	.0		

AVERAGE VALUE OF OVERFLOW 625.63

Figure 6-4 (continued)

TABLE 2 FLOW TIME
ENTRIES IN TABLE 1000

MEAN ARGUMENT 222.503

STANDARD DEVIATION 172.000

SUM OF ARGUMENTS 222504.000

NON-WEIGHTED

UPPER LIMIT	OBSERVED FREQUENCY	PER CENT OF TOTAL	CUMULATIVE PERCENTAGE	CUMULATIVE REMAINDER	MULTIPLE OF MEAN	DEVIATION FROM MEAN
0	0	.00	.0	100.0	-.000	-1.293
10	0	.00	.0	100.0	.044	-1.235
20	0	.00	.0	100.0	.089	-1.177
30	0	.00	.0	100.0	.134	-1.119
40	0	.00	.0	100.0	.179	-1.061
50	0	.00	.0	100.0	.224	-1.002
60	0	.00	.0	100.0	.269	-.944
70	1	.09	.0	99.8	.314	-.886
80	5	.49	.5	99.3	.359	-.828
90	12	1.19	1.7	98.1	.404	-.770
100	22	2.19	3.9	96.0	.449	-.712
110	30	2.99	6.9	93.0	.494	-.654
120	46	4.59	11.5	88.3	.539	-.595
130	68	6.79	18.3	81.6	.584	-.537
140	68	6.79	25.1	74.8	.629	-.479
150	98	9.79	34.9	65.0	.674	-.421
160	68	6.79	41.7	58.2	.719	-.363
170	60	5.99	47.7	52.2	.764	-.305
180	65	6.49	54.2	45.7	.808	-.247
190	63	6.29	60.5	39.4	.853	-.188
200	52	5.19	65.7	34.2	.898	-.130
210	45	4.49	70.2	29.7	.943	-.072
220	34	3.39	73.6	26.3	.988	-.014
230	31	3.09	76.7	23.2	1.033	.043
240	26	2.59	79.3	20.6	1.078	.101
250	23	2.29	81.6	18.3	1.123	.159
260	12	1.19	82.8	17.1	1.168	.217
270	13	1.29	84.1	15.8	1.213	.276
280	8	.79	84.9	15.0	1.258	.334
OVERFLOW	150	14.99	100.0	.0		

AVERAGE VALUE OF OVERFLOW 536.83

Any formal computer language has many characteristics. The relative importance of the characteristics depends on whose interests are being considered. For example, the learner's interests are different from the user's, and the user's are different from the system operator's. Although we shall try to include the considerations relevant to each of these groups, our first consideration is from the point of view of a user. The user wants a language that:

- facilitates model formulation
- is easy to program
- provides good error diagnostics
- is applicable to a wide range of problems

The first criterion requires that a language be problem oriented. That is, the commands and data designators in the language should be the same as an analyst would use to describe a real problem in his native language. The second and third criteria are partly a function of the problem orientation of the language and partly of the cleverness with which the translator is constructed. The last requires that any sort of state change that we might desire to represent can be represented in the language. Let us look at some simulation languages in terms of these three criteria: problem orientation, error detection, and general applicability.

The languages we will consider are:

GASP   a set of subroutines in FORTRAN that performs functions useful in simulations [Pritzker and Kiviat, 1967]

GPSS   a complete language oriented toward problems in which items pass through a series of processing and/or storage functions (latest version: GPSS/360) [IBM, 1967b])

SIMSCRIPT*   a complete language oriented toward event-to-event simulations in which discrete logical processes are common (latest version: SIMSCRIPT II [Kiviat et al., 1968])

CSMP†   a complete language oriented toward the solution of problems stated as nonlinear, integral-differential equations with continuous variables (CSMP permits a digital computer to simulate an analog computer.) [IBM, 1967a]

---

* SEAL, a language available from IBM, has similar properties. It is not discussed here.

† Several equivalents are available [Clancy and Fineberg, 1965]; the most famous is known as MIDAS.

DYNAMO   a complete language oriented toward expressing micro-economic models of firms by means of difference equations [Pugh, 1963]

JOB SHOP   a program package that can be set up to represent a
SIMULATOR   variety of job shops by means of parameters [Rowe, 1959]

These languages can be classified in terms of orientation and scope or generality of application as in Figure 6–5. The trade-off between generality (breadth of application) and problem orientation is clear.

Figure 6–5
Classification of simulation languages (relative location only).

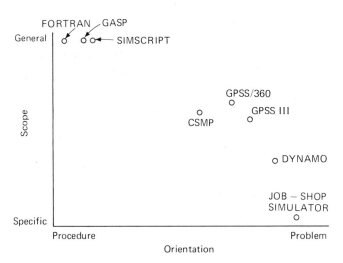

FORTRAN is included in Figure 6–5 as an example of a multipurpose language in which any sort of state-change process can be described. Even though it is not a simulation language, FORTRAN can be used to write simulation programs. ALGOL and PL/I are also suitable in this sense; PL/I has list-processing features that make it particularly suitable for simulations.

GASP and SIMSCRIPT differ in that the former is not a complete language. Both languages are very general, and both can do anything that can be done in FORTRAN. Although they offer valuable basic assistance in preparing simulators, they still demand that the analyst make most of the translations from the problem formulation to the state-change model, and also concern himself with some programming details.

GPSS/360 is very much oriented toward a particular kind of problem as indicated by the example programs already presented. Although it is problem oriented, GPSS has many features that permit it to be applied in a wide range of situations. Furthermore, the language can be augmented by subroutines written in Assembly Language. To illustrate how simulation languages improve, an earlier version of GPSS, GPSS III, is positioned in Figure 6–5. GPSS III is less general than the later version. For example, in GPSS III once processing (e.g., by a machine) has started on an item (e.g., a job lot), it cannot be stopped until the completion time that was computed originally. This restriction does not apply in GPSS/360. (As an example of a case in which this can be important, consider a machine with three bearings that fail occasionally. In a simulation model, we typically compute the *next* failure time of a bearing each time it fails. Now suppose we wish to test a maintenance policy that states that whenever one bearing fails, all are replaced. This policy requires that the failure times for the two running bearings must be changed before they fail. In programming terms it means changing an entry in the event list. Such a situation can be represented in GPSS/360 but not in GPSS III.)

DYNAMO [Pugh, 1963] and CSMP [IBM, 1967a] are examples of languages oriented toward problems formulated in terms of nonlinear differential or difference equations. Variables that are continuous almost everywhere in their range (some discontinuities can be handled) are assumed. DYNAMO was developed for defining models of business and CSMP for engineering design applications; however, their applications could be interchanged. Neither language is very general, but both are quite useful in specifying simulation procedures for specific types of problems.

The JOB SHOP SIMULATOR [IBM, 1960; Rowe, 1959] is illustrative of a program so specific that it is not a language at all; instead it is a program for the simulation of a particular problem. It is general only to the extent to which the size of the problem (e.g., number of machines) and some details of the operation (job routing rules, dispatching decisions) can be varied. Such packaged programs are not used extensively in simulation, since languages are much more general and are almost as easy to use on the particular problem as is a special program.

The foregoing languages are prominent in the United States, but they are by no means the only ones available. Three others might be mentioned: SIMULA [Dahl and Nygaard, 1965] a language similar to SIMSCRIPT, complies into ALGOL which is a multipurpose language widely used in Europe. It is a well-designed simulation language. GPS and CSL, languages developed in England, are similar to GPSS and are used for discrete-system problems. However, they have a different problem orientation than GPSS; they concentrate on starting and stopping processes rather than on the flow of items moving through processes. This difference will now be explored.

A subtle but important characteristic of discrete-simulation languages must be understood in order to select the most appropriate one for a particular problem. This has to do with the way a language permits the user to control the sequence of subroutines that represent the state changes. We will explain the alternative ways this control is handled by reference to the basic model of a discrete simulation presented in Figure 5–1. (For convenience, this model is reproduced here as Figure 6–6.)

Figure 6–6 shows the sequence of steps carried out by a simulation that is *event oriented*. This means that the system to be modeled is viewed as a world in which events occur that trigger changes in the system. Events can either initiate a process or they can indicate the end of a process.

141

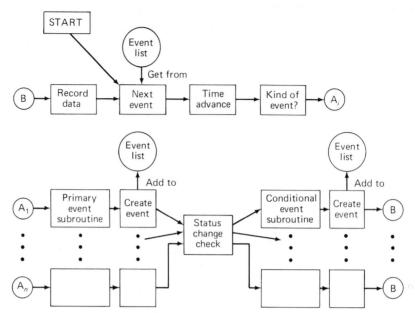

Figure 6–6 A basic form for discrete simulations.

Each event may be followed by a few conditional changes that are a direct consequence of the event. Thus the event list produces the dynamic behavior in the system. After every state change the event list must be scanned to determine the next event.

Another major process in event-oriented simulations is the state-change check (Figure 6–6). Here the state is scanned to determine which, if any, conditional events can occur. An important assumption in event-oriented simulations is that there will be only a few such conditional events. Thus, this simulation approach is most suitable where the system contains (or is analogous to) many items or transactions flowing through a series of relatively simple processes (e.g., a large number of different jobs being processed independently by a few machines). In these systems most events are process completions and most conditional events are the placement of the next transaction onto the process. This type of simulation is sometimes called *item* or *material oriented* [Laski, 1965] since it is most suitable for representing materials flowing through processes.

Most discrete-model languages available in the United States are based on event or material orientation (GPSS and SIMSCRIPT being typical examples). The language performs all the functions illustrated in Figure 6–6; that is, advancing the simulated time, searching for the next event, placing new events on the file, and testing for status matches to trigger conditional events. GPSS also provides many prewritten primary and conditional event subroutines. The procedural effect of some of the operations in the GPSS example program (Figure 6–1) are the following:

GENERATE   place an event in the event list to represent a new arrival
            (as in step 1 in Figure 5–9, the flow chart)

SEIZE   a conditional subroutine that is executed when (a) a transaction is waiting *and* (b) a facility is available (similar to steps 26 and 27 in Figure 5–9)

ADVANCE   place an event in the event list to represent the future completion of a process (similar to steps 30 through 33 in Figure 5–9)

The simulation program automatically obtains the next event whenever all of the state changes are completed; that is, whenever all items flowing as a result of the primary event have met a delay.

In some systems the assumptions of event-oriented simulators (many material items and few processes) are not met. For example, in a steel mill one material travels through very complex interacting processes. Each process involves several resources (e.g., a crane, a mill, an operator, and the batch of metal). Simulations of systems with complex interactive processing patterns are sometimes referred to as machine-oriented models. In these cases many conditions must be met before an *activity* or process can be started. Thus it is natural to search for a set of conditions that permits undertaking an activity. This set of conditions becomes the key to initiating the time-advance procedure. This approach is shown in Figure 6–7. Since this simulation form concentrates on the set of conditions that determines when activities can be started (or stopped), the form is known as *activity-oriented* simulation. (Note that the flow in Figure 6–7 is similar

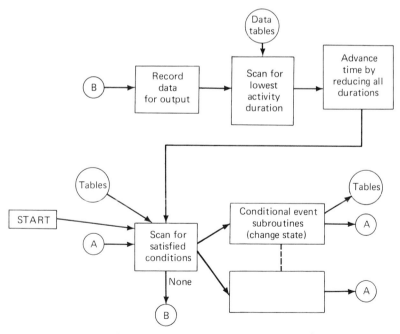

Figure 6–7   Basic form for activity-oriented process. Primary subroutines are treated as conditional but always occur.

143

to that in Figure 6–6; the emphasis is changed from event finding to activity starting and stopping.)

As Figure 6–7 shows, the state variables in activity-oriented simulations are updated through tables that contain data about each entity (e.g., machine status, job status, and so forth). At the start of an activity, the record of each entity involved contains the *relative* processing time required to complete its portion of the activity. In order to advance time, it is necessary to search through the time entries in the tables to find the lowest. The clock is advanced to this point, and all other entity durations are reduced by the amount of the advance. (Note that this is still event-time advance.) This time-advance procedure is more awkward than handling an event list, but it has three important advantages when dealing with machine-oriented systems:

(1) It is easier to determine which conditional subroutine to do first when several are enacted at the same time.

(2) It is easier to handle a hierarchy of conditional activities, such as, activity A creates conditions that affect activity B, which in turn can create conditions to affect activity A.

(3) It is easier to handle cases where one activity can change the duration of another, previously initiated, activity.

As we noted, the simulation languages that are activity oriented have been developed in England:

• GPS which is of historical interest as an early activity-oriented language; it was implemented only by the originators [Tocker].

• CSL which has been implemented for the IBM 7090's, 1620's, 1410's, and the Honeywell 200 and 400 series [IBM, 1963].

The current version of GPSS (i.e., GPSS/360) has been augmented beyond early versions so that it can handle interrelated processes almost as easily as activity-oriented languages. Some of the features in GPSS that permit reasonably efficient simulation of complex activities are:

TEST*   this feature holds up the flow of transactions until the state of the system meets a specified condition (e.g., queue is less than 10 items).

GATE   a command that is similar to TEST; however, TEST deals with conditions related to attributes of transactions and GATE to attributes of facilities. Since arbitrary indicators (called logic switches in GPSS) can be established, set, or reset, almost any combination of conditions can be represented.

*Refer to the *GPSS User's Manual* [IBM,1967b] for details of this and the following operations.

MATCH   a feature that prevents the flow of a transaction until conditions elsewhere in the system are met, such as when a transaction in another flow reaches a specified point.

GATHER   a technique that delays several transactions so that their processing can be controlled in consonance.

Before concluding this section we should say a little more about simulation languages that are designed for systems having variables that change in a continuous fashion. The most prominent language designed to represent industrial processes by continuous models is DYNAMO [Pugh, 1963]. DYNAMO represents the world as having:

"several *levels*"

"*flows* that transport the contents of one level to another"

"*decision functions* that control the rates of flows between levels"

"*information channels* that connect the decision functions to the levels" [Forrester, 1961, p. 68].

Levels and rates are related by simple difference equations

$$L_1(t + 1) = L_1(0) + \sum_{j=1}^{t+1} (R_i(j) - R_0(j))\Delta t$$

That is, the level at time $t + 1$ (for example, number of employees) is the level at $t = 0$ plus the cumulative flow (input less output, e.g., hiring less quits) to date. Δt is the time quanta being used. (This is not Forrester's notation, which is more computer-language oriented.) A decision equation changes rates, e.g.,

$$R(t + 1) = \frac{L_2(t)}{K}$$

as a function of other levels, such as L_2, in the system. Thus the hiring rate might be related to the level of the backlog of orders. The difference equations introduce lags or delays into the model and are used to approximate complex dynamic interactions assumed to describe an enterprise.

"A rate equation determines an immediately forthcoming action. If this action is sufficiently immediate (that is, the length of the solution interval, Δt is sufficiently short), it is evident that the decision cannot itself be affected by other decisions being made at the same instant in other parts of the system" [Forrester, 1968, p. 77].

That is, a parallel world in which several things happen at once is converted into a serial simulation model, in which difference equations are solved one after another within each time period. Industrial Dynamics also contributed to the art of applying simulation. It uses a flow diagram language, as does GPSS. Appendix 6A at the end of this chapter presents a simulation using DYNAMO.

There are a number of other languages (like CSMP) that are designed to simulate continuous systems. These are languages that program a digital computer to behave like an analog computer. Models are formulated as nonlinear integral-differential equations. These are then expressed in the language which in turn can be translated into an operating program. Unlike DYNAMO, most modern, continuous model languages use more efficient complex integration rules (e.g., Simpson's rule) to solve these equations.

6-5 choosing a simulation language

We have noted that the choice of a simulation language takes place at two levels. At one level a group must decide which languages it will make available on its computing facilities. At a second level, an analyst must choose from among the available languages for his particular problem.

We will look at the considerations and criteria for selection in each of these cases.

Selection of Simulation Languages for the Group

Two types of objectives are normally considered in selecting simulation languages. One is related to the operational characteristics of the language and the other is concerned with its problem-oriented characteristics.

Of primary operational interest are the programs and documentations necessary to implement and use the language; such considerations are

- the availability of intelligibly written user's manuals
- the compatability of the language compiler with available computer systems
- whether or not the language is supported by a major interest group (manufacturer, university, user's group, or software company) so that it will be updated and improved
- whether the language is easy to learn
- whether the language translator provides documentation and extensive error diagnostics
- the costs to install, maintain and update the language (in a few cases language translators are proprietary so that there are explicit charges for these services)
- the compiling and running time efficiency of the language

As to problem orientation, the group must examine the relationship between the characteristics of the language and those of the problems most likely to be encountered ["Panel . . . ," 1968]. This would include consideration of

- time advance methods
- event or activity orientation
- random number and random variate generation capabilities

- state and entity variable data storage and retrieval methods
- forms of output available and statistical analyses that can be performed on recorded data
- capability for inserting user-written subroutines

The most popular simulation language in the United States for discrete simulation is GPSS, with SIMSCRIPT generally assumed to be the second most widely used. For problems to be represented by continuous variables, MIDAS is fairly common and CSML is becoming so; use of DYNAMO is more limited. Translators are available and completely supported only for GPSS/360, SIMSCRIPT I.5, and GASP. (SIMSCRIPT I, available in the public domain [Markowitz, 1964] has rather poor documentation and diagnostics.) Most groups use GPSS/360 or SIMSCRIPT I.5 for discrete problems and MIDAS or CSML for continuous models.

Table 6–1 summarizes the major simulation languages and their translators available as of October 1968. (There have been no significant developments between that date and publication.)

Selection of a Simulation by an Analyst

When the need to construct a specific model arises, the analyst is usually pressed for time. He can afford neither to learn a new language nor to wait for a language translator to be installed and tested. Thus he is constrained to use a language that he already knows and for which translation is available. This situation usually forces the analyst to choose between one simulation language and one multipurpose language (e.g., GPSS or FORTRAN).

One of the primary considerations is whether the problem situation can be described naturally in the structure of the simulation language. (If the group has chosen its simulation language properly this usually should be the case.) For example, if the situation involves the flow of discrete items to be stored or processed in a set of facilities, GPSS or SIMSCRIPT would be natural languages to use. If the world view is of a system of continuously changing interacting variables, CSMP might be considered. If the situation involves complex decision processes or logical relationships, then it is best to use FORTRAN or an equivalent procedure language. If this is likely to occur frequently, GASP should be considered. As we will discuss in Chapter 10, if the problem is to represent a human thinking process, an interpretive, list-processing language, such as IPL-V [Newell, 1964] may be most suitable.

In general, if there is some chance that the simulation language will not be suitable, use of the procedure language will be the safest choice. If the analyst recognizes the general principles of simulation (as expressed in the basic simulation form of Figure 5–1), preparation of a FORTRAN simulation can be undertaken with a minimum of difficulty, even when the system being modeled is very complicated. There is at least one analysis group,* however, that has managed to do all its problems in GPSS.

* Norden Division of United Air Craft. Julian Reitman heads the group.

Table 6-1. Survey of Supported Simulation Language Translators

Manufacturer	Language	Description[1]	Translators for	Status[2]	Manual No.
Burroughs 6071 Second Ave. Detroit, Mich. 48202	DYNAMO		B5500	Current	Not available yet
	SIMULA	ALGOL-based	B5500	Due late 1968	Not available yet
Control Data Corp. 8100 34th Ave. S. Minneapolis, Minn.	SIMSCRIPT		3600	Current	60134600 (unsupported)
			6000 series	Current	60178300
	GPSS III		3600	CDC Data Center use only	
Data Saab 581 88 Linkoping Sweden	PROSIM	SIMSCRIPT-like ALGOL-based	D21, D22	Current	6361 (in Swedish)
Digital Equip. Corp. 148 Main St. Maynard, Mass. 01754	CSSL[4]	For continuous models	PDP–10	Under development	
GEC/AEI Automation East Lane North Wembley Middlesex, England	CONRAD	For continuous models	SDS92 SDS925 GE4020	Jan. 1969	80201
General Electric 13430 N. Black Canyon Hwy. Phoenix, Ariz. 85029	SIMSCRIPT		625, 635	Current	XCPB–1218
Honeywell EDP 200 Smith St. Waltham, Mass. 02154	GPSK	GPSS	H1200, 1250, 2200, 4200 (with scientific option)	Current	773
	CSL				524
IBM 112 E. Post Rd. White Plains, N. Y. 10600	GPSS/360		Any 360 model (64K, DOS)[5] (128K, OS)	Current	H20-0304 (intro.) H20-0326 (users)
	SIMSCRIPT I		7090/94	Current	SHARE documentation
	SIMSCRIPT I.5		360 (128 K)	Current	See footnote 3
	CSMP		1130; 360 (64K, OS)	Current	H20-0367
	SEAL	SIMSCRIPT-like	360 (256K)	Current	360 D 15.1.005 (unsupported)
International Computers, Ltd. Computer House Euston Centre London NW, England	SIMON		4100	Current	(No specific numbers)
	ESP		Series	Current	
	CSL		KDF9	Current	

Company / Address	Language	Description	Machine	Status	Number
Nippon Electric Co. 33–7 Shiba Gochome Minato-ku, Tokyo, Japan	EGPS	Like GPSS III	NEAC 2000	Current	Not yet available
	GPS-K	like GPSS,	NEAC 2000	Late 1969	Not yet available
	DYNAMO	activity-based	NEAC 200	Late 1969	(Osaka U. support)
Philco-Ford 3900 Walsh Rd. Willow Grove, Penn. 19090	SIMSCRIPT I		210, 211, 212	Current	PD 31
RCA Info-Systems Bldg. 204–2 Camden, N. J. 08101	Flow Simulator	Equivalent to GPSS/360	Spectra 70/35, 45, 55	Current	70–00–617
	SIMSCRIPT I.5		70/45, 55	Late 1968	Not yet available[3]
	5301 Flow Simulator	Equivalent to GPSS III	3301	Current	94–03–003
Scientific Data Systems 701 Aviation Blvd. El Segundo, Calif. 90245	SL–1	GPSS-like	Sigma 5, 7	Mid-1969	Not yet available
	DES–1	Continuous	9300	Current	980065
UNIVAC—Sperry Rand 2276 Highcrest Dr. Roseville, Minn. 55113	GPSS II		1107, 1108	Current	UP–4129
	SIMSCRIPT I.5		1107, 1108	Current	(see footnote 3)
	SIMULA		1107, 1108	Current	UP–7556
	UNS		494	Current	UP–7548

NONMANUFACTURER-SUPPORTED LANGUAGES

Company / Address	Language	Description	Machine	Status	Number
Prof. A. Pritsker Dept. of Industrial Engineering Arizona State University Tempe, Ariz. 85281	GASP II		Any system with FORTRAN IV compiler	Current	No number (charge for manual)
IBM—United Kingdom	CSL 2			Current	
Office of Naval Research	MILltran	SIMSCRIPT-like		Current	
California Analysis Centers, Inc. 225 Santa Monica Blvd. Santa Monica, Calif. 90401	SIMSCRIPT I.5		360 (OS, 128K) plus others noted above	Current	(Charge for translator system)
RAND Corp. 1500 Main St. Santa Monica, Calif 90406	SIMSCRIPT II			Available but unsupported	RAND P460PR

1 If not a standard language described in the text.
2 As of October 1968.

3 See under Calif. Analysis Center, Inc.
4 See SIMULATION, December 1967.

5 Minimum core size in bytes.

These analysts know the language in great detail and, by using the operators of the language in very sophisticated ways, they have managed to represent many situations for which the language was not designed explicitly. One way to achieve this is to make full use of the HELP command; a feature in GPSS that allows the programmer to add any subroutine, providing the subroutine is written in assembly language (FORTRAN subroutines can be used but slow the simulation).

In addition to choosing a computer language there are still several design decisions to be made. These are discussed in the next chapter. Next the analyst writes the simulation program. With the aid of the error detection diagnostics in the language, he then debugs the program. When he is satisfied that the program is isomorphic with the original flow chart, the basic model building is completed.

exercise

6–1 Write the GPSS simulator for Exercise 5–6. Run it and compare its program complexity and running time to those of the FORTRAN simulator.

references

Clancy, J., and M. Fineberg, "Digital Simulation Languages: A Critique and a Guide," *Proceedings of the IFIP Congress, 1965,* Sparton, Baltimore, 1965, pp. 23–36. (Continuous model images.)

Dahl, O., and K. Nygaard, *SIMULA, Introduction and User's Manual*, Norwegian Computing Center, Oslo, 1965.

Forrester, J. W., "Market Growth as Influenced by Capital Investment," *Industrial Management Review*, Vol. 9, No. 2, Winter 1968, pp. 68–77.

Forrester, J. W., *Industrial Dynamics,* M.I.T. Press, Cambridge, Mass., 1961.

IBM Corp., *System/360 Continuous System Modeling Program* (*360A–CX–16X*) *User's Manual*, H20–0367–1, New York, 1967a. (CSMP.)

IBM Corp., *General Purpose Simulation System/360, User's Manual*, H20–D326–0, New York, 1967b.

IBM Corp., *Job Shop Simulator, An IBM 704 Program Reference Manual*, New York, 1960.

IBM United Kingdom Ltd. and Esso Petroleum, *Control and Simulation Language— Reference Manual*, London, March 1963.

Kiviat, P. J., R. Villanueva, and H. M. Markowitz, *The SIMSCRIPT II Programming Language*, Prentice-Hall, Englewood Cliffs, N.J., 1968. (Companion references include: P. J. Kiviat et al., *The SIMSCRIPT II Programming Language: Reference Manual*, Prentice-Hall, 1968, and P. J. Kiviat, H. J. Shukiar, T. B. Urman, and R. Villanueva, *The SIMSCRIPT II Programming Language: IBM 360 Implementation*, RM–5777–PR, The RAND Corp., Santa Monica, Calif., 1968.)

Laski, J., "On Time Structure in Monte Carlo Simulations," *Operations Research Quarterly*, Vol. 16, No. 3, 1965, pp. 229–39.

Markowitz, H., B. Hansner, and H. Karr, *SIMSCRIPT*, Prentice-Hall, Englewood Cliffs, N.J., 1964. (Original and most widely available version of SIMSCRIPT.)

Newell, A. (ed.), *Information Processing Language—V*, 2nd ed., Prentice-Hall, Englewood Cliffs, N.J., 1964.

"Panel on Goals for Improvements in the Language (GPSS)," *IEEE Transactions on Systems Science and Cybernetics,* Vol. SSC–4, November 1968, pp. 433–37.

Pritzker, A., and P. J. Kiviat, *GASP II : A FORTRAN Based Simulation Language,* Dept. of Industrial Engineering, Arizona State University, Tempe, September 1967.

Pugh, A., *DYNAMO User's Manual,* 2nd ed., M.I.T. Press, Cambridge, Mass., 1963.

Rose, A., "Toward a Theory of Scheduling," *Contributions to Scientific Research in Management,* Proceedings of a Conference, Western Data Processing Center, Graduate School of Business, University of California, Los Angeles, January 29–30, 1959.

Teichroew, D., and J. Lubin, "Computer Simulation—Discussion of the Technique and Comparison of Languages," *Communications of the Association for Computing Machinery,* Vol. 9, No. 10, October 1966, pp. 723–41.

Tocher, K., *Handbook of the General Simulation Program,* Vol. I (revised), Rept. 77 ORC 3/Tech., Vol. II, Rept. 881 ORC 3/Tech., Dept. of Operational Research and Cybernetics, The United Steel Co. Ltd., Sheffield, England.

appendix 6A

An Example Simulation in DYNAMO*

One can identify a system only in terms of an objective. Here the objective is to identify and to explain one of the systems which can cause stagnation of sales growth even in the presence of an unlimited market. In particular, we deal here with that system which causes sales stagnation, or even sales decline, to arise out of an overly cautious capital investment policy. In this system inadequate capacity limits the growth in product sales.

Figure 6A–1 illustrates the scope of the system being considered. The closed boundary surrounds the relationships shown. No other influences from the outside are necessary for creating the sales growth and stagnation patterns which will presently be developed.

Within the closed boundary the system consists of interacting feedback loops as illustrated in Figure 6A–1. Three major loops are shown. Loop 1 is a positive-feedback loop involving the marketing effort here described in terms of hiring of salesmen. It provides the driving power for sales growth. Only positive-feedback loops can produce sustained growth. A positive loop is one in which activity changes the condition of the system in such a direction as to produce still greater activity. Assuming a favorable set of conditions around the loop, here is a situation in which salesmen book orders followed by product delivery which generates review which produces the sales budget which permits hiring still more salesmen. In short, salesmen produce revenue to pay for the further expansion of the sales effort.

However, Loop 2, on the upper right, involves delivery delay and sales effectiveness and can make the product sufficiently unattractive that the sales loop is no longer able to generate revenue greater than its current

* Extracted with permission from Jay W. Forrester "Market Growth as Influenced by Capital Investment," *Industrial Management Review,* Vol. 9, No. 2, Winter 1968, pp. 86–92, 102–104, Copyright *Industrial Management Review.*

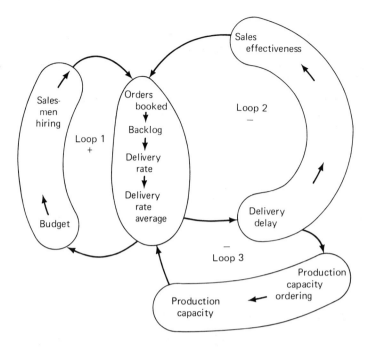

Figure 6A–1
Loop structure
for sales growth,
delivery delay,
and capacity
expansion.

expenditures. The delivery delay in Loop 2 can convert the salesmen-hiring in Loop 1 from positive-feedback growth behavior to negative-feedback goal-seeking behavior. Negative loops are goal seeking and adjust activity toward some target value. Here Loop 2 is a negative-feedback loop and tends to adjust the incoming order rate to equal the production capacity. It is common to think of the order rate as determining the production capacity, but under many circumstances production capacity is instead determining the order rate. This phenomenon takes place within Loop 2. Orders booked increase the order backlog which increases the delivery delay which makes the product less attractive and reduces the order rate. Were the order rate to be sustained above the production capacity, the backlog and the delivery delay would continue to increase until the product could no longer be sold.

Production capacity is determined in Loop 3. Here a very simplified capital investment policy will be represented to keep the example within permissible size. The ordering of new production capacity is a function of delivery delay only. Rising order backlog, as indicated by delivery delay, is taken as an inadequate capacity, and orders for more capacity are placed. These orders, after an acquisition delay, add to the production capacity. Loop 3 is a negative-feedback loop which is attempting to change production capacity to adjust the order backlog to a value determined by a management goal for proper delivery delay. As the delivery delay rises, production capacity is raised to bring down the delivery delay.

These loops will be examined in turn to show their detailed structure and their behavior. The flow diagrams and system equations define a complete simulation model of the simplified company-market system so that the time sequences implied by the system description can be computed and plotted.

Salesmen-Hiring Loop

The detailed structure of the positive-feedback loop governing the hiring and level of salesmen is shown in Figure 6A–2.

In the flow diagrams, the level equations are shown as rectangles, as for salesmen in this figure. The rate variables are shown by the valve symbol as for salesmen hired. The circles are "auxiliary" variables which are algebraically substitutable into the following rate equations and are structurally part of the rate equation.

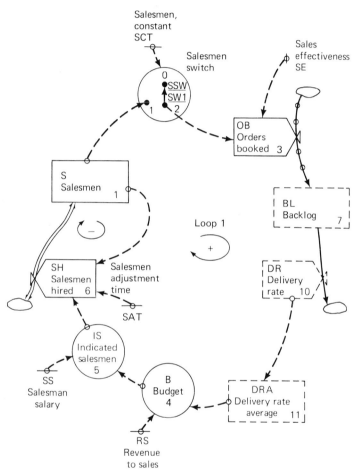

Figure 6A–2
Salesmen-hiring
loop with sales
generating
revenue to
support selling
effort.

Considering that the auxiliary variables are part of the associated rate variables, we see in Figure 6A–2 the alternating rate and level substructure within a feedback loop. The salesmen-hiring rate feeds the salesmen level. The salesmen level controls the orders booked rate. Orders booked as a rate flows into the backlog level. The backlog level is depleted by the delivery rate. The delivery rate is an input to the delivery rate average, which is a level. (All averages are generated by an accumulation process and by both mathematical form and structural location are necessarily system levels.) The delivery rate average, being a level, feeds into the salesmen-hired rate.

In Figure 6A–2 the Salesmen Switch (SSW) at the top of the figure has been put in to agree with the specific equations in Figure 6A–5. The switch allows activation or deactivation of the loop in simulation model runs. For the purpose of this discussion it should be considered in Position 1.

The positive-feedback character of Loop 1 shown in Figure 6A–2 gives the market system its growth tendencies. With a sufficiently attractive product and a sufficiently high fraction of revenue devoted to the sales budget, conditions are such that salesmen produce orders booked which increase backlog which increases delivery rate which increases the budget which increases the indicated salesmen that can be supported which causes a salesmen-hiring rate which increases the number of salesmen.

Such a positive-feedback loop has an exponential growth character as shown in Figure 6A–3. Here, Loop 1 alone causes ever-increasing growth without limit in the loop variables. The growth rate depends on the delays around the loop and on the conversion coefficients that determine loop amplification. Delays around the loop occur in the order backlog, in the delivery rate averaging, which here represents the billing and collection delay, and in the salesmen adjustment time (SAT), which here represents the delays in budgeting and the delay in finding and training salesmen. The value of 20 months for SAT is probably shorter than correct for most systems; if any of these delays are increased, the growth rate will be slower.

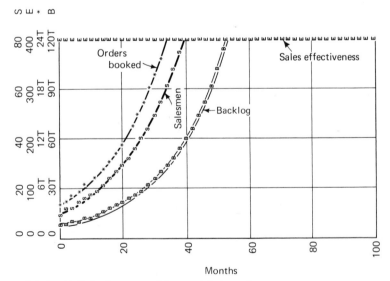

Figure 6A–3 Unlimited exponential growth in loop 1.

The effect of changing the gain around the salesmen-hiring loop in Figure 6A–2 can be shown by making a large change in sales effectiveness. If sales effectiveness is reduced, it means that a given number of salesmen will book fewer orders and produce less revenue and thereby support a smaller sales budget. If the sales effectiveness were made small enough, a given number of salesmen would produce revenues too small to support themselves. Under these circumstances the indicated salesmen would be less than the existing number of salesmen and salesmen-hiring would become salesmen reduction. Under such circumstances, the positive-feedback loop would have been converted to a negative-feedback loop tending toward zero salesmen and zero activity. This change in sales effectiveness is shown in Figure 6A–4. Here conditions are as in Figure 6A–3 until week 36. At week 36 the sales effectiveness has been reduced from 400 units/man-month (400 units per month sold by each salesman) to 100 units/man-month. In other words, the imaginary condition has been created where the product is four times harder to sell. Orders booked drop immediately but rise again by a small amount because the number of salesmen is still increasing. After the time for the lower order rate to propagate through the order backlog and the delay in delivery rate averaging, the number of salesmen starts to decline, and, along with the declining salesmen there is a corresponding decline in orders booked and in backlog. Figure 6A–4 is included to give a feeling for the behavior of the loop in Figure 6A–2. The sudden change in product attractiveness and the fourfold decrease in sales effectiveness would of course not be expected in an actual system.

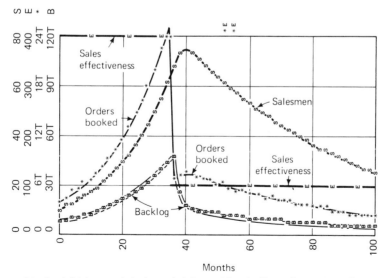

Figure 6A–4   Initial growth in loop 1 followed by decline when sales effectiveness is reduced.

Figure 6A–5 is the full set of equations as they appear in the model. The basic system structure extends through Equation 27–2. Control cards follow and then the variations of coefficients used to produce the different computer runs.

(Equations 0–1 through 6–1 represent the model in Figure 6A–2. The remaining equations represent parts of the model not described here. See the full article for a discussion of these.)

0–1		MARKET LOOPS
0–2	RUN	STD
0–3	NOTE	U. OF ILL.--CONVERSE AWARDS SYMPOSIUM, APRIL 13, 1967
0–4	NOTE	
0–5	NOTE	POSITIVE LOOP--SALESMEN
0–6	NOTE	
1	1L	S.K=S.J+(DT)(SH.JK+0)
1–1	6N	S=10
2	49A	SSW.K=SWITCH(SCT,S.K,SW1)
2–1	C	SCT=60
2–2	C	SW1=0
3	12R	OB.KL=(SSW.K)(SE.K)
4	12A	B.K=(DRA.K)(RS)
4–1	C	RS=12
5	20A	IS.K=B. K/SS
5–1	C	SS=2000
6	21R	SH.KL=(1/SAT)(IS.K−S.K)
6–1	C	SAT=20
6–4	NOTE	
6–5	NOTE	NEGATIVE LOOP--MARKET
6–6	NOTE	
7	1L	BL.K=BL.J+(DT)(OB.JK−DR.JK)
7–1	6N	BL=8000
8	20A	DDM.K=BL.K/PC.K
9	58A	PCF.K=TABHL(TPCF,DDM.K,0,5,.5)
9–1	C	TPCF*=0/.25/.5/.67/.8/.87/.93/.95/.97/.98/1
10	12R	DR.KL=(PC.K)(PCF.K)
11	3L	DRA.K=DRA.J+(DT)(1/DRAT)(DR.JK−DRA.J)
11–1	6N	DRA=DR
11–2	C	DRAT=1
12	20A	DDI.K=BL.K/DRA.K
13	3L	DDRC.K=DDRC.J+(DT)(1/TDDRC)(DDI.J−DDRC.J)
13–1	6N	DDRC=DDI
13–2	C	TDDRC=4
14	3L	DDRM.K=DDRM.J+(DT)(1/TDDRM)(DDRC.J−DDRM.J)
14–1	6N	DDRM=DDRC
14–2	C	TDDRM=6
15	58A	SEDM.K=TABHL(TSEDM,DDRM.K,0,10,1)
15–1	C	TSEDM*=1/.97/.87/.73/.53/.38/.25/.15/.08/.03/.02
16	51A	SEDC.K=CLIP(SEDF,SEDI,TIME.K,SEDCT)
16–1	C	SEDF=1
16–2	C	SEDI=1
16–3	C	SEDCT=36
17	49A	SEDS.K=SWITCH(SEDC.K,SEDM.K,SW2)
17–1	C	SW2=0
18	12A	SE.K=(SEDS.K)(SEM)
18–1	C	SEM=400
18–4	NOTE	
18–5	NOTE	CAPITAL INVESTMENT
18–6	NOTE	
19	3L	DDT.K=DDT.J+(DT)(1/TDDT)(DDRC.J−DDT.J)
19–1	6N	DDT=DDRC
19–2	C	TDDT=12
20	15A	DDOG.K=(DDT.K)(DDW)+(DDMG)(DDWC)
20–1	7N	DDWC=1−DDW
20–2	C	DDW=0
20–3	C	DDMG=2
21	27A	DDC.K=(DDRC.K/DDOG.K)−DDB
21–1	C	DDB=.3
22	58A	CEF.K=TABHL(TCEF,DDC.K,0,2.5,.5)

```
22–1    C       TCEF*=−.07/−.02/0/.02/.07/.15
23      49A     CEFSW.K=SWITCH(0,CEF.K,SW3)
23–1    C       SW3=0
24      12R     PCO.KL=(PC.K)(CEFSW.K)
25      39R     PCR.KL=DELAY3(PCO.JK,PCRD)
25–1    C       PCRD=12
26      1L      PCOO.K=PCOO.J+(DT)(PCO.JK−PCR.JK)
26–1    12N     PCOO=(PCO)(PCRD)
27      1L      PC.K=PC.J+(DT)(PCR.JK+0)
27–1    6N      PC=PCI
27–2    C       PCI=12000
27–5    NOTE
27–6    NOTE    CONTROL CARDS
27–7    NOTE
27–8    PLOT    OB=*,PC=C(0,24000)/SE=E(0,400)/S=S(0,80)
27–9    NOTE    B42, RERUNS OF B41
28      NOTE
28–1    RUN     A
28–2    NOTE    UNLIMITED EXPONENTIAL GROWTH
28–3    SPEC    DT=.5/LENGTH=100/PRTPER=100/PLTPER=2
28–4    PRINT   1)S
29      C       SW1=1
29–1    C       PCI=100000
29–4    PLOT    OB=*(0,24000)/SE=E(0,400)/BL=B(0,120000)/S=S(0,80)
29–5    RUN     B
29–6    NOTE    GROWTH AND DECLINE
30      C       SW1=1
30–1    C       SEDF=.25
30–2    C       PCI=100000
30–5    RUN     C
30–6    NOTE    NEGATIVE LOOP OSCILLATION
31      C       SW2=1
31–3    PLOT    OB=*,DR=D(0,24000)/SE=E(0,400)/DDRM=R(2,6)/BL=B(0,120000)
31–4    RUN     D
31–5    NOTE    SALES STAGNATION
32      C       SW1=1
32–1    C       SW2=1
32–4    PLOT    OB=*(0,24000)/SE=E(0,400)/SH=H(0,2)/DDRM=R(2,6)/S=S(0,80)
32–5    RUN     E
32–6    NOTE    INCREASED SALES BUDGET ALLOCATION
33      C       SW1=1
33–1    C       SW2=1
33–2    C       RS=13.6
33–5    RUN     F
33–6    NOTE    CAPACITY EXPANSION
34      C       SW1=1
34–1    C       SW2=1
34–2    C       SW3=1
34–5    PLOT    OB=*,PC=C(0,24000)/SE=E(0,400)/DDRM=R,DDOG=G(2,6)/S=S(0,80)/CEF=
34–6    X1      F(−.06,.18)
34–7    RUN     G
34–8    NOTE    GOAL=TRADITION WITH DELIVERY DELAY BIAS PRESSURE
35      C       SW1=1
35–1    C       SW2=1
35–2    C       SW3=1
35–3    C       DDW=1
```

Figure 6A–5   Typical DYNAMO model.

7

model design

In addition to choosing a language, the analyst must decide how he is going to trigger time advances in the model and whether to use a stochastic or deterministic representation of the system. In this chapter, we will present the considerations and the techniques for these decisions.

types of time advances 7-1

In Section 1–7 we noted that one of the problems in designing a simulator is to choose an appropriate time interval. In the examples in Chapters 2 and 5 we saw that there are two methods of advancing time: unit-by-unit and event-to-event (or simply unit- and event-time advance). Here we will investigate the nature of the trade-off. The considerations involved are quite straightforward if we recall the basic simulation sequence shown in Figure 7–1.

The computations are simplified in unit-time advance because there is no event list nor associated processing. But there are a number of periods when no events occur, so that the time-advance computations are inefficient. In the case shown in Figure 7–1, event advance is preferable because the added calculations for the event list do not exceed the time wasted in uneventful periods. If events occur on a fairly regular basis, time-advance periods can be established in a way that minimizes the chance of advancing to periods of inactivity. In this case, time advance is likely to be preferred.

Unit-Time vs. Event Advance

Unit-time-advance simulation models can be used to represent any system, but event-advance simulators cannot. Event-advance simulators

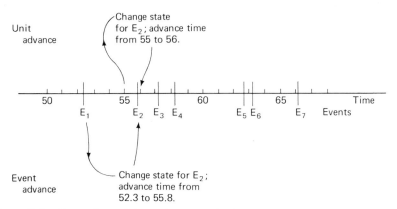

Figure 7–1   Comparison of time-advance methods.

are inappropriate when one or more of the state variables change in a continuous fashion and cannot be approximated by discrete events. For example, it is difficult to use event-advance methods to model a chemical process where one of the state variables is the continuously changing temperature of the reaction. Events (which occur at the molecular level in this example) happen at such short intervals that they must be aggregated into a continuously changing variable (i.e., temperature).

We now compare the relative effectiveness of the two methods of advancing time in more detail, necessarily limiting our discussion to situations in which both methods are appropriate; that is, systems where variables can be represented in discrete states.

In "Mean Value Estimation from Digital Computer Simulation" Gafarian and Ancker [1966] have compared the relative efficiency of event-advance simulation models and unit-time-advance models in estimating the expected (or average) output of the system. They examined the two time-advance methods for an equivalent simulated time (which is not necessarily the same as equivalent computer running time) and judged the efficiency of each in terms of the variance of its estimate of the mean effect. Gafarian and Ancker show that information about the behavior of the system is always lost by using the unit-advance simulators—no matter how small the time increment. The loss of information shows up in Figure 7–1 as the uncertainty about where the events occur within each unit of time. Therefore, for an equivalent simulated time, an analyst can always obtain the estimate with the smallest variance (i.e., the most reliable estimate) by using event-advance simulation models.

We cannot conclude from the Gafarian and Ancker analysis that event-advance methods necessarily dominate time-advance methods because their study did not include computer running time as a factor in the evaluation.

In "Some Problems of Digital Computer Simulation" Conway, Johnson, and Maxwell [1959] sought to define the conditions in a problem that would lead the analyst to conclude whether unit-advance simulators would require less computer time to obtain data (for a specified simulation period) than event advance. They assumed that computer running time is approximately proportional to the number of paired comparisons required for each occasion when the simulation is advanced. This assumption is fairly crude because it does not include the time required to update the status of the system after each comparison; this time is likely to be longer for event-advance simulators, since a change of status always occurs each time the simulation is advanced. Nevertheless, the assumption is sufficient for the authors' purpose, which is to isolate the factors that are relevant to decisions about timing rather than to formulate explicit trade-offs between methods.

In their paper Conway et al. deal with a hypothetical problem that has the following characteristics:

(1) The state of the system at any time can be described in terms of k variables.

(2) Each variable has a particular value for an average of m time periods.

(3) The simulation model is to be run for t simulated time periods.

The unit-time-advance simulator has a time interval of $1/t$. In each interval, the simulator checks the current status of each of the k state variables. Thus the total simulation will involve kt comparisons. To determine the number of comparisons in the event simulator, it is necessary to compute the expected number of events that will occur during the run. Assuming that events occur independently, the probability of an event occurring in any particular time interval is k/m and the expected number of events is tk/m. Each time an event occurs, the event list must be updated. With k state variables, the update can be achieved by $k - 1$ paired comparisons in the event list. Thus the total simulation using event-advance methods will involve $tk(k - 1)/m$ comparisons.

Conway et al. found that an approximate estimate of the relative running efficiency of the two time-advance procedures is obtained by comparing tk with $tk(k - 1)/m$. By comparing these formulas they concluded that event-advance simulators become more advantageous as the mean time between events increases (i.e., m gets larger), whereas the unit-advance method becomes preferable when the number of state variables increases (i.e., k becomes larger). Thus simulators of large systems (e.g., enterprise) in which there is a high probability of something happening in a time unit should use unit-time-advance methods. This confirms the intuitive impression given by Figure 7–1.

Event vs. Activity Orientation

We have already discussed another choice in the timing procedure: between event and activity orientation (see Section 6–4). Both activity- and event-oriented models assume that time is a continuous variable. In event advance, single events trigger partial state-change routines. In activity advance, a complete series of state changes is triggered at the time all conditions are satisfied to permit an activity to start or stop.

Laski [1965] examined the relative advantages of event- and activity-oriented simulators. He concluded that activity-oriented methods are most useful when the activities cause many events and there is a high degree of interaction between the status of events. Event-oriented methods, however, are usually more efficient from a computational standpoint. Therefore, the trade-off is between the computational advantages of event-oriented methods and the structural advantages of activity-oriented methods (see Section 6–4 for a detailed discussion of these methods).

7-2 event-advance vs. unit-time-advance methods in the machine failure problem

We have summarized the specific conclusions of several analyses of time advancing. Since methods which best represent the time variable depend on the characteristics of the particular problem, we cannot state absolute rules for this choice. Now we will look at the relative efficiency of event-advance and unit-time-advance models in the specific context of the machine adjustment problem introduced in Chapter 2. Since the efficiency of the unit-time-advance model depends on the choice of time interval, we will also discuss how this choice is made.

In the course of developing the simulator for the machine adjustment problem (Chapter 2), we briefly discussed the problem of choosing an appropriate time interval. The time-advance interval, δt, had to be small enough so that at most only one event (i.e., either a machine breakdown or the completion of an adjustment) was likely to occur in δt. This is easily achieved in the analytic model by using the mathematical concept of a limit. For the simulation, by examining the mean breakdown and repair rates (fifteen and five minutes, respectively), a simulation time-advance interval of one quarter of a minute was judged to be a reasonable approximation to the analytic conditions. The one-quarter-minute interval made the probability of a repairman completing a repair in $\delta t = 0.05$ and the probability of a working machine failing in $\delta t = 0.0167$ (see Tables 2–4 and 2–5). There is a probability (0.055) that a multiple event should occur, but it would not be so processed by the simulator.

In very complex models it is not possible to calculate the probability of multiple occurrences. A rule of thumb that the authors and others have found to provide an estimate of a reasonable time interval in these cases is: "choose the time interval to be one tenth of the shortest expected inter-event time." More analytic procedures for choosing the time interval are discussed in the next section.

We begin our analysis of time-advance procedures by examining the sensitivity of the output of the machine repair problem simulator to alternative time-advance intervals. For this comparison, we deal only with the fixed adjuster version of the problem because it has a known analytic solution. Table 7–1 presents the results of rerunning the simulator for time-advance intervals of three quarters of a minute and one and a half minutes. For completeness we also include the one-quarter-minute observation reported in Chapter 2 as well as the theoretical steady-state conditions derived from the analytic model. The measure used to compare simulation outputs is the probability of down configurations and also expected machines idle. These indicate the bias introduced into the simulator by choosing a time interval that is too large. We see that when the time interval used for the simulator becomes larger, the model becomes an unrealistic representation of the behavior of the system. The errors occur because, as the time unit gets larger, (1) the probabilities of events occurring are no longer properly estimated and (2) the probability that two or more events should occur (whereas only one is simulated) increases.

| | P_i = Probability of i machines not operating | | | | | | | Expected |
	P_0	P_1	P_2	P_3	P_4	P_5	P_6	Machines Idle
Theoretical simulation results	0.155	0.308	0.254	0.168	0.083	0.027	0.004	1.811
$\delta t = \frac{1}{4}$ min	0.149	0.303	0.248	0.170	0.091	0.033	0.005	1.868
$\delta t = \frac{3}{4}$ min	0.141	0.284	0.269	0.182	0.090	0.029	0.005	1.903
$\delta t = 1\frac{1}{2}$ min	0.110	0.244	0.278	0.212	0.112	0.038	0.005	2.104

Table 7–1. A Comparison of Theoretical and Simulation Results of a Six-Machine Two-Adjuster Problem for Various Time-Advance Intervals

The time variable in event-advance simulators is treated as continuous because time is advanced at the exact instance when there is a change in the status of the system. The time when each such change occurs is predicted by searching for the minimum time in a future events list. Thus, event simulators correctly order the occurrence of events, no matter how close in time, by making this decision a consequence of the time-advance procedure. The only "noise" in the system is due to time being represented in the simulator by a digital number of finite precision. In most computers the precision is high enough so that this effect is negligible.

To compare the methods of time advance we have reprogrammed the machine failure problem with two fixed repairmen as an event simulator. The flow chart and the annotated FORTRAN program are presented in Figures 7–2 and 7–3, respectively. In Table 7–2 we compare the predic-

Time-Advance Method	Expected Number of Machines Idle	Computer Running Time for 200 Simulated Hours of Operation
Theoretical	1.811	
Unit-time advance ($\frac{1}{4}$-min intervals)	1.868	0.36 min
Event advance	1.835	0.12 min

Table 7–2. A Comparison of Accuracy and Running Time for Unit-Advance and Event-Advance Simulation Models of a Six-Machine Two-Adjuster case

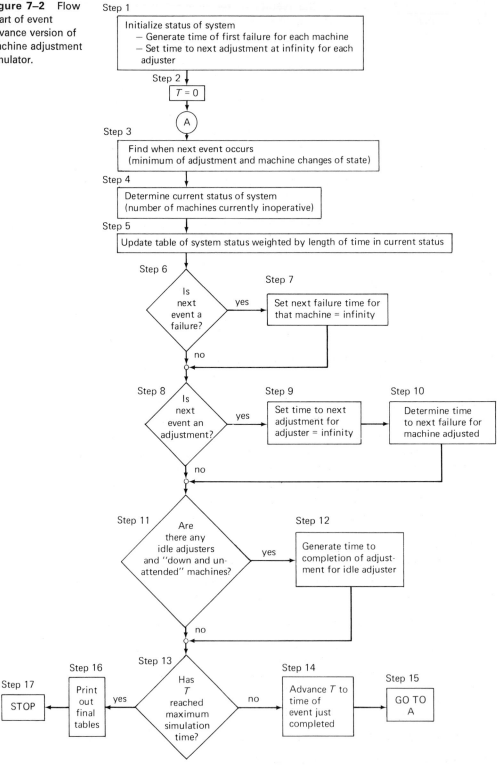

Figure 7–2 Flow chart of event advance version of machine adjustment simulator.

Step 1
Initialize status of system
— Generate time of first failure for each machine
— Set time to next adjustment at infinity for each adjuster

Step 2
$T = 0$

A

Step 3
Find when next event occurs
(minimum of adjustment and machine changes of state)

Step 4
Determine current status of system
(number of machines currently inoperative)

Step 5
Update table of system status weighted by length of time in current status

Step 6
Is next event a failure?

yes

Step 7
Set next failure time for that machine = infinity

no

Step 8
Is next event an adjustment?

yes

Step 9
Set time to next adjustment for adjuster = infinity

Step 10
Determine time to next failure for machine adjusted

no

Step 11
Are there any idle adjusters and "down and unattended" machines?

yes

Step 12
Generate time to completion of adjustment for idle adjuster

no

Step 13
Has T reached maximum simulation time?

no

Step 14
Advance T to time of event just completed

Step 15
GO TO A

yes

Step 16
Print out final tables

Step 17
STOP

sec. 7-3
choice of time
unit in unit-advance
models

tions for steady-state conditions of the event-advance simulator with the time-advance simulator. The computational efficiency of each, measured by the computer time required to simulate 200 hours of operation, is also reported. Both models were run on an IBM 360/65. The superiority of the event-advance method in this case is clear. We could show this only after we had selected the best time interval for the unit-advance model. In the next section, we will examine ways of determining this time interval.

choice of time unit in unit-advance models 7-3

If the analyst chooses the unit-time-advance method, he must next choose the size of the time unit. (The equivalent in event advance is the choice of the precision of the time variable. This is usually chosen as equal to the full precision of a computer word and is more precision than needed in nearly all cases. It costs no more than some lesser precision.)

The general rule for choosing a time unit is: choose the largest unit such that the probability that more than one decision will have to be made during a unit of time is negligible. Within this rule there is a subsidiary rule: if the consequences of the decisions are to be determined by simulating individual events (and unit advance is used), the unit must be still smaller; small enough so that the probability of multiple events occurring in a unit of time is negligible.

Gafarian and Ancker [1966] deal with improving the information output of unit-time advance. Their concern is to determine methods whereby unit-advance simulators provide parameter estimations that provide as much information as event-advance simulators. Specifically they examine the problem of choosing the size of the time "slice" that results in a variance estimate of the steady-state conditions that is approximately the same as an event-advance model.

In their analysis, Gafarian and Ancker make two critical assumptions. First, they analyze simulation output that is already in steady-state conditions (they do not worry about running time required to achieve steady state). Second, they make the assumption that there is an exponentially decreasing covariance between time-spaced observations; that is, the effect of an event on future events decreases as time goes by and the rate of decrease is exponential.

For a continuous process the covariance assumption can be stated as follows:

By definition:

$$R(\tau) \equiv E\{[X_t - E(X_t)][X_{t+\tau} - E(X_{t+\tau})]\}$$

By assumption:

$$R(\tau) = \sigma^2 e^{-c\tau}$$

165

Figure 7-3 Program for simulation of machine adjustment case with event time advance.

```
C    MACHINE ADJUSTMENT MODEL WITH EVENT ADVANCE.
C
C    F(I) REFERS TO STATUS OF MACHINE I.  R(J) REFERS TO STATUS OF REPAIRMAN J.
     DIMENSION F(10),R(10),Q(10),AQ(10),AQQ(10)
     DO 9 I=1,10
     F(I)=0.0
     R(I)=0.0
     Q(I)=0.0
9    AQ(I)=0.0
     DUMMY=3261547.0
     ANF=99999.0
C    STEP 1 - INITIALIZE STATUS OF SYSTEM
     DO 10 I=1,6
     YFL=RANNOS(DUMMY)          (RANNOS random number subroutine
     ZFL=ALOG(YFL)                          not shown)
10   F(I)=-15.0*ZFL
     R(1)=ANF
     R(2)=ANF
C    STEP 2
     T=0.0
C    STEP 3
100  DT=AMIN1(F(1),F(2),F(3),F(4),F(5),F(6),R(1),R(2))
C    STEP 4
     IND=1
11   DO 11 I=1,6
     IF (F(I).EQ.ANF) IND=IND+1
C    STEP 5
     Q(IND)=Q(IND)+DT-T
C    STEPS 6 AND 7
12   DO 12 I=1,6
     IF (DT.EQ.F(I)) F(I)=ANF
C    STEP 8
     DO 14 I=1,2
     IF (DT.NE.R(I)) GO TO 14
C    STEP 9
     R(I)=ANF
C    STEP 10
     DO 13 J=1,6
     IF (F(J).NE.ANF) GO TO 13
     YFL=RANNOS(DUMMY)
     ZFL=ALOG(YFL)
     F(J)=DT-15.0*ZFL
     GO TO 14
13   CONTINUE
14   CONTINUE
```

0001
0002
0003
0004
0005
0006
0007
0008
0009
0010
0011
0012
0013
0014
0015
0016
0017
0018
0019
0020
0021
0022
0023
0024
0025
0026
0027
0028
0029
0030
0031
0032
0033

```
              C         STEP 11
0034                    IND=0
0035          140       DO 140 I=1,6
0036                    IF (F(I).EQ.ANF) IND=IND+1
0037                    KND=0
0038                    DO 141 J=1,2
0039          141       IF (R(J).EQ.ANF) KND=KND+1
0040                    IF (IND.EQ.KND) GO TO 16
0041                    DO 16 I=1,6
0042                    IF (F(I).NE.ANF) GO TO 16
              C         STEP 12
0043                    DO 15 J=1,2
0044                    IF (R(J).NE.ANF) GO TO 15
0045                    YFL=RANNOS(DUMMY)
0046                    ZFL=ALOG(YFL)
0047                    R(J)=DT-5.0*ZFL
0048                    GO TO 16
0049          15        CONTINUE
0050          16        CONTINUE
              C         STEP 13
0051                    IF (T.GE.20000.0) GO TO 902
              C         STEP 14
0052                    T=DT
              C         STEP 15
0053                    GO TO 100
              C         STEP 16
0054          902       PRINT 901,T
0055          901       FORMAT (1X,7HTIME = ,F8.1)
0056                    DO 17 J=1,7
0057          17        AQ(J)=Q(J)/T
0058                    PRINT 900,(AQ(J),J=1,7)
0059          900       FORMAT (1X,10F8.3)
              C         STEP 17
0060                    CALL EXIT
0061                    END
```

Cumulative time spend with zero through
six machines down.

```
TIME =  20000.1
 0.145   0.298   0.251   0.178   0.088   0.035   0.005
```

where $R(\tau)$ = covariance between observations that are τ time periods apart.

σ^2 = variance of individual observations

c = positive constant and is a measure of how rapidly the effect (autocorrelation) between two samples decreases

For the unit-time-advance simulator, the variance of the mean-value estimate of an autocorrelated time series is

$$\sigma_{\theta_1}^2 = \frac{\sigma^2}{N} + \frac{2}{N} \sum_{j=1}^{N-1} \left[1 - \left(\frac{j}{N} \right) \right] R(jt_0) \qquad (7\text{–}1)$$

where N = number of simulated observations of the variable being estimated

t_0 = size of time slice for time-advance simulation runs

For the continuous (event) case, the variance of the mean-value estimate is [see Parzen 1962]

$$\sigma_{\theta_2}^2 = \frac{2\sigma^2}{T^2} \int_0^T dt \int_0^t e^{-c\tau} \, d\tau \qquad (7\text{–}2)$$

Garfarian and Ancker define the *efficiency* (actually a measure of unit-time-advance error) of the time-advance simulator as

$$E = \frac{\sigma_{\theta_2}^2}{\sigma_{\theta_1}^2} \qquad (7\text{–}3)$$

where $\sigma_{\theta_2}^2$ = variance estimate from event-advance simulator

$\sigma_{\theta_1}^2$ = variance estimate from time-advance simulator

$E \to 1$ as $t_0 \to 0$

By plotting E as a function of N and ct_0, they show that unit-time-advance simulators approach the efficiency of event-advance methods when t_0 (the time slice) is less than $1/c$ (the decay rate of the covariance function).

The Gafarian and Ancker paper is important because it provides a quantitative method for determining the size of the time slice that should be selected in order to obtain good approximations of continuous-time representation. The general rule for the types of situations discussed in the paper is:

"The more rapidly the decrease in correlation between time-dependent variables (i.e., the larger the value of c and thus the more independent the successive observations) the greater the advantage in using small time slices for discrete observations."

In continuous models, the choice of the time unit should be a fraction of the shortest time constant or delay time. In conjunction with the use of DYNAMO, Forrester [1961, p. 79] says:

"The interval . . . should be less than half the (shortest) delay. . . . The above is a rule of thumb. The most expedient test will be to vary the length of the . . . interval, to observe its effect on computed results."

sec. 7-4
choice of
deterministic
or stochastic
models

When a shortened interval does not have a significant effect of the output values, the next higher interval will be satisfactory.

choice of deterministic or stochastic models 7-4

A primary objective in developing a simulation model is to provide a realistic representation of the behavior of the real system. Therefore, the title of this section may be a little puzzling, since intuitively a variable should be represented in the form that best characterizes the observed phenomena. We can justifiably argue that the choice of the form of representation should be dictated only by external evidence about the phenomenon. If historical data or direct observation suggests that unexplainable variations exist in the value of some phenomena, then the phenomena should be represented in the simulator as a stochastic process. The term *unexplainable* as used here means that the analyst is unable or unwilling (e.g., for economic reasons) to seek a deterministic cause for the phenomena.

The foregoing modeling procedure may, in some cases, be abandoned temporarily if only gross differences are being studied or to facilitate validation.

In some studies where, for example, two or three alternatives are being considered, only major differences among the alternatives may be significant. In this case, expected values may give enough information; the exact nature of the distribution of performance values is not significant. An example of a situation where this occurred is a study we did of an urban school district. For reasons of facilitating validation a deterministic, aggregate model of the district's financial operations was developed. (A very simplified version of this model is presented in the appendix to this chapter.) The model was then used to examine a range of alternative operating policies. This model showed that three years hence the cost of even the least expensive, feasible alternative would be $40 million more than revenues (a difference of twenty percent). The gap would become larger in later years. It was not necessary to use a stochastic refinement of the model to see that the district had a major problem and should concentrate on obtaining more revenues. (Three years later the district *did* submit a budget with a $40 million deficit and only by exerting the greatest political pressure at local and state levels did it acquire the required revenues.)

If it is necessary to detect alternatives that differ less dramatically and, especially if confidence estimates are desired, then a stochastic model will be needed. Also, there are cases in which making a model deterministic would change the situation qualitatively. Where the stochastic variable represents a time sequence (as interarrival times in the job shop of Chapter 5) or the routing of goods (in a shop or in a transportation system), deterministic abstractions are not appropriate. This is because queues form as a result of the statistical variation in arrival and service times; to substitute periodic arrivals and/or fixed service times makes the model invalid.

A preliminary deterministic model may be used to make validation easier. One of the most frequently used methods of validation is to compare the output of the simulator with previous actual behavior of the system under similar conditions. This method of validation becomes exceedingly difficult when the simulator contains a large number of stochastic variables. Even with a large number of replications it is difficult to conclude whether the time series produced by the simulation compares favorably with the historical data. Thus the analyst might decide not to introduce all the desired real-world complexity into the early versions of the simulation model. Instead, a two-phase simulation design procedure would be used. In the first phase the analyst tests structural assumptions in the model by treating exogenous variables deterministically (setting them at mean values). In the second phase the real-world complexities are introduced through distributions.

The primary value of a two-phase validation procedure is that the initial phase provides a means of testing the reasonableness of the more basic assumptions that have been made in modeling the system. If the output of the Phase I model does not show a general correspondence with the real system, the analyst must re-examine the plausibility of these assumptions. When the simulation model passes this initial test, validation can be attempted at a more detailed level. Often the Phase I model is useful in providing direct insights into the system and in predicting consequences of actions to aid in decision making. The deterministic abstraction captures the essence of the system sufficiently well to draw conclusions about the effects of decisions. Further, the effect of variation in exogenous variables *can* be studied with a deterministic model. This is achieved by making several runs with various settings of the parameters; that is, by a sensitivity analysis. If this is done in an organized manner, statistical analyses can be performed and much can be learned about how performance is affected by such variations. At a minimum, this analysis makes it possible to determine what parameters are *not* critical and, therefore, need not be represented stochastically in a Phase II model.

7-5 random numbers and variates

If a stochastic model is needed, the simulation must include the representation of random variates—variables having values that are specified according to a distribution. Since stochastic models are most common in simulation, we will devote the remainder of this chapter to methods for creating and using random variables.

Use of Random Numbers for Monte Carlo Analysis

In Section 1–4 we made clear the distinction between Monte Carlo methods and simulation. Monte Carlo analysis is used to solve a *deterministic,* analytic problem by converting it to a probabilistic analog having the same mathematical formulation. Then random sampling techniques are used to estimate the solution to the deterministic problem. Simulation methods on the other hand are applied to dynamic problems for which no closed form mathematical representation can be constructed. A simulation model is constructed to best represent the observed behavior of a real system, rather than to provide an analog to an analytic model of the system.

Much of the confusion between Monte Carlo methods and simulation arises because both use random numbers. To illustrate the difference we have constructed a simple problem typical of that to which Monte Carlo analysis might be applied. Specifically, the problem is to find the area under the curve $y = 2x$ between $x = 1$ and $x = 2$. It is obvious from integral calculus or geometric considerations that the answer is 3. But there are other situations where analytic or geometric analysis does not yield a solution. Evaluating multidimensional integrals is one such case. It is in these situations that numerical analysis procedures, like Monte Carlo methods, are used. For purposes of illustration, however, we will deal with this simple example.

Figure 7–4a is a graph of the functional relationship whose area we wish to estimate. Monte Carlo analysis requires a probabilistic analog to this problem. This is achieved by positioning the area inside a larger rectangle whose area we already know. Figure 7–4b shows this rectangle. The probabilistic analog used to estimate the shaded area is: a point that lands at random in the rectangle (i.e., it has an equal chance of falling anywhere on the rectangular surface) will fall in the shaded area with a probability equal to the shaded area over the total rectangular area. Therefore, observing a large number of random points in the rectangle provides an estimate of the proportion of the rectangle that is shaded, and thus of the shaded area.

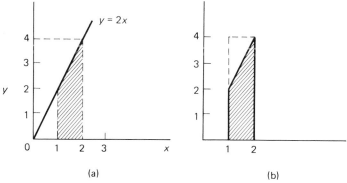

(a)　　　　　　　　　(b)

Figure 7–4　Monte Carlo analysis. (a) Problem: determining the area of $y = 2x$; (b) area imbedded in a rectangle.

171

Various sampling procedures can be applied to obtain statistically reliable Monte Carlo estimates using the minimum number of random numbers. We will not discuss Monte Carlo sampling procedures further since this book is limited to simulation methods. (We suggest that those readers who are interested in more information on Monte Carlo analysis refer to Hammersley and Handscomb [1964].)

Use of Random Numbers for Simulation

In simulation analysis, random variables are used to represent the behavior of uncontrollable factors in the system—factors whose real-world counterpart fluctuates in an unpredictable but statistically describable way.

Some of the ways in which random variables are used in simulations are:

(1) Exogenous variables are usually represented by random variables. As these variables are the result of processes outside the system, their values cannot be estimated by a procedure; however, based on observation or theory, their statistical properties are known. The interarrival time of jobs and the job charactertistics in the example in Chapter 5 (Figure 5C–1) are created by generating random variables.

(2) Some processes could, in principle, be completely deterministic, such as the processing of a job on a machine. To achieve this determinism, however, the details of the machine set-up and running would have to be represented. Adequate results are obtained with much simpler models, however, if the process is aggregated into one statistically determined effect. Here the random variable is used to represent a subsystem (the processing) that in detail is deterministic.

(3) Another example of the use of random variables is to simplify representation of scheduling rules. Take, for example, simulating the flow of automobile traffic through city streets. We could assign each simulated car a route (an exogenous uncontrollable). The direction a particular car is to take at any intersection is then completely determined. It is, however, often simpler to enter cars into the system with no routing information. At each intersection the direction in which the car proceeds is determined as a random variable.

In all cases the distribution from which the random variable is to be drawn must be established from observed data or from theoretical considerations. (See Kendall and Stuart [1966] for such methods.)

Since a computer must follow unique procedures, probabilistic occurrences—random variates—must either be generated by a device separate from the computer or be simulated by a deterministic calculation within the computer. It is possible to introduce random variables into a simulation by means of a device that physically generates random events. This is expensive and requires changes in the computer hardware. Usually *pseudorandom* variables are used, variables that are generated by a process that is deterministic but gives sequences that appear random and are independent of the rest of the simulation.

There are two steps in translating probabilistic events into deterministic ones. First, we need a method for creating random *numbers* using a procedure that is totally independent of the simulation model. A number of pseudorandom number generators have been developed, and we discuss the major ones below. When a source of random numbers is available, we need to translate the random numbers into random *variates;* that is, to use a random number to create an observation from the distribution that the analyst believes describes the probabilities of the random variable taking on various values. We will discuss this translation step after we consider random number generators.

Random Number Generators

Before examining specific methods of generating random numbers, it is useful to make explicit the characteristics that these numbers must satisfy. We say that a procedure that can produce numbers having any of *n* discrete values is producing *random numbers* if any of the values is equally as likely to occur (i.e., the probability of a value's occurrence is $1/n$), and each new value is completely independent of any previous output of the generator. Statistically, this means the numbers are uniformly distributed, independent variables.

A number of tests have been developed to determine whether a series of numbers meets the criterion of randomness. Before presenting the more commonly used tests, we should put into perspective the implications that can be drawn from such tests. Those readers familiar with statistical testing procedures will realize that we cannot reject a hypothesis with absolute certainty if it fails a statistical test; all that we can conclude is that if the hypothesis were true, the results that were observed are an unlikely occurrence. The choice of rejection level determines how unlikely such an occurrence must be before the hypothesis is rejected (known in statistics as a Type I error). Clearly there will be occasions when such rare situations do occur. For example, if a one-digit random number generator produced five of one of the digits in a series of ten numbers, we would probably not consider this truly random. However, this situation will occur about 14 times out of every thousand times a truly random number generator produces 10 digits. It is clear that the more tests to which we submit the output of a random number generator, the greater the likelihood that it will be rejected on at least one of them. Therefore we suggest that random number generators be tested only on characteristics of randomness most critical to the accuracy of the implications that will be drawn from the simulator. Very large samples of such numbers should be tested.

Suppose we wish to test whether a sequence of numbers $R_1, R_2, \ldots, R_m$ meet the randomness criterion. If each observation R_i is an n-digit decimal number, there are two ways of testing randomness:

(1) Test the randomness and independence of each observation as a complete number (where there are 10^n possible values that can occur).

(2) Test the randomness of each of the digits of R; $r_{i1}r_{i2}r_{i3}r_{i4} \ldots r_{in}$. (Here the sequence is such that the leading digit of R_{i+1} follows the lowest order digit of R_i in the tests for independence.)

The advantages of the first method are first that for an equal number of observations, randomness tests can be constructed over a longer sequence of output and second that the tests put implicit emphasis on the randomness of the leading digits of the numbers. The disadvantage of this method is that it may lead to the acceptance of numbers that are not random in lower order digits. The second method places equal importance on the randomness of all digits and is preferred if the simulation depends on lower order randomness.

The two most frequently used tests of randomness are the *frequency test* and the *serial test*. Both rely on the χ^2 statistic for analyzing output. The frequency test examines whether all numbers are equally likely to occur; it does not examine whether the numbers in the sequence are independent. To see how the test is used, suppose we have a sequence of M single-digit random numbers that we wish to evaluate.

Let f_i = frequency that digit i occurred in the sequence;
$i = 0, 1, 2, \ldots, 9$

E_i = expected number of times digit i would have occurred if the sequence were completely random

Then the frequency test is:

$$\chi_F^2 = \sum_{i=0}^{9} \frac{(f_i - E_i)^2}{E_i} \qquad (7\text{--}4)$$

Obviously $E_i = M/10$ if the sequence were truly random.

The statistic is distributed χ^2 with, in this case, 9 degrees of freedom. By checking the χ^2 table in a statistics handbook with 9 degrees of freedom (one less than the number of classes) and with a likelihood of Type I error we are willing to risk, the sequence can be tested for frequency randomness.

The serial test is used to determine whether pairs, triples, and so forth, of digits occur randomly. This is the primary test for independence of sequences of number. The serial test was originally proposed by Good [1953]. To illustrate its use, suppose we wished to test the independence of consecutive pairs of digits in a sequence of M single-digit random numbers.

Let f_{ij} = frequency of the pair in which the first number is digit i and the second j

E_{ij} = expected number of times digit i would have been followed by digit j if the sequence were completely random and independent

Then the serial test is:

$$\chi_S^2 \quad \sum_{i=0}^{9} \sum_{j=0}^{9} \frac{(f_{ij} - E_{ij})^2}{E_{ij}} - \sum_{i=0}^{9} \frac{\left(\sum_{j=0}^{9} f_{ij} - \sum_{j=0}^{9} E_{ij}\right)^2}{\sum_{j=0}^{9} E_{ij}} \qquad (7\text{-}5)$$

Clearly

$$E_{ij} = M/100 \quad \text{and} \quad \sum_{j=0}^{9} E_{ij} = M/10$$

The serial test is distributed as χ^2 with ninety degrees of freedom (number of classes in the pairs of numbers minus the number of classes in the single digits, $100 - 10$). Again the sequence is accepted or rejected by a χ^2 table value at the desired probability of rejection.

A host of additional tests can be run in addition to these. One of the most frequently used is the *runs test* [IBM, 1959]. Several types of runs can be examined, such as the number of consecutive observations above or below the average output, or the consecutive number of observations in which the sequence continually increases or decreases in value. Another test is known as the *gap test*. Starting at one digit we examine the number of nonmatching digits that occur before a match occurs. As we have already indicated, the particular tests that an analyst selects should reflect the seriousness with which a particular type of non-randomness will affect his results. Therefore, if the analyst did not feel his results would be much different if the generator failed the runs, gap, or other tests, he should concentrate his analysis on other areas of randomness.

Let us turn our attention to some of the methods that have been and are being used to generate random numbers. Before computers, random numbers were based on outputs of physical devices; for example, a balanced roulette wheel or die, or a coin, should yield outputs that pass tests for randomness. These devices are adequate if only a few such numbers are required. However, as greater use was made of random numbers, these methods became very inefficient. Other random physical devices were sought to generate the numbers more quickly. These utilized electronic principles. Perhaps the most famous use of a second-generation generator was by the RAND Corporation. It relied on an electronic pulse generator driven by a noise source and generated numbers quite rapidly. A book, *One Million Random Numbers* [RAND, 1955], was based on the output of this device. (These numbers are also available on magnetic tape from RAND.)

Random number generators based on electronic sources gave way to the third-generation generators which rely on mathematical recursive relationships. The physical source methods had two difficulties:

(1) It was difficult to provide and maintain a physical device to which a computer has direct access.

(2) The numbers generated by the device are not reproducible; therefore correlated simulation runs (which we will discuss later) under controlled conditions are possible only if the random variables are stored and reused, a process that is both time and memory consuming.

The random number generators based on mathematical relations are not truly random, since the sequence is completely deterministic. These sequences will pass most statistical tests and from the point of view of the user, the output, with one exception, is indistinguishable from that of physical sources. As soon as pseudorandom series reaches a point where its input is the same as at some previous stage, all successive numbers will be the same as in the previous sequence. The number of entries before such a repeat is called a *cycle*. Numbers generated using mathematical procedures are referred to as *pseudorandom numbers.*

The first popular pseudorandom number generator was known as the *midsquare method.* The procedure for generating an *n*-digit random number was simply to take the middle *n* digits of the square of the previous random number. Several problems led people to reject the midsquare method. For one thing it tended to have a short cycle. Furthermore it was difficult to determine without direct experimentation the length of a cycle that would be achieved for a given starting number.

The procedure that replaced the midsquare method and the one that is most popular today is known as the *congruential method* (first proposed by Lehmer [1951]). There are two forms of the congruential method commonly used. The multiplicative method uses the following recurrence relationship:

$$X_{i+1} = aX_i \ (\text{mod } m) \tag{7–6}$$

The expression means to take the last random number, X_i, multiply it by the constant *a* and take the result, modulo *m* (that is, divide by *m* and treat the remainder as X_{i+1}). Thus the random numbers all range between zero and $m - 1$. If *m* is chosen as the largest possible integer in the computer, division to take the modulo is done implicitly by the multiplication process and some computer time is saved. The RANDU subroutine in Figure 5C–1 is an example of this method.

The other form of the congruential method is known as the mixed method and uses the following recursive relationship:

$$X_{i+1} = aX + c \ (\text{mod } m) \tag{7–7}$$

Chambers [1967] compared the two forms of the congruential method and concluded the following:

(1) The mixed method has the longer cycle.

(2) The multiplicative method passes more of the tests for statistical randomness.

(3) The multiplicative method is usually faster (although this depends on the machine being used).

Hammersley and Handscomb [1964] and the *IBM Manual* [IBM, 1959] show how to evaluate alternative ways of determining the best choice of *c* and *a* in the recurrence relationship.

Another method of generating random numbers (there are many) was reported by MacLaren and Marsaglia [1965]. They used the mixed congruential method on random numbers originally obtained from the RAND Tables. Thus their method was

$$X_i = aX'_i + c \ (\text{mod } m)$$

where X'_i is a value from the RAND Table. This method has the advantage that a table of numbers originally stored can be used to generate other numbers. However, the method has the disadvantage that storage is required for the original table of numbers.

Figure 7–5 illustrates a subroutine for producing uniformly distributed random variables using the mixed method. A sample of the output of the subroutine beginning with $X_0 = 876543$ is also provided.

With this introduction to random number generators, we turn to methods of converting the uniformly distributed random numbers to random variates with other distributions.

Conversion of Uniform Random Numbers to Random Variates

There are three commonly used methods for converting a random number into a random variate with a specified distribution. The most efficient method is known as the *inverse transformation.* However, this method applies only if the distribution of interest can be inverted analytically. If it cannot, the *rejection method* is sometimes used. This procedure requires no particular assumptions about the functional form of the distribution; however, the method is quite inefficient because it requires at least two (and usually more) random numbers to produce one random variate from the desired distribution. To avoid the inefficiencies of the rejection method, the method of *rectangular approximation* is usually employed. In this case, the random variates do not correspond exactly to the functional form of the desired distribution; however, each uniformly distributed random number produces a variate corresponding to the approximation of the distribution and the method is efficient. We will next discuss each method in more detail.

177

```
        C    PROGRAM TO GENERATE AND LIST RANDOM NUMBERS.
        C
0001         DIMENSION A(10)
0002         WRITE(6,10)
0003    10   FORMAT(1H1)
0004         DO 3 J=1,20
0005         DO 1 I=1,10
0006    1    A(I)=RANNOS(876543)    Calls random number generator
0007         WRITE(6,2) (A(I),I=1,10)
0008    2    FORMAT(1X, 5F14.10)
0009    3    CONTINUE
0010         WRITE(6,10)
0011         STOP
0012         END


0001         REAL FUNCTION RANNOS(SEED)
        C        SUBROUTINE COMPUTES A PSEUDO-RANDOM NUMBER BETWEEN 0 AND 1.
0002         REAL RNEW
0003         INTEGER PLUS / Z1000000 / , IBIT / Z40000000 / , HEX / Z10003 /
0004         INTEGER OLD,NEW, SEED
0005         LOGICAL*1 NORMAL /.FALSE./
0006         EQUIVALENCE (NEW,RNEW)
0007         IF(NORMAL) GO TO 10        NORMAL = TRUE means that this is
0008         OLD= IABS(SEED)            not the first time the routine is used
0009         NORMAL = .TRUE.            so that the SEED [R(0)] is not needed
0010    10   OLD=OLD*HEX
0011         NEW=OLD/256                Uses relation = R(I) = R(I − 1) · 65539
0012         IF(NEW.LE.0) NEW=NEW+ PLUS HEX = 65539
0013         NEW=NEW+IBIT               Division by 256 and addition of IBIT places
0014         RANNOS=RNEW+0.0            result for conversion to floating
0015         RETURN
0016         END
```

Resulting random numbers follow:

```
0.3755969405   0.2517451644   0.1300982833   0.5148830414   0.9184131622
0.8765314817   0.9934706688   0.0720409155   0.4910098910   0.2976909280
0.3670566082   0.5231211782   0.8352172971   0.3032133579   0.3023250699
0.0850300789   0.7892548442   0.9702576995   0.7182529569   0.5771983266
0.9989136457   0.7986969948   0.8019595146   0.6234841347   0.5232690573
0.5282574296   0.4601230621   0.0064220428   0.8974248767   0.3267502189
0.8836778402   0.3613148332   0.2147886753   0.0368984342   0.2882924080
0.3976684213   0.7913787365   0.1692563295   0.8931298256   0.8354716301
0.9746613503   0.3287233114   0.2003881931   0.2438190579   0.6594205499
0.7621514201   0.6381234527   0.9693781734   0.0731581450   0.7145460248
0.6288521886   0.3421991467   0.3935256600   0.2813614011   0.1464371681
0.3463702202   0.7602869272   0.4443891644   0.8237529397   0.9430148005
0.2443121672   0.9787405133   0.6736330390   0.2331334352   0.3361039162
0.9184224010   0.4855985641   0.6477901340   0.5163531899   0.2680077553
0.9608684182   0.3531404138   0.4710271358   0.6478989720   0.6481493711
0.0578054786   0.5134891272   0.5606851578   0.7427091002   0.4100882411
0.7761480808   0.9660936594   0.8112295866   0.1725344062   0.7341408134
0.8520347476   0.5049415231   0.3613363504   0.6235446334   0.4892403483
0.3235407472   0.5380814075   0.3166214824   0.0569964647   0.4923852682
0.4413435459   0.2165935636   0.3274693489   0.0154739022   0.1456191540
0.7344496846   0.0961254239   0.9667058587   0.9351059794   0.9102831483
0.0457449555   0.0819218755   0.0798263550   0.7416611910   0.7315295935
0.7142267227   0.7015942335   0.7815251350   0.3748030066   0.2150920033
0.9173250794   0.5681220889   0.1528067589   0.8037420511   0.4471909404
0.4494677782   0.6720882058   0.9873186350   0.8751181364   0.3648409247
0.3129829764   0.5943293571   0.7491286993   0.1458082795   0.1326916814
0.4838753343   0.7090266943   0.8992816210   0.0144492984   0.9931617739
0.8289268613   0.0351050496   0.7502889633   0.1857880354   0.3621279001
0.5006751418   0.7448994517   0.9633207321   0.0758293867   0.7850902677
0.0280764103   0.1026467085   0.3631922007   0.2553328872   0.2632673383
0.2816081643   0.3202427030   0.3869823813   0.4397100210   0.1554185152
0.9751209617   0.4519588947   0.9356650114   0.5463595390   0.8571724892
0.2257989645   0.6402418613   0.8092600703   0.0933837295   0.2769621015
0.8213191628   0.4352555871   0.2196615338   0.4006686807   0.4270579815
0.9563297629   0.8944561481   0.7597691417   0.5085096955   0.2131357193
0.7022276521   0.2951440811   0.4508162737   0.0486005545   0.2342569232
0.9681365490   0.7005064487   0.4898096323   0.6343001723   0.3975140452
0.6763832569   0.4806724787   0.7965860963   0.4534635544   0.5515071750
0.2278704643   0.4036583900   0.3711162806   0.5937719941   0.2225848436
0.9915614724   0.9461047053   0.7525748610   0.0005069971   0.2298688293
```

Figure 7–5   Program to demonstrate the generation of random numbers.

Inverse Transformation

To show how the inverse transformation yields distributionally dependent random variables, let us begin by making standard notational definitions ($P \equiv$ "probability that"). Define the probability density function $f(x)$ and cumulative density function $F(x)$ as

$$f(x) = P\{X = x\} \tag{7-8}$$

$$F(x) = P\{X \le x\} = \int_{-\infty}^{x} f(t)\, dt \tag{7-9}$$

For random numbers (uniform random variables) generated in the interval 0, 1, the distributions have the following characteristics:

$$u(r) = dr \qquad 0.0 \le r \le 1.0 \tag{7-10}$$
$$U(r) = r \qquad 0.0 \le r \le 1.0 \tag{7-11}$$

Let us now examine the form of the probability distribution for the cumulative density function $F(x)$ for any other distribution. Clearly $F(x)$ is the probability that a random number between zero and one is less than or equal to $F(x)$; that is,

$$F(x) = P\{X \le F(x)\} = \Phi(F(x)) \qquad 0.0 \le F(x) \le 1.0$$

From the characteristic of the uniform distribution in Equation 7–11, it is clear that $F(x)$ follows a *uniform* distribution because the cumulative probability function, Φ, is equal to the argument of Φ (see Equation 7–11). Therefore we can use the uniformly distributed random numbers r to generate the distribution of $F(x)$, regardless of the *functional form of the distribution*. It follows that

$$r = F(x) \tag{7-12}$$

and therefore

$$x = F^{-1}(r) \tag{7-13}$$

where $F^{-1}(r)$ is the inverse of the original cumulative distribution (the value of the original distribution whose cumulative is r).

To illustrate the inverse transformation method, consider the negative exponential distribution

$$f(x) = e^{-x} \qquad x \ge 0.0$$
$$F(x) = 1 - e^{-x}$$

using Equations 7–12 and 7–13

$$r = F(x) = 1 - e^{-x} \tag{7-14}$$
$$x = -\log_e (1 - r) \tag{7-15}$$

Thus the exponential random variable x is obtained by generating a uniform variable r between zero and one and applying formula 7–15. If the reader examines the FORTRAN program for the event-advance model of the machine repair problem (Figure 7–2, step 10) he will see that the inverse transformation method was used to generate exponential variates.

There are many distributions for which the inverse transformation method cannot be used because it is impossible to analytically invert the cumulative density function (as we did in going from Equation 7–14 to 7–15). The normal distribution is such a case. When inversion *is* possible, this procedure is by far the most efficient.

Rejection Method

The rejection method can be applied to the probability distribution for any bounded variable (that is, for which upper and lower bounds can be placed on the range of values that can occur). In theory, this restriction eliminates using the method on such infinite tail distributions as the normal or exponential. However, finite limits can usually be set beyond which an observation almost never occurs.

To see how the method works, suppose we have the probability density function shown in Figure 7–6 from which we wish to generate random variates. Suppose we generate a large number of random variables uniformly in the rectangle defined by *a*, *b*, and *c* and consider only those points that fall below the probability curve. It should be clear that the distribution of points that we have *not* rejected take on values between *a* and *b* in precisely the same likelihood as predicted by the distribution $f(x)$. (This is a use of Monte Carlo to generate random variates.) Thus the points that are not rejected are equivalent to random variables from that distribution. If two random numbers, r_1 and r_2, are generated, the rejection method is used as follows:

(1) Let $X_1 = a + (b - a)r_1$ (Scale the variable on the X axis.)

(2) Let $X_2 = cr_2$ (Scale the variable on the Y axis.)

(3) If $X_2 \leq f(X_1)$, accept X_1 as the next random variate.

(4) Generate two new random numbers and return to step 1.

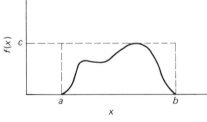

Figure 7–6 The rejection method.

Let us determine the probability that a pair of random numbers will successfully yield a random variate. Clearly this is the probability that the first random number takes on a value X [which is $dx/(b - a)$] times the probability that the second number is less than $f(x)/c$ (which is equal to $f(x)/c$ since the random number is uniformly distributed between zero and one). Thus,

P {successful pair} $= P$ {first number takes value of x and the second number is less than $f(x)/c$}

$$= \int_a^b \frac{dx}{(b-a)} \cdot \frac{f(x)}{c} = \frac{1}{c(b-a)} \int_a^b f(x)\,dx$$

$$= \frac{1}{c(b-a)} \tag{7-16}$$

The rejection method is very inefficient when $c(b-a)$ becomes large since a large number of random numbers would have to be generated for every random variable produced. This would be the case with a distribution such as in Figure 7–7. In such cases the distribution is sometimes broken into pieces and the pieces are sampled in proportion to the amount of distributional area each contains. For example, Figure 7–7 might be broken into three sections with the middle one (i.e., the spike) accounting for most of the sampling points. Such a method is known as the *method of mixtures* [Tocher, 1963, Ch. 8]. The process is identical to the rejection method for each piece of the distribution, plus a straight-forward sampling of the pieces.

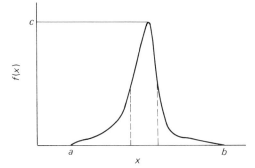

Figure 7–7 A distribution for which the rejection technique is inefficient.

Rectangular Approximation

This method is used when no explicit functional form represents the probability density function. Instead, the probability density function of the distribution is approximated by a set of rectangles. The widths of the rectangles are proportional to a range of observed values x to $x + \delta$ and the heights are approximately proportional to $\int_x^{x+\delta} f(t)\,dt$ (Figure 7–8).

When the rectangular approximations have been completed, the cumulative density function can be derived by integration. Since the integral of a linear piece is a line segment, the cumulative distribution is piecewise linear. For the probability density function in Figure 7–8 the cumulative distribution is that of Figure 7–9.

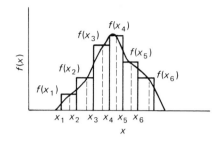

Figure 7–8 Rectangular approximation of probability density function.

Figure 7–9
Cumulative
density
function
approximation.

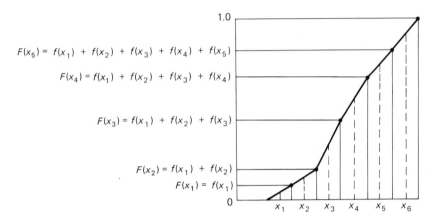

The cumulative density function can then be used to generate random variables. For example, if $F(x_1) \leq r \leq F(x_2)$, then the variate x would be approximated by the following linear interpolation:

$$X = x_1 + (x_2 - x_1) \frac{r - F(x_1)}{F(x_2) - F(x_1)}$$

Figure 5C–1, lines 75–83, is an example of the rectangular approximation method.

This method also can be used for discrete distributions in which the variable takes only specific, discrete values and a probability is associated with each. The cumulative distribution is rectangular in this case and X is found by generating r and doing a table-lookup to determine $F(r)$. See Subroutine MODP in Figure 5C–2 as an example.

Since the rectangular method requires fewer random numbers than the rejection method, it is usually, but not necessarily, more efficient. The computer must search a table of the cumulative function, find the appropriate value of x, and do an interpolation on x. The trade-offs between the methods depend on the forms of the probability distributions.

There are a number of special approximations for computing random variates with the common distributions, e.g., normal, log normal, exponential [Tocher, 1963, Ch. 8; IBM, 1968; Mize and Cox, 1968]. Where these are needed, the references contain the algorithm and often the FORTRAN program.

exercise

7–1 Write the FORTRAN programs to generate a random variate with an exponential distribution, with a mean on 1.0, in each of these three ways:

(a) according to the inverse cumulative distribution formula (Equation 7–15)

(b) by the rejection method

(c) by approximating the inverse cumulative distribution with a piece-wise linear approximation (that is, approximating the exponential with a rectangular distribution) and using it to obtain the variates by linear interpolation

Run these generators and compare their running times and the degrees to which the exponential distribution is approximated (using χ^2 test).

references

Chambers, R., "Random Number Generation," *IEEE Spectrum,* Vol. 4, No. 2, February 1967, pp. 48–56.

Conway, R. W., B. M. Johnson, and W. L. Maxwell, "Some Problems of Digital Systems Simulation," *Management Science,* Vol. 6, No. 1, October 1959, pp. 92–110.

Ehrenfeld, S., and S. Ben Tuvia, "The Efficiency of Statistical Simulation Procedures," *Technometrics,* Vol. 4, May 1962, pp. 257–75.

Forrester, J. W., *Industrial Dynamics,* M.I.T. Press, Cambridge, Mass., 1961.

Gafarian, A. V., and C. J. Ancker, "Mean Value Estimation from Digital Computer Simulation," *Operations Research,* Vol. 14, No. 1, January–February 1966, pp. 25–44.

Good, I., "The Serial Test for Sampling Numbers and Other Tests of Randomness," *Proceedings of the Cambridge Philosophical Society,* Vol. 49, 1953, pp. 276–84.

Hammersley, J. M., and D. C. Handscomb, *Monte Carlo Methods,* Wiley, New York, 1964.

IBM Corp., *Random Number Generation and Testing, Reference Manual,* C20–8011, New York, 1959.

IBM Application Program, *System/360 Scientific Subroutine Package (360A–CM–03X), Version III, Programmer's Manual,* H20–0205–3, New York, 1968, pp. 221–29.

Kendall, M., and A. Stuart, *The Advanced Theory of Statistics,* Vol. 3, Hafner, New York, 1966.

Laski, J., "On Time Structure in Monte Carlo Simulations," *Operations Research Quarterly,* Vol. 16, No. 3, 1965, pp. 229–39.

Lehmer, D., "Mathematical Methods in Large-Scale Computing Units," *Annals of the Computer Laboratory,* Harvard University, Vol. 26, 1951, pp. 141–46.

MacLaren, M. D., and G. Marsaglia, "Uniform Random Number Generators," *Journal of the Association for Computing Machinery,* Vol. 12, No. 1, January 1965, pp. 83–89.

Mize, J. H., and J. G. Cox, *Essentials of Simulation,* Prentice-Hall, Englewood Cliffs, N.J., 1968.

Parzen, E., *Stochastic Processes,* Holden-Day, San Francisco, 1962.

RAND Corp., *A Million Random Digits with 100,000 Normal Deviates,* Free Press, New York, 1955.

Tocher, K. D., *The Art of Simulation,* Van Nostrand, Princeton, N.J., 1963.

appendix 7A

School District Financial Simulator

This example is included to illustrate an aggregate year-by-year simulation. This model is very much simpler than one that would be used for decision aiding, but it illustrates the basic structure of aggregate models. It is typical of models used in industry and commerce and in the public sector to forecast the overall financial and operational (e.g., manpower) effects of changes in basic policies.

In this example the policy being investigated is the student–teacher ratio.

School District Model—Variable Dictionary

ENR	enrollment*†
STFA	staff available*†
STFH	staff hired
CTDT	total cost
T	year
P(I)	student/staff ratio for run I*
SOVHD	staff overhead factor (administrative costs per staff)
REV	revenue*†
EOVHD	enrollment overhead (administrative costs per student)*†
STOPYR	last year to be simulated*
STFBUD	portion of revenues available for staff salaries (total revenues less overheads)
ENRINC	fraction by which enrollment increases per year*
REVINC	fraction by which revenues increase per year*
ATRN	staff attrition fraction*
AVESAL	average salary (in millions dollars)*†
HLIM1	breakpoints in curve
HLIM2	relating new hires *desired* to *actual* new hires (a gross representation of limitations on staff availability)*
LEV1	actual new hire
LEV2	levels corresponding to HLIM breakpoints*
INF	inflation factor (on salaries)*
CSTF	total staff salary cost

B	blank character*	
B3	3 blank characters*	for output
D	"DEF" means deficit*	
E	*	

HNEG   signal that required staff was less than available staff

Subroutines Used

ESTENR	estimates enrollment for year
REVNU	estimates revenue
STAFF(IP)	computes staff hired, staff available, and staff cost for student/staff ratio IP
COSTS	computes total costs (adds overheads)
OUTPUT	formats and writes output

---

* This variable set to its initial value in BLOCK DATA.
† Reset at the start of each run.

```
       C     SIMULATION OF SCHOOL DISTRICT FINANCES AND OPERATIONS.
       C
0001           COMMON /COM/ ENR,STFA,STFH,CTOT,T,P(3),SOVHD,REV,EOVHD,STOPYR,
              1    STFBUD  ,ENRINC,REVINC,ATRN,AVESAL,HLIM1,HLIM2,LEV1,LEV2,INF
              2    ,CSTF,B,B3,D,E
0002           COMMON /NEG/  HNEG
0003           INTEGER T,STOPYR,HNEG
0004           REAL LEV1,LEV2,INF
0005           WRITE(6,11)
0006    11     FORMAT(/////1X,'COSTS IN MILLIONS'/)
0007           DO 4 IP=1,3                          Three simulation runs in one computer run
0008           WRITE (6,10) P(IP)
0009    10     FORMAT(1H0,'STAFF POLICY -',1X,F4.1,1X,'STUDENT/STAFF')
0010           HNEG=0
0011           T=67
0012    1      T=T+1
0013           IF (T.EQ.68) STFA=13000.             Initial condition reset for
0014           IF(T.EQ.68) ENR=298000.              each new run
0015           IF(T.EQ.68) REV=218.
0016           IF (T.EQ.68) EOVHD=.0002
0017           IF(T.EQ.68) AVESAL= .007
0018           IF(T.EQ.STOPYR) GO TO 2
0019           CALL ESTENR                          Main simulation sequence
0020           CALL REVNU
0021           CALL STAFF(IP)
0022           CALL COSTS
0023           CALL OUTPUT
0024           GO TO 1
       C
0025    2      IF(HNEG.EQ.1) WRITE (6,3)
0026    3      FORMAT(1X,'* - EXCESS STAFF, SINCE IF MORE STAFF THAN NEEDED, NO
              1LAYOFFS')
0027    4      CONTINUE
0028           WRITE (6,12)
0029    12     FORMAT (1H1)
0030           STOP
0031           END




0001           SUBROUTINE ESTENR
0002           COMMON /COM/ ENR,STFA,STFH,CTOT,T,P(3),SOVHD,REV,EOVHD,STOPYR,
              1    STFBUD  ,ENRINC,REVINC,ATRN,AVESAL,HLIM1,HLIM2,LEV1,LEV2,INF
              2    ,CSTF,B,B3,D,E
0003           INTEGER T,STOPYR
0004           REAL LEV1,LEV2,INF
0005           ENR=ENR+ENRINC*ENR                   Computes estimated enrollment
0006           RETURN
0007           END




0001           SUBROUTINE REVNU
0002           COMMON /COM/ ENR,STFA,STFH,CTOT,T,P(3),SOVHD,REV,EOVHD,STOPYR,
              1    STFBUD  ,ENRINC,REVINC,ATRN,AVESAL,HLIM1,HLIM2,LEV1,LEV2,INF
              2    ,CSTF,B,B3,D,E
0003           INTEGER T,STOPYR
0004           REAL LEV1,LEV2,INF
0005           EOVHD=EOVHD*(1+INF)                  Computes overhead
0006           REV=REV+REVINC*REV                   Computes estimated revenue
0007           STFBUD=(REV-ENR*EOVHD)/(SOVHD+1.)    Budget for staff is
0008           RETURN                               revenues less overhead
0009           END




0001           SUBROUTINE STAFF(IP)
0002           COMMON /COM/ ENR,STFA,STFH,CTOT,T,P(3),SOVHD,REV,EOVHD,STOPYR,
              1    STFBUD  ,ENRINC,REVINC,ATRN,AVESAL,HLIM1,HLIM2,LEV1,LEV2,INF
              2    ,CSTF,B,B3,D,E
0003           COMMON /NEG/  HNEG
0004           INTEGER T,STOPYR,HNEG
0005           REAL LEV1,LEV2,INF
0006           STFN=ENR/P(IP)                       Staff based on student/staff policy
0007           STFA=STFA-ATRN*STFA
0008           STFH=STFN-STFA
```

Figure 7A–1 Program for simulation of the financial and manpower aspects of a school district.

```
0009                IF(STFH.LE.0.) GO TO 3              Staff hired may be less than that
0010                IF(STFH.LT.HLIM1) GO TO 1          required due to recruiting limitations
0011                IF(STFH.GE.HLIM2) GO TO 2
0012                STFH=((((LEV2-LEV1)/ (HLIM2-HLIM1))*(STFH-LEV1))+LEV1
0013                GO TO 1
0014         2      STFH=LEV2
0015         1      STFA1=STFA+STFH
0016                GO TO 4
0017         3      HNEG=1
0018         4      AVESAL=AVESAL*(1+INF)
0019                CSTF=AVESAL*STFA1                   Staff hired may be limited by
0020                IF(CSTF.LE.STFBUD) GO TO 5          budget limitation
0021                STFT=STFBUD/AVESAL
0022                IF(STFT.LT.STFA) GO TO 6
0023                STFA=STFT
0024                CSTF=STFBUD
0025                RETURN
0026         6      CSTF=AVESAL*STFA
0027                RETURN
0028         5      STFA=STFA1
0029         7       RETURN
0030                END



0001                SUBROUTINE COSTS
0002                COMMON /COM/ ENR,STFA,STFH,CTOT,T,P(3),SOVHD,REV,EOVHD,STOPYR,
               1     STFBUD  ,ENRINC,REVINC,ATRN,AVESAL,HLIM1,HLIM2,LEV1,LEV2,INF
               2     ,CSTF,B,B3,D,E
0003                INTEGER T,STOPYR
0004                REAL LEV1,LEV2,INF
0005                CTOT=(1+SOVHD)*CSTF+EOVHD*ENR
0006                RETURN
0007                END



0001                SUBROUTINE OUTPUT
0002                COMMON /COM/ ENR,STFA,STFH,CTOT,T,P(3),SOVHD,REV,EOVHD,STOPYR,
               1     STFBUD  ,ENRINC,REVINC,ATRN,AVESAL,HLIM1,HLIM2,LEV1,LEV2,INF
               2     ,CSTF,B,B3,D,E
0003                INTEGER T,STOPYR
0004                REAL LEV1,LEV2,INF
0005                IF(T.EQ.68) WRITE (6,10)
0006         10     FORMAT (1X,'YR',T11,'ENROLL',T21,'STAFF',T31,'STAFF',T41,'STAFF',
               1 T51,'TOTAL',T61,'REVENUE'/
               2 1X,T11,'(THOUS)',T21,'AVAIL.',T31,'HIRED',T41,'COST',T51,'COST',
               3 T61,'(MILLIONS)' //)
0007                ENRT=ENR/1000.
0008                F=B                                 Converts data to output
0009                DEF=B3                              units, adds codes
0010                IF(STFH.LT.0.) F=E                  and writes out
0011                IF((REV-CTOT).LT.0.) DEF=D
0012                WRITE(6,11) T,ENRT,STFA,STFH,F,CSTF,CTOT,REV,DEF
0013         11     FORMAT (1X,I2,T11,F6.1,T21,F7.0,T31,F7.0,T39,A1,
               1 T41,F6.1,T51,F6.1,T61,F6.1,T71,A3)
0014                RETURN
0015                END



0001                BLOCK DATA
0002                COMMON /COM/ ENR,STFA,STFH,CTOT,T,P(3),SOVHD,REV,EOVHD,STOPYR,
               1     STFBUD  ,ENRINC,REVINC,ATRN,AVESAL,HLIM1,HLIM2,LEV1,LEV2,INF
               2     ,CSTF,B,B3,D,E
0003                INTEGER T,STOPYR                    Initial data for
0004                REAL LEV1,LEV2,INF                  all parameters and
0005                DATA STOPYR,P(1),P(2),P(3)/78,23.,21.,25./  variables to set
0006                DATA B,B3,D,E/' ','   ','DEF','*'/          conditions for 1967
0007                DATA EOVHD,SOVHD/.0002,1./
0008                DATA ENR,ENRINC/298000.,.005/
0009                DATA REV,REVINC/218.,.025/
0010                DATA STFA,ATRN,AVESAL,HLIM1,HLIM2,LEV1,LEV2,INF
               1 /13000.,.04,.007,700.,2000.,700.,1500.,.02/
0011                END
```

Figure 7A–1 (continued)

Resulting output of three school district simulations.

COSTS IN MILLIONS

STAFF POLICY - 23.0 STUDENT/STAFF

YR	ENROLL (THOUS)	STAFF AVAIL.	STAFF HIRED	STAFF COST	TOTAL COST	REVENUE (MILLIONS)	
68	299.5	12480.	541.	89.1	239.3	223.4	DEF**
69	301.0	11981.	950.	87.3	237.1	229.0	DEF
70	302.5	11502.	1285.	85.4	235.1	234.8	DEF
71	304.0	11536.	1500.	87.4	240.6	240.6	
72	305.5	11592.	1500.	89.6	246.6	246.6	
73	307.1	11649.	1500.	91.8	252.8	252.8	
74	308.6	11705.	1500.	94.1	259.1	259.1	
75	310.1	11762.	1500.	96.5	265.6	265.6	
76	311.7	11820.	1500.	98.9	272.3	272.3	
77	313.2	11877.	1500.	101.3	279.1	279.1	

STAFF POLICY - 21.0 STUDENT/STAFF

YR	ENROLL (THOUS)	STAFF AVAIL.	STAFF HIRED	STAFF COST	TOTAL COST	REVENUE (MILLIONS)	
68	299.5	12480.	1365.	89.1	239.3	223.4	DEF
69	301.0	11981.	1500.	87.3	237.1	229.0	DEF
70	302.5	11502.	1500.	85.4	235.1	234.8	DEF
71	304.0	11536.	1500.	87.4	240.6	240.6	
72	305.5	11592.	1500.	89.6	246.6	246.6	
73	307.1	11649.	1500.	91.8	252.8	252.8	
74	308.6	11705.	1500.	94.1	259.1	259.1	
75	310.1	11762.	1500.	96.5	265.6	265.6	
76	311.7	11820.	1500.	98.9	272.3	272.3	
77	313.2	11877.	1500.	101.3	279.1	279.1	

STAFF POLICY - 25.0 STUDENT/STAFF

YR	ENROLL (THOUS)	STAFF AVAIL.	STAFF HIRED	STAFF COST	TOTAL COST	REVENUE (MILLIONS)	
68	299.5	12480.	-500. *	89.1	239.3	223.4	DEF
69	301.0	11981.	59.	87.3	237.1	229.0	DEF
70	302.5	11502.	598.	85.4	235.1	234.8	DEF
71	304.0	11536.	958.	87.4	240.6	240.6	
72	305.5	11592.	975.	89.6	246.6	246.6	
73	307.1	11649.	979.	91.8	252.8	252.8	
74	308.6	11705.	984.	94.1	259.1	259.1	
75	310.1	11762.	988.	96.5	265.6	265.6	
76	311.7	11820.	993.	98.9	272.3	272.3	
77	313.2	11877.	997.	101.3	279.1	279.1	

* - EXCESS STAFF, SINCE IF MORE STAFF THAN NEEDED, NO LAYOFFS

**DEF means a deficit predicted for that year.

Figure 7A-1 (continued)

8

analyzing a simulation run

Using the techniques we have already described, the analyst should be able to design, program, and debug a simulator. In this chapter we show how the output generated by the simulator should be analyzed to aid decision making. We will describe the methods of analysis as if they play a part only after the simulator has been debugged; however, this is done only for pedagogical convenience. The reader should keep in mind that decisions about the structural characteristics of a model are made in parallel with decisions about how the model is to be used; for example, decisions about how detailed the simulator should be are affected by what output is desired.

We begin by defining the terms that will be used throughout this chapter. Then we examine ways the output of the simulator can be efficiently recorded and used to analyze the problem. This is followed by a discussion of how the analyst should validate that the simulator is a correct representation of the system and that his recommendations are reliable and accurate.

definitions 8-1

The terms used to describe simulation results are defined here. A simulation *run* is an uninterrupted recording of the system's performance under a specified combination of controllable variables. A *replication* of a run is a recording under the same combination, but with different random variations. An *observation* of the simulated system is a segment of a run sufficient for estimating the value of each of the performance measures. (Note that an observation can extend over a considerable period of simulated time.)

We say that a system has reached *stable* or *steady-state* conditions when successive observations of the system's performance are statistically indistinguishable. *Steady state* means that it is possible to define an observation such that it provides no new information about the future behavior of the system.

> Our definition of steady state is different from a strictly mathematical one which requires that a system's behavior be stationary; that is, the probability distribution $g(t)$ describing the performance at t is identical to the distribution $g(t + \delta)$ for all $\delta > 0$. This mathematical criterion of steady state is too restrictive for our purposes because it excludes all systems that have perfectly predictable cyclical behavior. The definition that we have adopted does not exclude cyclical behavior.

Because an observation is defined as a *segment of a run* (rather than an instant in the run) we are able to treat each cycle as one observation, as in the machine adjustment example. Therefore, if each observation (i.e., each cycle) is statistically identical, we will define the system as being in steady state. The reader may feel we are splitting hairs in making this distinction between what is or is not steady state; however, as we shall soon show the properties of the experimental design needed for data analysis are much less restrictive when we can assume a system is in steady state.

A system whose behavior does not satisfy steady-state conditions is usually described as being in a *transient* state. Models may exhibit transient properties for either of two reasons:

(1) If the starting conditions used to initialize the model were atypical of operating conditions, but steady-state conditions are expected to be exhibited eventually, then there is a transient period until the effects of the starting conditions become insignificant. A good experimental design insures that the results during such a transitional phase are insignificant or are not included in the analysis.

(2) A transient phenomenon may occur in the situation being simulated.

For some kinds of systems no steady-state conditions are expected. This would be true, for example, for a simulation whose output is the annual GNP for the United States. There is no reason (based on past experience) to assume that the GNP will satisfy steady-state conditions in the future. It is the transient phase itself that is to be studied.

8-2 methods of removing unwanted transients

Many simulation models are developed and run under the assumption that there are steady-state operating conditions. If this is the case, transients occur because the analyst has started the simulation run with atypical values. Therefore, the analyst must first select starting conditions that keep the transient period short. Then he must decide how to eliminate the effect of the transients that do occur so that the simulator's performance is judged only on its steady-state behavior.

For a single run of a simulator, there are two basic strategies for setting starting conditions. One is to begin in an empty and idle status; that is, assume that the system is completely clean of activity and run the simulator until the transient effects are insignificant. It is easy to start the simulator under these conditions, but the transient period is likely to be quite long. The other alternative is to start the simulator at the a priori steady-state conditions expected under the operating rules. This should reduce the transient period but may bias the results to preconceived conclusions if data is collected before the transient effects have been removed.

A further complication arises when two (or more) runs are to be made under different conditions. Presumably the two runs, say A and B, will lead to different simulated operating conditions. If a priori steady-state estimates are to be used to initialize the runs, should A and B be started at levels that each is expected to achieve in the steady state? To avoid biasing the results, we recommend that both runs be started at the conditions that represent an average of the two initial positions. This procedure is also proposed by Conway [1963].

The effects of transients must be removed when performance measures are recorded in a simulation run. The result of not doing this is shown clearly in Figure 2–4 where the state probabilities do not settle down for 10,000 time units. If means and variances were computed before steady-state conditions existed, incorrect conclusions would be drawn.

Two methods are commonly used to remove the effects of transients. The first is to use long simulation runs so the data from the transient period is insignificant relative to the data in the steady state. This was the method used in the machine adjustment simulator in Chapter 2. The method is very simple to arrange, but it is costly in terms of computer running time.

The second method, and the one more commonly used, is to introduce a nonrecording period to get the simulator into steady-state conditions. This is done by running the simulator until steady-state conditions are achieved, then clearing all statistical accumulations (but leaving the state of the simulated system as it is) and then continuing the run. The conditions at the end of the transient period become an a priori estimate of the steady-state conditions and, in effect, are used to start a new run. This method is often easier to program than its alternative: to explicitly insert steady-state starting conditions into the model. The plastic shop example in Chapter 5 illustrates this method of removing transient effects. In the FORTRAN program of Figure 5C–1, the section denoted step 4.3 clears the statistical accumulations and then reads in a new number of jobs to be processed in the main run. The transient effects can be seen in the output; after 10 jobs (the assumed transient period) and then after the next 100 jobs. Note the difference between step 1 in Figure 5B–1 in which the initial conditions are inserted and step 4.3 in Figure 5C–1

191

in which the initial conditions are set by starting idle and running until 10 jobs have been processed. In GPSS a RESET control operator facilitates this clearing and restarting process. This operator, which clears statistical and other output accumulations without changing the model, is used in Figure 6–4, the GPSS version of the model.

There are no fixed rules for determining when steady-state conditions can be assumed. A simple method we have found to be useful involves examining a sequence of observations from the run. If the number of observations in which the output is greater than the average to a given point is about the same as the number in which it is less, then steady-state conditions are likely to exist. Another method is to compute a moving average of the output and to assume steady state when the average no longer changes significantly over time.

8-3 the use of simulation models to study transient phenomena

Some simulations are developed specifically to study the transient rather than the steady-state characteristics of the system. There are two main reasons for analyzing a transient phase of a simulation model:

(1) Steady-state conditions may not exist in the system at all. This would be true if we were simulating a constantly changing process.

(2) We might be interested in analyzing problems associated with a start-up or transition. This would be true, for example, if we were simulating the initial operation of a new plant or the initial effects of a structural change in an existing plant.

In the second situation the simulation model would ultimately settle down to a steady state. The steady state might even be predictable using analytic models. It is less likely that analytic models could be used to predict the transient conditions. This is a case with current theories for inventory control; there are many analytic models available that predict steady-state conditions (for example, see Wagner [1962]). But there is a well-known transient effect from the installation of a new inventory system. Stock levels rise initially in the system and later settle to the desired steady-state conditions. This occurs because those materials that are carried at too low a level are immediately ordered to the desired level, whereas those that are too high are reduced only by withdrawals from the system. Predicting the maximum inventory level that will occur in the transient period and how long it will take for this transient phase to die out is very difficult analytically, but it can be done by simulation.

The simulation output that is important for transient analysis may not be the same as that used for steady state. In the study of steady-state conditions, we are generally interested in average or typical occurrences

in the system. In transient analysis we may be more interested in exceptional or extreme conditions which exist during the course of the transient
period. For example, we may be interested in the *maximum* number of
months required to install a computer system, the probability of *exceeding*
a safety level in starting up a new plant, or the probability of the *failure*
of a new business enterprise.

As we will show later, in studying steady state a larger statistical sample
can often be obtained efficiently simply by making the run longer. The
longer run helps improve confidence in the estimate. In studying transients
with a stochastic model, the run *must* be replicated by restarting to obtain
a distribution of results. Further, if the output of interest is the possibility
of an exception or an estimate of an extreme, a larger number of replications may be required to ensure a high probability of including the unlikely
events in the sample.

In some cases the transient can be converted into conditions where
steady-state analysis is appropriate by discounting the future values of
the effects. (Any basic text on finance or engineering economics describes discounting methods.) This method would be used typically for
economic simulation studies; here the value of income and costs in the
future is translated into its approximate present worth by discounting
factors. Then comparisons can be made between alternatives by studying
the *present* value of all future conditions (i.e., the time variable is removed).
Transient conditions in other systems (e.g., in starting a new organization)
cannot be handled in this way.

measuring performance 8-4

The formulation of the simulation problem determines what variables
will be generated by the simulator and how they will be related into a
performance objective (see Chapter 4). In some cases the output is the
occurrence of a single event; more likely it is a continuous variable whose
average value and/or distribution is to be predicted by the simulation run.
We now want to examine how the analyst can use the output from the
simulator in the most efficient way to infer what the performance measures
are under the operating conditions.

If the simulator is deterministic, there are no problems of inference;
the output of the simulation at the end of the run *is* the required measure.
For example, the school district simulator described in Appendix 7A is a
deterministic model. Since there are no stochastic variables, the deficits
predicted by one run of the simulator provide the only basis for inference;
no replications of the run are needed. (On the other hand, neither is there
a basis for stating a confidence level.)

The analysis of steady-state conditions when the simulation model is
stochastic is not as straightforward. The problems are illustrated in Figure 8–1. Measure P_1 is illustrative of the kind of data that changes every
time period or on a continuous basis. Variable P_2 represents data that
changes whenever a certain kind of event occurs (e.g., lateness associated

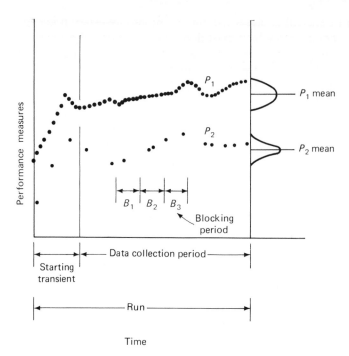

Figure 8–1
Analyzing
stochastic
simulation data.

with a job completion). It is not difficult to estimate the average value of each parameter. This is merely the mean of the values observed in that portion of the run. However, it is much more difficult to state a level of confidence that the mean so computed is in fact the true mean. For this we need to know the variance of the data. To supply this variance, we must know more about the relationship between the observations in the sample. With this additional information, we can use basic statistical inference to make statements about confidence in the estimates. The key to the statistical inference is how the samples are selected, and it is this question on which we concentrate. (For a good discussion of these issues, see Brenner [1965].)

One obvious way of obtaining a sample (of several observations) is to rerun, or replicate the run, several times. The mean from each run is then treated as one observation and the set of observations, or the sample, is used to estimate the desired statistics. This immediately brings up the issue of how long each run should be. Clearly, from Figure 8–1, replicating runs is inefficient in that the wasteful starting transient is repeated on each replication.

Assume for the moment that we have determined that the appropriate run length for replicate-run sampling is B units long (in simulated time). Another way of creating a new observation would be to run the initial simulator B units longer and, therefore, avoid the transient period required if a rerun were made. Call the B unit period the *blocking period*. In most situations, this approach will not work because the observations, or blocking periods, are not independent. That is, the average performance in the second of two adjacent periods depends, in part, on what happened during the first period. This results from simulating complex dynamic systems. In the plastic shop example, a long job starting in the first period will affect lateness in the second period. The technical term for this inter-dependence is *autocorrelation.* (We return to this problem in a subsequent section.)

A single run can often be considered as a sample of observations consisting of the individual recordings taken at each event or time unit. This is convenient, since, from basic statistics, the distribution of sample means (for reasonable sample sizes) is distributed normally. Thus, it makes sense to talk of the variance of the observation means where a run is an observation and to use this variance to estimate confidence intervals.

For stochastic models we are left with three questions to be answered before we can infer results from the simulation runs:

(1) Should the run be replicated or continued?

(2) How long should the blocking or observation period be?

(3) What can be done to eliminate or reduce the effects that auto-correlations between adjacent observations have on sample re-quirements?

In the next section we describe ways of answering these questions.

methods of analyzing stochastic 8-5
simulation runs

The efficiency with which information on the steady-state behavior of a simulator under two different operating conditions is obtained can be improved through the use of correlated random variables. To illustrate how, refer again to Figure 8–1. We can statistically describe the fluctuations of a single observation around the true performance by its variance, σ^2. By observing the output of the simulator, we can estimate the average performance of the system as

$$\hat{\mu} = \sum_{i=1}^{n} \frac{x_i}{n}$$

where x_i's = the individual observations

         n = the number of observations in the sample

If each of the x's is independent, the confidence we place in the estimate of the mean is given by

$$\hat{\sigma}_{\mu}^2 = \frac{\sigma^2}{n}$$

195

Analysis Assuming No Autocorrelation

For the time being, we will assume each of the observations are independent of each other (i.e., there is no autocorrelation between the x's). Later in this section, we will show the effect of removing this assumption.

Since we want to compare the steady-state performance of the simulator under different operating rules, it is clear that we want $\hat{\sigma}_\mu^2$ to be small enough so that we will not make a mistake in concluding that one set of operating conditions is superior to another. The chances of making such a mistake are reduced if the simulation is run for a very long time because the number of observations will become very large and $\hat{\sigma}_\mu^2$ will get smaller. However, this increased confidence level is achieved only through additional computation. Therefore, we want to analyze the simulation runs in a way that a desired confidence in the results is achieved with the least computational cost.

Let us examine the effect of replicating a run and introducing a correlation between the replications. (We continue to assume that the observations within a replication are independent.) Suppose we make two replications of a simulation run, X and Y, where both have the same observational variance σ^2. As shown in Figure 8–2, X and Y can be averaged to produce an estimate of the mean and variance of the performance measure. Suppose that each replication has an equal number of independent observations, $n/2$, and that we purposely introduce a correlation, ρ between the replications.

> From statistics, the estimate of the mean is still the average of the two replications
>
> $$\hat{\mu} = \sum_{i=1}^{n/2} \frac{(X_i + Y_i)}{2}$$
>
> but the confidence in this estimate is now given by
>
> $$\hat{\sigma}_\mu^2 = \frac{\sigma^2}{n}(1 + \rho)$$
>
> If the two replications are independent, $\rho = 0$ and the variance estimate is identical to one replication of twice the length. If, however, we introduce a *negative correlation* between pairs of observations in the two replications (i.e., when the value X_i tends to be high, the value Y_i will tend to be low and vice versa), the variance to the sum of observations $(X_1 + Y_1), (X_2 + Y_2), \ldots, (X_{n/2} + Y_{n/2})$ will be less than the variance of one continuous run of n observations. This is illustrated in Figure 8–2.

The variables produced by purposely introducing negative correlation between pairs are known as *antithetic variates* [Hammersley and Handscomb, Ch. 5, 1964].

The procedure most commonly used to generate negatively correlated variates is to use uniformly distributed random numbers (on the interval

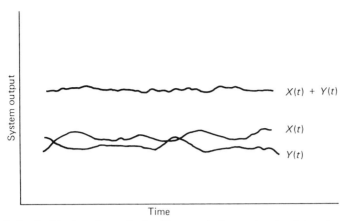

Figure 8–2 Antithetic variates obtained by negatively correlated variate pairs.

$0.0 \leq R \leq 1.0$) to generate probabilistic events on one run and to use $1.0 - R$ for the *equivalent* event in the second run. In using antithetic variate procedures, it is important to maintain the event equivalence (relative to the random variables) between runs; otherwise the desired negatively correlated outputs will not be achieved because the processes get out of phase.

The effects of correlated variates can be put to further use when the analyst compares two alternative courses of action in the simulation; that is, for comparing two runs under *different* controllable values.

Suppose we have estimated independently the mean and variance of a simulation output under two sets of controllable conditions (say A and B) and have estimated these effects as $\hat{\mu}_A$, $\hat{\sigma}_A^2$, and $\hat{\mu}_B$, $\hat{\sigma}_B^2$, respectively. The analyst must now decide whether one course of action is significantly better than the other. The mean and variance of the difference between runs is

$$\hat{\mu}_D = \hat{\mu}_A - \hat{\mu}_B$$
$$\hat{\sigma}_D^2 = \hat{\sigma}_A^2 + \hat{\sigma}_B^2$$

We can test whether $\hat{\mu}_D$ is significantly different from zero by using standard statistical analysis. Whether any difference is significant depends, in part, on how small $\hat{\sigma}_D^2$ is. We can reduce this variance by introducing a *positive* correlation between runs A and B. This is because the variance of the difference between correlated pairs is given by

$$\hat{\sigma}_D^2 = \hat{\sigma}_A^2 + \hat{\sigma}_B^2 - 2\rho\hat{\sigma}_A\hat{\sigma}_B$$

Thus, if we analyze two different courses of action using the *same* random numbers for equivalent events, we can reduce the variance at no increase in computer running time. This procedure is equivalent to a technique known as *blocking* in physical experimental design (see Davies [1960], Ch. 5).

197

Let us summarize the two ways that correlated observations can improve the efficiency of gathering information from a simulation run. We have two operating conditions, A and B, and we are interested in obtaining an estimate of the difference between those runs that has a small variance (i.e., $\hat{\sigma}_D^2$ is small). If each operating condition is replicated once (i.e., if there are four sets of output, A_1, A_2, B_1, and B_2), the total variance can be expressed as

$$\hat{\sigma}_A^2 = \sigma_A^2(1 + \rho_{A_1A_2})$$
$$\hat{\sigma}_B^2 = \sigma_B^2(1 + \rho_{B_1B_2})$$

$$\hat{\sigma}_D^2 = \hat{\sigma}_A^2 + \hat{\sigma}_B^2 - 2\rho_{AB}\hat{\sigma}_A\hat{\sigma}_B \tag{8-2}$$

(8-1)

In words, the procedure is:

(1) Introduce a *negative* correlation between replications of a run, thus yielding a reduced variance for the within-run estimate (Equation 8–1, $\rho_{A_1A_2}$ and $\rho_{B_1B_2}$ negative).

(2) Introduce a positive correlation between runs under different operating conditions, thus yielding a reduced variance for the difference between runs (Equation 8–2, ρ_{AB} positive).

The discussion so far might lead the reader to conclude that the most efficient experimental design methods involve several replications of each run with correlations between replicate pairs. This conclusion is not necessarily correct because it is based on the assumption that no initial transient phase exists. It may be that the time required to pass over the transient starting conditions will negate the advantages of correlated runs once steady-state conditions exist. In "Some Tactical Problems in Digital Simulation," Conway [1963] argues that estimating mean effects using one long run is usually more efficient than several correlated replications of shorter length. Whether this is the case depends on how accurately the analyst can estimate what the stable conditions will be before he makes the runs, and on how long it will take transient effects to disappear as the run progresses.

Analysis Assuming Autocorrelation

In "The Allocation of Computer Time in Comparing Simulation Experiments," Fishman [1967a] examined ways of efficiently allocating computer time between two simulation experiments when the objective is to compare differences in mean effects. Fishman concluded, among other things, that optimal run lengths are very sensitive to the amount of autocorrelation within each run. In our analysis so far, we have assumed that the observations within a replication of a run are independent. We will now examine the effects of correlation between observations in a replication.

Two methods are generally used to deal with autocorrelated simulation output. Each method has a different effect on the performance of the simulator; their relative values depend on the properties of the simulator and on the analyst's requirements for reliability of his results. The methods are:

(1) Estimate precisely the autocorrelation function and include its effects in the estimation of the mean and variance of state variables.

(2) Group the time-series output data into blocks of consecutive observations such that each block represents an independent observation. Then use standard statistical estimation methods.

If the autocorrelation function is estimated, the following steps are involved:

(1) Run the simulator to obtain test output data under steady-state conditions.

(2) Use the test data to estimate the correlation between an observation at any simulated time, and an observation at $t + s$; that is, estimate

$$\rho(s) = \frac{E\{[X_t - \mu][X_{t+s} - \mu]\}}{\sigma^2}$$

where X_t = individual observation of output at t

μ = average output over test simulation run

σ^2 = variance of an individual observation over the test run

These estimates are made for all positive values of s for which $\rho(s)$ is significantly different from zero.

(3) Once the autocorrelation function has been estimated, the simulation model is run to compare performance characteristics under alternative operating characteristics. The autocorrelation function is used to refine the estimated variance of the performance output. Specifically, if the production run under specific conditions yields n-correlated observations, the estimate of the output is

$$\hat{\mu} = \sum_{i=1}^{n} \frac{X_i}{n}$$

$$\hat{\sigma}_\mu^2 = \frac{\sigma_x^2}{n}\left[1 + 2\sum_{s=1}^{n-1}\left(1 - \frac{s}{n}\right)\rho(s)\right]$$

(Note that if observations are independent, $\rho(s) = 0$ for all s and the formula for the variance reduces to the standard form already presented.)

If the blocking method is used to remove the effects of autocorrelated observations, the following steps are involved:

(1) If a production run consists of n-autocorrelated observations, denoted $X_1, X_2, \ldots, X_n$, observations are grouped into k consecutive blocks with the following properties:

(a) An observation is redefined to be the average of the m observations within a block. Call these new observations $Y_1, Y_2, \ldots, Y_k$ where

$$Y_1 = \frac{X_1 + X_2 + \cdots + X_m}{m}$$

$$Y_2 = \frac{X_{m+1} + X_{m+2} + \cdots + X_{2m}}{m}$$

$$\vdots$$

$$Y_k = \frac{X_{m(k-1)+1} + X_{m(k-1)+2} + \cdots + X_n}{m}$$

Note that $m = n/k$.

(b) The block size is chosen large enough so the Y's are independent of each other; that is, $\rho(s) = 0$ for all s.

(2) The mean and variance of the blocked output can now be estimated as follows:

$$\hat{\mu} = \sum_{i=1}^{k} \frac{Y_i}{k} = \sum_{j=1}^{n} \frac{X_j}{n}$$

$$\hat{\sigma}_\mu^2 = \frac{\sigma_y^2}{k}$$

In "Some Tactical Problems in Digital Simulation," Conway [1963] examines the mathematical implications of the two methods for treating autocorrelated simulation data. He concludes that although efficiency of estimating the mean value is the same using either procedure, the efficiency for estimating variance is not. In fact, Conway shows that the method that explicitly uses the autocorrelation function *always* provides the minimum variance estimate. Thus, if an analyst intends to run the simulator until the variance estimate is within a specified limit, he can always achieve this with the smallest number of observations by first estimating the autocorrelation function. The mathematical conclusions that Conway derives are not really surprising since, on an intuitive basis we can see that the blocking method always loses at least some independent information through aggregation.

It is difficult to draw direct conclusions from Conway's findings because they show only how to find the minimum variance for a specified simulation run length. More reasonable criteria for this decision include estimates of computer running time. For example, either of the following criteria would be a more acceptable basis for comparing methods:

(1) The procedure that minimizes computer running time for a specified confidence interval on the variable being estimated.

(2) The procedure that provides the minimum confidence interval for a given computer time.

"Design Problems in a Process Control Simulator" [Hauser, Barish, and Ehrenfeld, 1966] reports tests of both autocorrelation and blocking methods using the first of these criteria. Their results cannot be generalized because the authors depend on the specific simulation model used for the analysis; however, it is interesting that the conclusions are different than ones obtained using the number of observations as an effectiveness criterion. Hauser et al. found that the computer time needed to estimate the autocorrelation function was so large that it overwhelmed the gain resulting from the fewer observations ultimately required to obtain the desired confidence interval. For the particular model used in the analysis (an inventory simulator) the data blocking methods provided equivalent results in approximately half the computer time required for the auto-correlation estimation procedure.

The implication of the Hauser et al. article is that the blocking procedure has an advantage because it does not require an explicit estimation of the autocorrelation function. However, the blocking method does demand some knowledge of the form of this function. The knowledge is required before the analyst can determine the number of consecutive observations (*m*) that provide independent (between-block) estimates of the output factor. The choice of a number that includes too many observations increases running time; choosing one that is too small causes incorrect estimates of the true confidence limit on the output of the simulator.

Which of the two procedures should be used to remove autocorrelation effects depends on the characteristics of the simulation situation. We make the following observations about the *relative* advantage of each method. (We emphasize relative because it is nearly impossible to determine absolute conditions for when one procedure will be superior to the other.) The relative advantage of the autocorrelation estimation procedure increases as:

(1) The cost in computer time to obtain an individual observation of the system's behavior increases.

(2) The size of the variance of the estimated behavior becomes smaller.

The first observation comes directly from Conway's analysis; namely, using the autocorrelation function always provides a specified confidence interval in fewer observations than the blocking method. As a consequence we see that as computer cost per simulation observation increases, the relative advantage of estimating the autocorrelative function increases. The second observation is related to the nature of the computer cost to obtain the autocorrelation estimate. Once the estimation has been made, the cost is essentially fixed and thus independent of the number of observations needed to obtain the desired confidence limit. Assuming that the variable cost of a simulation observation is approximately linear with the number of observations, the cost under alternative procedures as a function of the desired confidence limit will be of the form shown in Figure 8–3.

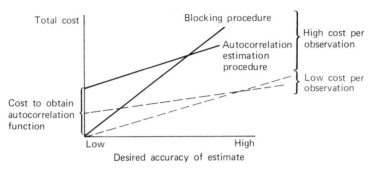

Figure 8–3   Total computer cost as a function of confidence interval desired.

To conclude this section, we briefly examine the potential future applications for spectral analysis, a technique just beginning to be used in simulation. Blackman and Tukey [1958] provide an excellent description of the basic elements of the technique. Fishman and Kiviat [1967b] have surveyed the use of spectral analysis to analyze simulated time series. (For a general discussion of time series, see Cox and Lewis [1966].)

Essentially, spectral analysis attempts to decompose a time series into basic components that can be represented as sine and cosine functions. When these periodic effects are exposed, the process becomes easier to interpret and analyze.

The most important future use of spectral analysis seems to be in providing a way to convert an apparent nonsteady-state time series into one in which such conditions can be assumed. By removing periodic effects that might otherwise go unnoticed, spectral analysis enables the researcher to define an observation in such a way that time dependency is removed; that is, autocorrelation no longer exists. For this to occur, however, spectral analysis must be powerful enough to detect fairly subtle cycles in the data. In an unpublished paper, Stankard purposely introduced cyclical behavior into dummy data and attempted to detect it using spectral analysis. Only the very obvious cycles were detected using the technique. Unless some improvements are made in the analytic procedures, therefore, spectral analysis will have only limited use with simulation models.

Before we discuss how to validate that the simulation output provides a realistic representation of the system, we must analyze how the generation of input data affects the output. This is normally not a problem, because the input conditions are developed independently of the construction of the model. In the next section we discuss an alternative way of generating input data—a way that affects methods of validating the model.

Analysts sometimes find themselves in the situation where they have formulated a model and are unable to find data to estimate the parameters in it. This happens for analytic as well as simulation models. The analyst may be forced to restructure it to a form for which data are available to estimate parameters. Parameter estimates can sometimes be obtained without restructuring the model. We illustrate how by referring to an advertising study conducted by one of the authors [Emshoff and Mercer, 1969].

A simulation model had been constructed to represent the behavior of consumers in oligopolistic markets. The model treated the purchase decision as a function of psychologically related variables that operate on the consumer at the time of his purchase. The value of the psychological variables were assumed to be affected by decision variables controlled by the manufacturer-distributor-retailer network for each brand (decisions such as advertising, pricing, and distributing policies). Thus, the simulation model was represented in two stages. In Stage I, sales of a brand (S_i for Brand i) are predicted as a function of the psychological characteristics of the consumers ($X_1, X_2, \ldots, X_n$). Notationally,

$$S_i = f(X_1, X_2, \ldots, X_n) \qquad (8\text{--}3)$$

The Stage II model predicts the effects of controllable decisions such as pricing and advertising ($Y_1, Y_2, \ldots, Y_m$) directly on the psychological variables, and thus indirectly on purchasing behavior. That is,

$$X_1, X_2, \ldots, X_n = g(Y_1, Y_2, \ldots, Y_m) \qquad (8\text{--}4)$$

The question is how to test the validity of Equations 8–3 and 8–4. It is very unlikely that historical data are available on the distributional characteristics of X. Field survey work might be carried out; however, this would be very expensive and time consuming. If historical data exist on actual sales S_i and the levels of controllable variables ($Y_1, Y_2, \ldots, Y_m$) that correspond for each time period, an alternative method is available. With such information, the simulation model can be used "backwards" in order to answer the question, "What would the values of the psychological parameters have to be in order for the sales and controllable variables to take on the values they did?" If enough data are available, part of them can be used to obtain best estimates of the psychological parameters. This is called *parameter identification* (see Section 9–3).

This method can be used only if there are enough historical data so that some remain unused to serve as a basis for validating the model. Too often analysts fail to save data and are left with no basis for testing their model. One of the most serious mistakes made by a novice when faced with this problem is to reuse the data on which the parameters were estimated as a way of testing whether the simulator reproduces historical conditions. This exercise does not serve as a test of the model.

8-7 validity

The most vexing question asked about a simulation model is, "How do you know it is valid?" Suppose, for example, an analyst feels his simulation is an accurate representation of a system and he presents it to management for their use in decision making. The latter then asks, "How do we know it is valid? How do we know its predictions will come true?" These questions must be answered at some point in every simulation study.

How can we be sure that the predictions made by a simulation model— or any model—will be correct or at least will be better than the predictions made by some other method (e.g., by judgment)? Ultimately this becomes a question of the credibility of the model. Therefore, we must examine what evidence is required by a manager before he will utilize a model as an aid in his decision making. Mathematical models have an advantage in this regard over simulation models. If, for example, a situation can be shown to fit the assumptions of a linear programming model, then the manager has the support of evidence that shows that linear programming models have proven effective in other (albeit different) situations. The only possible evidence of validity for a simulation model that has been developed specifically for a situation is that the model has made satisfactory predictions in the past. If this is the first time the model is being used, such evidence is not available. This difficulty is most severe with a simulation model of a nonexistent system, for the analyst cannot even test it using historical data.

Hermann [1967] presents five preliminary approaches to validation for these "first-time" models. These are:

1. "Internal validity." Does the simulation have a low variance of outputs when replicated with all exogenous inputs held constant? This question is especially significant for game-type simulation in which there are uncontrolled internal elements; that is, the players. We require low variability because a stochastic model with a high variance owing to internal processes (while perhaps an interesting finding in itself) will obscure changes in output resulting from changes in controlled or environmental variables. It is difficult to believe in models with high internal variability.

2. "Face validity." This is the surface or initial impression of a simulation or game's realism and is obtained by asking people who know the real system (e.g., managers) to judge whether the model is reasonable. From the scientific point of view, this is not validity at all and we prefer to call this a test of the reasonableness or credibility of the model.

3. "Variable-parameter validity." Do the simulation's variables and parameters compare with their assumed counterparts in the observable universe? Sensitivity testing is a form of variable-parameter validity. In a sensitivity test one or more factors are changed to determine (a) if they affect the output and (b) if they help make the model produce results that match historical data more closely. Factors to which the output is insensitive need not be closely estimated.

4. "Hypothesis validity." Do pairwise (or higher level) relationships in the model correspond to similar relationships in the observable universe? In other words, are subsystem models valid? [Amstutz, 1967]. Hermann notes that "an operating model [a simulation] would be increasingly valid as its operation was distinguishable from systems which it was not intended to represent, as well as by evidence of its convergence with the performance of the intended reference system." This test of the *negation* is rarely properly investigated.

5. "Event or time-series validity." This is validation in the scientific sense. Does the simulation predict observable events, event patterns, or the variations in output variables? Since the model is never perfect nor completely detailed, an important question is, "How close do simulated and real events have to match?" The distinction between events and event patterns is important. Speaking of simulations of political systems, Hermann asks, "Is it as important that a simulation replicate a diplomatic message (a rather frequent class of events) as it is that it replicate the elimination of head of state (a less frequent class of events)?" In most situations effective models need not be detailed and only distributions of events (such as the distribution of sales) need be compared. But in other situations (such as a study of corporate mergers) predicting the occurrence of singular events is critical.

Tests 1 through 4 are important to help assure us that a first-time model is worth using for further research or for decision aiding. But a model is completely valid only when it has been demonstrated to be a reliable and accurate predictor of event sequences and value variations. Furthermore, a model is *useful* only when the decision maker believes (rightly or wrongly) that it is valid in this sense.

Credibility, the only kind of validity we have for a first-time model, requires a detailed examination of the internal structure of the model and of the data used for estimated parameters. It requires careful comparison with such historical data as is available. It requires good communication between the analyst and the decision maker, and some faith on the part of the decision maker that the analyst is qualified. Simulations in production, distribution, and data processing have been shown to be valid and useful by repeated applications. The validity of most behavioral simulations is yet to be demonstrated. "Insofar as their validation is concerned, it is premature to reject or accept the value of most simulations and games in the behavioral sciences" [Hermann, 1967].

When an analyst produces a new simulation model all that can be hoped for is a test of reasonableness and an act of faith that its use will improve decisions. Obviously, in these circumstances it is unlikely that the model will be used for decision *making*. The simulator may well be used for qualitative or quantitative decision *aiding*, since in this use the decision maker is not counting on the model alone. He may use other evidence to confirm or revise the model results. After a model has been used for some time (even though it has changed somewhat over the period of use) and has been shown to make satisfactory predictions, the model may actually be used for decision making. This is especially true if the decision maker has used the model directly to gain insights.

In summary, the validity of the model is tested in this sequence:

(1) The analyst assures himself that the model performs the way he intends it to, using test data, and if available, real historical data. This is debugging.

(2) Reasonableness is checked by:

    (a) showing that key subsystem models predict their part of the world well (using historical data);

    (b) showing, where parameter identification is required, that parameters can be fit (that the search terminates with a close match to historical data), and that the parameters have reasonable values;

    (c) having people who are knowledgeable about the situation (preferably including the decision maker) review the model in detail and agree to its structure and parameters.

(3) The decision maker has an opportunity to explore the use of the model to become familiar with its predictions and to examine the interactions it implies. At this point the analyst and decision maker may be able to agree as to what is a close enough fit between simulator output and actual data.

(4) The model is used for decision aiding. Careful records are kept of its predictions and of actual results. (This may involve a time span of years, so that the evaluation procedure has to be set up carefully.)

There is no reason why several models cannot be in this process at one time.

It is never possible to completely validate a decision-aiding model since there is never real data about the alternatives not implemented; this problem is common to any decision-aiding procedure, not only to simulation. If the decision makers believe the model is useful and use it, the analyst has done his job.

exercise

8–1 Determine whether the data on page 207 have any autocorrelation. Suggest a blocking arrangement so that independent observations can be taken.

9780.	11277.	11019.	10236.	9041.	9879.	10287.	10296.	8916.	8968.
10615.	9451.	9758.	9762.	9411.	10442.	9943.	9302.	10613.	10173.
10204.	10389.	9467.	9370.	9644.	10625.	9997.	10725.	10805.	10751.
11122.	10314.	10678.	10063.	8785.	9133.	9390.	9910.	9965.	9845.
9369.	10594.	8890.	9387.	9579.	10115.	10435.	10540.	11186.	11311.
11116.	10320.	9409.	10414.	9266.	9768.	10259.	10129.	9217.	9217.
8966.	9705.	9686.	9369.	11159.	10550.	9011.	10072.	10664.	9882.
10805.	9044.	10376.	10159.	9650.	10700.	10540.	8947.	9910.	9398.
9890.	9211.	9329.	9507.	10016.	9412.	9491.	10425.	10222.	10875.
10638.	9363.	10260.	10005.	10678.	8907.	10371.	10767.	9426.	9426.
9038.	9778.	9320.	9967.	8884.	9250.	9645.	10485.	9244.	10646.
9995.	10924.	9988.	9691.	9488.	10225.	10369.	10977.	10154.	8981.
9820.	9100.	11118.	10695.	9736.	10068.	10963.	11219.	10930.	10234.
10682.	9976.	9889.	10353.	9005.	9822.	9635.	10787.	10057.	10304.
10900.	8999.	10915.	10938.	10831.	10695.	9946.	10336.	9342.	11117.
10280.	9894.	9123.	8930.	9731.	10318.	9238.	10499.	10683.	9594.
10700.	10090.	10292.	10122.	9765.	9661.	10213.	10768.	10834.	9708.
9506.	10341.	10606.	10477.	9751.	9751.	10555.	10493.	10864.	10050.
9867.	9769.	11097.	10466.	9294.	9687.	10160.	9576.	9227.	9660.
10850.	9569.	10486.	9253.	9866.	10891.	9366.	10844.	9445.	10537.
9374.	9703.	9620.	9044.	10057.	8787.	10203.	10544.	9206.	10764.
10060.	10590.	9389.	9694.	9057.	9784.	10037.	10191.	9431.	9689.
9660.	10870.	10882.	9636.	10048.	9677.	9552.	9364.	9583.	9831.
9350.	10083.	9893.	10382.	9114.	9599.	9739.	9591.	10040.	10171.
10457.	11158.	9129.	10276.	9699.	10696.	10013.	9554.	9859.	8824.
10353.	10724.	10906.	9425.	10198.	10482.	10293.	10555.	9258.	9630.
10687.	9981.	9826.	9447.	9151.	9437.	10821.	9840.	10800.	10570.
11000.	10122.	9369.	11257.	9254.	9627.	10516.	10767.	10237.	10239.
10901.	11002.	9718.	9439.	11063.	10439.	10268.	9880.	9256.	10605.
9692.	9409.	10278.	10967.	10589.	10657.	9546.	8979.	10605.	9401.
9911.	9152.	11072.	8767.	10371.	9625.	10696.	10754.	9401.	10594.
10255.	10116.	8590.	9132.	8823.	9201.	9240.	10143.	10594.	10319.
9059.	10621.	10132.	11324.	10150.	10342.	9921.	11265.	10319.	10663.
10524.	9608.	9867.	10752.	11168.	10758.	9508.	10292.	11228.	9478.
10119.	10588.	10726.	10082.	9612.	10851.	9885.	9887.	10888.	10429.
10509.	10188.	9539.	10631.	10068.	9131.	10537.	9306.	10827.	10642.
9023.	10626.	10941.	9044.	9621.	10464.	9802.	9860.	9607.	9812.
9892.	9358.	10525.	8985.	9071.	10238.	10269.	9631.	9104.	10655.
8821.	8814.	9358.	10779.	9333.	11040.	10823.	9181.	10482.	10275.
10643.	10429.	10969.	10645.	9458.	10932.	10804.	9227.	10387.	9452.
10047.	10878.	10286.	10473.	9215.	9934.	10806.	11012.	9776.	9936.
10296.	10395.	9531.	10541.	9820.	9716.	10849.	10192.	10109.	9980.
8892.	9248.	9588.	10329.	10243.	9186.	11079.	10086.	9643.	10535.
10672.	10672.	10854.	9852.	10422.	9428.	10872.	10675.	9137.	10037.
10468.	9707.	10257.	9785.	10608.	9541.	9133.	10433.	9638.	9287.
9195.	9958.	9818.	9733.	9816.	10175.	9500.	10601.	10558.	10503.
9879.	9122.	10029.	8898.	10305.	9234.	10035.	9346.	9424.	9059.
9763.	9179.	9282.	9700.	9524.	9806.	10059.	9614.	8696.	10396.
9939.	9592.	10270.		9478.	9998.		8843.	9337.	9138.
9795.	9304.	10121.		10591.			9681.	9106.	10550.
								10918.	

references / bibliography

Amstutz, A. E., *Computer Simulation of Competitive Market Response,* M.I.T. Press, Cambridge, Mass., 1967, pp. 386–412.

Balakrishman, A. V., and L. W. Neustadt (eds.), *Computer Methods in Optimization Problems,* Academic Press, New York, 1964.

Blackman, R. B., and T. W. Tukey, *The Measurement of Power Spectra,* Dover Publications, New York, 1958.

Brenner, M. E., "Relation Between Decision Making Penalty and Simulation Sample Size," *Operations Research,* Vol. 13, No. 3, May–June 1965, pp. 433–43.

Brenner, M. E., "Selective Sampling—A Technique for Reducing Sample Size in Simulation of Decision-Making Problems," *Journal of Industrial Engineering,* Vol. 14, No. 6, November–December 1963, pp. 291–96.

Conway, R. W., "Some Tactical Problems in Digital Simulation," *Management Science,* Vol. 10, No. 1, October 1963, pp. 47–61.

Conway, R. W., B. M. Johnson, and W. L. Maxwell, "Some Problems of Digital Systems Simulation," *Management Science,* Vol. 6, No. 1, October 1959, pp. 92–110.

Cox, D., and P. Lewis, *The Statistical Analysis of Series of Events,* Wiley, New York, 1966.

Davies, O. (ed.), *Design and Analysis of Industrial Experiments,* 2nd ed., Hafner, New York, 1960.

Emshoff, J. R., and A. Mercer, "Aggregate Models of Consumer Purchases." 37th Session of the International Statistical Institute, London, 1969.

Fishman, G. S., *Digital Computer Simulation: The Allocation of Computer Time in Comparing Simulation Experiments,* RM–5288–PR, RAND Corp., Santa Monica, Calif., 1967a.

Fishman, G. S., with P. J. Kiviat, *Statistical Considerations,* RM–5387–PR, RAND Corp., Santa Monica, Calif., 1967b.

Hammersley, J. M., and D. C. Handscomb, *Monte Carlo Methods,* Wiley, New York, 1964.

Hauser, N., N. Barish, and S. Ehrenfeld, "Design Problems in a Process Control Simulator," *Journal of Industrial Engineering,* Vol. 18, February 1966.

Hermann, C., "Validation Problems in Games and Simulations," *Behavioral Science,* Vol. 12, May 1967, pp. 216–30.

Parzen, Emanuel, "Mathematical Considerations in the Estimation of Spectra," *Technometrics,* Vol. 3, May 1961, pp. 167–90.

Wagner, H., *Statistical Management of Inventory Systems,* Wiley, New York, 1962.

experimental optimization

In this chapter we address the question of how to use a simulation model to help the decision maker; more formally, how to find the best setting of controllable variables to obtain the best total performance of the system.

design of the simulation experiments 9-1

When a simulation model has been constructed, debugged, and validated, the analyst must design an efficient method for using it to solve the problems he had first formulated. To use the notation developed in Section 4–2, the analyst uses the simulator to find the set of controllable variables C_i^* that yield the best measure of performance, i.e., maximizes V. A well-designed simulation experiment should systematically incorporate the analyst's updated knowledge about the relationship between the controllable variables, the uncontrollable variables, their effects on the measure of performance, and the estimated computational costs to obtain information on the system's behavior [Burdick and Naylor, 1966].

The objective of experimental design is to determine the best (or approximately the best) solution to the problem with the minimum expected computation costs. Currently no procedure is available for determining how to design the best simulation experiment. Therefore this section describes *aids* that have been found useful in designing these experiments.

The problem-formulation phase identifies the controllable variables that are to be manipulated in search of a best, or approximately best, solution to the problem. The various combinations of controllable variables define *courses of action* or *alternatives* that could be tested in the model. If the controllable variables take on discrete values only, there are a finite—but often very large—number of courses of action to be considered. The experiment should be designed to choose the best of these courses of action with the least computational cost. In the plastic shop problem in Chapter 5, for example, each specific dispatching rule is an alternative.

If the controllable variables can be changed in a continuous fashion, there are virtually an infinite number of courses of action to be considered. This would have been the case in the machine repair problem in Chapter 2 if we had permitted rotating repairmen to spend any portion of time between 0 and 100 percent on each line. Eliminating unacceptable courses of action in continuous situations is facilitated by organized search.

Continuously Controllable Variables

Where the variables can be changed continuously, the problem of finding the optimum is analogous to finding the peak of a hill, but usually in a multidimensional space. The most complex situations are equivalent to finding the peak in a range of hills; we not only have to find a peak but must also be sure it is the highest of all peaks.

A problem in which the analyst is sure that there is just one optimum is called *unimodal*. In these cases there are a number of techniques for finding the optimum rather efficiently. In multimodal situations, the analyst has to make a random search over the space, find the local peak from each point, and hope that the highest of these *is* the optimum. (The problem is not as bad as it sounds, since there is usually historical or theoretical guides as to where the optimum is likely to be.)

The whole situation is further complicated when the measure of performance is a random variate. A number of replications are required at each point so that the *mean* shape of the hill is determined and the *mean* peak of it found.

The general method of finding the peak of a unimodel situation is to go uphill from each point. The techniques for this are called hill-climbing or gradient searches. We will describe them more fully in a later section of this chapter.

Discrete Controllable Variables

Where the controllable variables can change only to specific values, other approaches are needed. If the discrete variables have an underlying scale so it is theoretically possible to think of them as continuous, it may be possible to assume temporarily that they are continuous and then round off results. However, this method often does not lead to optima. If the discrete variables represent only the names of procedures with no other significance (e.g., the job sequencing rules in the example of Chapter 5), then values between the discrete points have no meaning whatsoever and the problem *must* be handled in its discontinuous form.

The most common method of studying the effects of changes in discrete variables is factorial analysis; for continuous variables search methods are used. Figure 9–1 summarizes the procedures for obtaining the optimum.

(The methods for simply comparing simulation outputs were presented in Chapter 8.)

In the next section we present a brief example to illustrate how factorial analysis is used. (Those interested in the theoretical basis of factorial analysis and further information on its use should consult one of the standard texts on the subject, such as Davies [1960], Brownlee [1960], or Kempthorne [1952]. Geisler [1964] discusses the sampling aspects of factorial analysis in regard to simulation.) Following the example we discuss the use of search procedures for optimizing continuous-variable simulation problems.

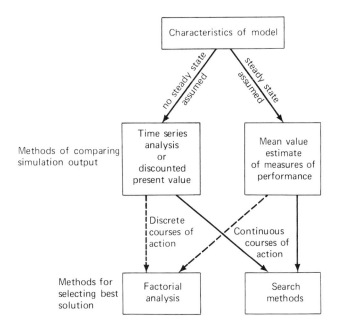

Figure 9–1
Methods for finding "optima" with simulations.

example of factorial analysis 9-2

In the situation of Exercise 5–6, design and run an experiment to determine the effect of varying (a) the probability of failure (e.g., by improving the equipment) and (b) the repair time distribution (e.g., by using repairmen of various skills). The data are as follows:

Repair Time	Original, %	Skilled, %
1	30	45
2	20	30
3	20	15
4	10	5
5	20	5
Cost of labor per time unit	$5	$7

Repairmen are paid for 8 hours per shift (i.e., 32 time units).

Failure Rate per Unit Time	Added Depreciation Cost
0.1 (existing machines)	0
0.02 (new machines)	$1 per unit time

Cost of downtime is $12 per unit time.

The factorial analysis of this problem follows.* For this problem a simple 2^2 factorial experiment (two factors at two levels) was designed.

Factors

A. Change in Cumulative Service Time Distribution

Repair Time	Low Level	High Level
1	0.3	0.45
2	0.5	0.75
3	0.7	0.90
4	0.8	0.95
5	1.0	1.00

B. Probability of Failure

Low Level	High Level
0.02	0.1

Design

Treatment Combinations	Total	A	B	AB
(1)	+	−	−	+
a	+	+	−	−
b	+	−	+	−
ab	+	+	+	+

Note: + indicates the treatment variable at high level.

Number of Trials

Four trials were run. The output data are summarized in Table 9–1.

	Trial Numbers			
	1	2	3	4
Conditions				
Repair rate	Low level	High level	Low level	High level
Failure rate	Low level	Low level	High level	High level
Cost				
Labor cost	$4,800	$6,720	$4,800	$6,720
Depreciation cost	960	960	0	0
Downtime cost	1,992	1,488	9,708	6,660
Total cost	$7,752	$9,168	$14,508	$13,380

Table 9–1. Data for Factorial Analysis

* Prepared by H. P. Johri, University of Waterloo, Waterloo, Ontario, Canada.

Analysis of Data

It is now possible to separate out the *main effects* and the *interactions.* Main effects are the effects of each variable alone: repair skill and quality of equipment. Interaction measures the combined effects of both variables. Reference to factorial analysis procedure indicates that we can designate the results as follows (for a 2 $\times$ 2 design):

Case	Symbol	Note	Value in This Example
1. Base case	(1)		$7,552
2. One variable changed	*a*	No interaction	9,168
3. One variable changed	*b*	No interaction	14,508
4. Both changed	*ab*	Interaction effect	13,380

Calculation of Effects

We can designate the

effect of repair skill on costs as   *A*

effect of equipment as   *B*

interaction (joint effect) as   *AB*

The procedure then says that

$$A = \tfrac{1}{2}[-(1) + a - b + ab]$$
$$B = \tfrac{1}{2}[-(1) - a + b + ab]$$
$$AB = \tfrac{1}{2}[(1) - a - b + ab]$$

In this case (multiplying by 2):

$$2A = -7752 + 9168 - 14{,}508 + 13{,}380 = 288$$
$$2B = -7752 - 9168 + 14{,}508 + 13{,}380 = 10{,}968$$
$$2AB = 7752 - 9168 - 14{,}508 + 13{,}380 = -2544$$

This is interpreted thus:

(1) Average *decrease* in cost for changing repair time distribution

$$\text{Yield} = \frac{\text{Average yield under high level}}{} - \frac{\text{Average yield under low level}}{}$$

$$= \frac{9168 + 13{,}380}{2} - \frac{7752 + 14{,}508}{2}$$

$$= 144$$

(2) Average *decrease* in cost for changing probability of failure

$$\text{Yield} = \frac{14{,}508 + 13{,}380}{2} - \frac{7752 + 9168}{2}$$

$$= 5484$$

(3) Average increased yield for changing *both* factors together

$$\text{Yield} = \frac{\text{Average when both}}{\text{factors at same level}} - \frac{\text{Average when one factor}}{\text{high and one low}}$$

$$= \frac{7752 + 13,380}{2} - \frac{9168 + 14,508}{2}$$

$$= -1272$$

Conclusions

1. Both factors A and B have a beneficial effect on the total cost (calculations 1 and 2). Taken together their cumulative effect is not beneficial (calculation 3).

2. The effect of factor B is very predominant.

3. The best strategy to obtain minimum total cost is to arrange the probability of failure (e.g., by improving the equipment) and *not* to change the repair time distribution. This is intuitively clear since by changing the probability of failure, the number of failures decrease so much that the influence of repair time distribution is not felt.

9-3 the application of search methods to simulation problems

Search procedures have been used in conjunction with simulation analysis in two ways. They are widely used as a way of selecting the best system operating conditions. Therefore, we will begin with a discussion of the properties of search that enable us to use the routines for model optimization. A second use of search, as discussed in Section 8–6, is to estimate model parameters when no data on them are available. In this section we show how simulation models can be "inverted" and search procedures applied to make such estimates.

All search procedures are sequential methods of finding a better solution to the problem [Wheeling, Ch. 9, 1969]. An analogy to finding the best solution to a simulation problem involving two continuous, controllable variables is to be blindfolded, placed on the side of a hill, and told to reach the top. Each step taken on the hill is analogous to running the simulator with new combinations of the controllable variables. The result of a step (a run of the simulator) is a higher or lower position on the hill (i.e., improved or worse performance than that previously obtained). Clearly, the objective is to get to the top of the hill (reach the optimum) in the minimum number of steps (minimum runs of the simulator). Search procedures are designed to use the information already obtained about the shape of the response function (the hill) to decide both the direction and the size of step to take next to yield the optimum in a minimum number of trials.

The biggest problem in designing a useful search procedure is that it must be efficient over a wide range of response surfaces. A characteristic of surfaces that no current procedures can effectively overcome is non-unimodality; that is, the surface has more than one local maximum or minimum. At a local optimum any *small* change in values of the variables, regardless of the direction, leads to a worse situation. For most search procedures, this is exactly the criterion used to stop the algorithm and conclude that the optimum has been reached. It is true that local maximum will have been found, but there is no way to guarantee that it is the optimum over the whole surface. The only way this can be determined is to evaluate all the local maxima and choose the largest. The expense is generally prohibitive in terms of computer time [Clough, 1969].

A method that is sometimes used when nonunimodality exists is known as the Las Vegas technique. The method requires the analyst to use the search procedure several times to estimate the distribution of the local optima. The response measure for each local search is then plotted against the search number as in Figure 9–2. Those local searches which produce a response greater than any previous response are then identified and a smooth curve is fitted through the response points. This estimated effectiveness curve can then be used to project the estimated incremental response that will be achieved from one more search. The Las Vegas rule for determining the number of searches is to continue until the valve of the estimated improvement in the solution is less than the cost of completing one additional search.

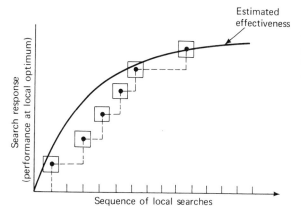

Estimated effectiveness

Figure 9–2 Las Vegas technique for estimating effectiveness of additional search.

Search procedures require only that there be a functional relationship that predicts a response for each combination of the controllable variables. For simulation problems, the response is usually stochastic. Although this makes experimental design more difficult, it does not affect the way the search procedure operates. A well-designed experiment produces sufficient replication of conditions, so that the average response can be treated as a deterministic number for search comparison.

Since replications are expensive, it is sometimes possible to smooth over steps or trials in the process, although each trial is at a different setting of the controllables [Wilde, 1964]. The process is analogous to exponential smoothing and is portrayed in Figure 9–3 for the case of one control variable. The theory behind smoothing is sophisticated and should be reviewed before this approach is used.

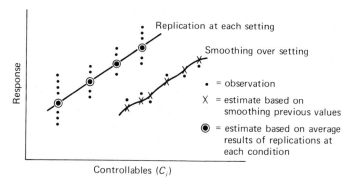

Figure 9–3 Smoothing techniques as an alternative to replicating output which is stochastic.

To apply search techniques to estimating model parameters, represent the model as

$$V = f(X_i, Y_j, a_k)$$

where V = measure of performance
X_i = controllable variables
Y_j = uncontrollable variables
a_k = parameters

Often explicit estimates of some of the parameters are unavailable (see Section 8–6). However, historical records may be available on the performance, $V(t)$, and the corresponding level of variables and $X_i(t)$ and $Y_j(t)$. In this situation, the analyst may use part of the historical data to estimate the a_k by assuming the model structure is correct and determining the values of a_k that cause the model to simulate the history most closely. That is, the objective is to find the minimum of the difference between model output and historical data as a function of a_k:

$$\min_{a_k} \sum_t [V_t^h - f(X_i^h(t), Y_i^h(t), a_k)]^2$$

where f is the simulation model and superscript h refers to the historical data. Here the measure of closeness is least squares, but other measures can also be used. (This search for best parameters is sometimes called the parameter identification problem [Zadeh, 1956].)

This method was used by the authors to estimate personality parameters in a simulation model of conflict behavior [Emshoff, 1970; Sisson and Ackoff, 1966]. One of the difficulties with inverting the model for parameter estimation is that validation becomes more difficult. The data used for parameter estimation cannot be reused for validation. Generally historical data are not readily accessible and too few are available to estimate parameters and test output adequately.

The general procedure for simulation search can be summarized by a flow diagram, as in Figure 9–4.

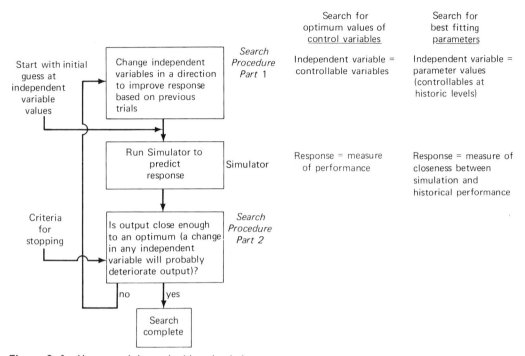

Figure 9–4   How search is used with a simulation.

specific search procedures   9-4

In this section we will show how some of the more commonly used search procedures work. Our intent is to show the method each uses to iterate toward an optimum. We will not go into the detailed mathematical considerations that must be examined before some of the more complicated procedures can be programmed. For each method we include a reference that contains complete information; therefore, the reader interested in applying any of the methods can have access to the information he needs. Many of the search procedures are embodied in available computer program packages. After discussing search methods, a section is devoted to information on a few of the available packages. (Those interested in a general treatment of optimum searching methods are referred to Davies [1956], Wilde [1964], or Wilde and Beightler [1967].)

One-Dimensional Searches

As we will show in the following subsections, the general procedure for finding the optimum in a multidimensional response surface is to

217

convert the search into a series of one-dimensional searches. A ray (a line) is defined in the multidimensional space and the problem is to find the point along the ray where the response is greatest. Thus one-dimensional searches are important in general as well as in cases where there is only one controllable (or one parameter).

Two factors must be set to make a one-dimensional search:

(1) The direction to go (from the present point).

(2) The size of the step (that is, the distance to the next trial point).

Choosing a very small constant step size and proceeding step-by-step along the line in a direction that improves response is safe but very expensive. Many steps are required and the simulator must be run at each to estimate the response. If the optimum can be located as being between two points, thus defining a range, a binary search is much more efficient. In the binary search, the range is divided into half and a determination is made as to which half the optimum is in. Then that half is treated as the range and the process is repeated. This approach converges very quickly on the optimum. (A binary search on an alphabetical listing of all the people in the United States would require about twenty-five such divisions.) In effect, the step size changes as the search proceeds; starting large when there is large uncertainty about the location of the optimum and becoming small as it is pinpointed. Figure 9–5 shows the

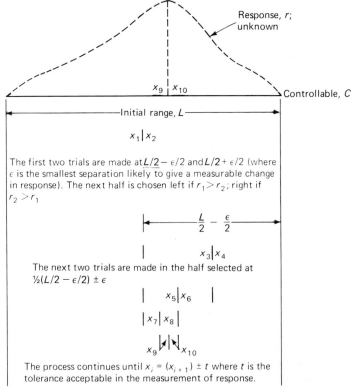

The first two trials are made at $L/2 - \epsilon/2$ and $L/2 + \epsilon/2$ (where ϵ is the smallest separation likely to give a measurable change in response). The next half is chosen left if $r_1 > r_2$; right if $r_2 > r_1$

The next two trials are made in the half selected at $\frac{1}{2}(L/2 - \epsilon/2) \pm \epsilon$

The process continues until $x_i = (x_{i+1}) \pm t$ where t is the tolerance acceptable in the measurement of response.

Figure 9–5 Binary search procedure.

complete binary search procedure. (There are other, even more efficient one-dimensional search techniques, described fully in Wilde [1964].)

Single-Factor Search

As the name suggests, this procedure sequentially varies one controllable factor at a time until it is no longer possible to vary any factor individually and improve the response. (This method was first proposed by Friedman and Savage [1947].)

To see how the method works, consider the two variable response surfaces shown in Figure 9–6. The points of equal response are indicated by the contour lines. The initial selection of controllable variables, P_0, $[X_{01}, X_{02}]$, is chosen as the best guess of the experts as to the optimal operating condition. The simulator is run under these conditions and performance is predicted by the model; that is, $V_0 = f(X_{01}, X_{02})$. The value of X_2 is held constant and X_1 is changed until a value is found where any increase or decrease in X_1 yields a worse performance for the system. That is, a one-dimensional search is performed along $X_2 = X_{02}$. The point where X_1 yields a conditional maximum is designated P_1 and yields a performance measure $V_1 = f(X_{11}, X_{02})$ where $V_1 > V_0$. Now, X_1 is held constant and X_2 is changed until a new conditional optimum, P_2, is achieved. This yields $V_2 = f(X_{11}, X_{22})$. The method continues until no improvement in performance results from changes in any individual factor. Use of the single-factor method on problems involving more than a two-dimensional search is a simple extension of the procedure just outlined.

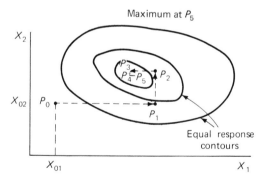

Maximum at P_5

Figure 9–6 Two-dimensional examples of single factor search method.

Equal response contours

There are two weaknesses to the single-factor search method. First, it can involve excessive runs of the simulator because more points are examined than with diagonal searches involving multiple-factor changes. Second, the method does not perform well on surfaces where ridges exist. For example, the single-factor method on Figure 9–7 would stop the search at P_1 (the ridge) and conclude it had reached an optimum. The method of steepest ascent was developed to overcome these deficiencies.

Steepest Ascent Search

In this procedure, all variables are changed simultaneously, and the direction of movement is made proportional to the estimated sensitivity

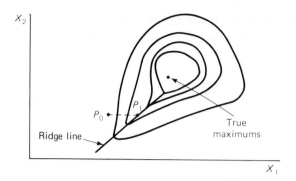

Figure 9–7
Single factor
search on
ridged surface.

of the performance to each variable. (This method was first proposed by Box and Wilson [1951].) The most common form of the steepest ascent procedure assumes that the performance is linearly related to the changes in the controllable variables for small changes. If this is not appropriate for particular response functions, quadratic functions are sometimes used. For this discussion, we assume the linear form is a good approximation.

The equation describing the linear relation between n-controllable variables and the system's performance is given by

$$V = a + b_1X_1 + b_2X_2 + \cdots + b_nX_n$$

where a = intercept when all controllable variables are zero

        b_i = slope of the function in the ith dimension

The basis of the linear steepest ascent method is that each controllable variable is changed in proportion to the magnitude of its slope. The set of slopes $b_1, b_2, \ldots, b_n$ at a particular point is called the *gradient* of the surface. Hence, this is sometimes called a gradient search. To determine the gradient at any point, it is necessary to determine sequentially the system's response when each controllable variable is changed by an amount δ. For a surface containing n-controllable variables, this requires n points around the point of interest. Computationally,

$$b_i = \frac{V_{i\delta} - V_0}{\delta}$$

where $V_{i\delta}$ = the performance when X_i is moved by an amount δ and all other X's remain the same

        V_0 = performance at the point of interest

A one-dimensional search is then undertaken along the ray defined by the slopes b_i. The new direction is proportional to the slopes in the original dimensions, so one of these directions can be used arbitrarily to determine step size in the one-dimensional search. If Yb_1 is chosen to be the step size for the variable X_1, the equation for the change in value along the steepest ascent direction is

$$\Delta V = Y(b_1 + b_2 + \cdots + b_n)$$

where Yb_1 = change in variable X_1

Yb_2 = change in variable X_2

Yb_n = change in variable X_n

The search is completed when all the b_i's are negative and the gradient direction yields a decrease in performance.

Although the steepest ascent method generally outperforms the single-factor search, it is fairly inefficient on certain surfaces. A method known as partan (parallel tangent method) was devised to improve efficiency and still retain the gradient concept.

Partan Search Method

This procedure uses steepest ascent methods, but has the added feature that it introduces planes into the n-dimensional space to reduce the region in which the optimum may occur [Shah, Beuhler, and Kempthorne, 1964]. The search procedure is such that the optimum of an n-dimensional elliptical surface will be found in $2n - 1$ searches.

The partan search method can best be described in terms of a schematic diagram such as the one presented in Figure 9–8. The process begins by the arbitrary picking of a point P_0 in a plane π_0. Then a search is conducted on any line not tangent to plane π_0. This one-dimensional maximum occurs at some point P_2. From P_2 the gradient steepest ascent method is used to determine the direction of search within a plane π_2 that is parallel to π_0. The maximum of this directed search is a point P_3. The next search is along the line connecting P_0 and P_3. The maximum occurs at P_4. A new gradient search is performed in a plane π_4 that is parallel to π_0 and π_2. This point is P_5. Connecting points P_2 and P_5 yields the direction of search producing P_6. By building planes parallel to preceding planes, the directions of future searches are successively restricted and, if the surface has quadratic properties, the optimum will be reached on the $(2n - 1)$th search for an n-dimensional surface. If the surface is not quadratic, we can either start the partan method over from the $2n - 1$ maximum or continue the process by constructing each plane parallel to the most recent $n - 1$ planes.

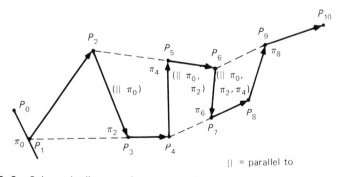

Figure 9–8 Schematic diagram of partan search.

Conjugate Direction Method

The final search procedure is a robust procedure which, unlike steepest ascent and partan, requires no derivative estimation. The method finds the optimum of an n-dimensional quadratic surface after at most n iterations [Fletcher and Powell, 1963].

The conjugate direction procedure attempts to redefine the n dimensions so that single-factor search methods can be used successfully to find the optimum. Single-factor procedures are ideally suited to surfaces where dimensions can be treated independently; that is, where

$$f(X_1, X_2, \cdots, X_n) = g_1(X_1) + g_2(X_2) + \cdots + g_n(X_n) \qquad (9\text{--}1)$$

In this case, optimization along each dimension leads to optimization of the entire surface. Two directions are defined to be *conjugate* if cross-product terms are all zero; that is, if Equation 9–1 holds for $n = 2$. The conjugate direction method tries to find a set of n dimensions that describes the surface, and each direction is conjugate to all others. If this can be achieved (or closely approximated), single-factor optimization methods can be applied successfully to the surface.

The conjugate direction method is based on an important theorem related to quadratic surfaces:

If X_0 is a step wise (single-factor) optimum in a space containing direction q and X_1 is also an optimum in the same space, then, the direction defined by the points X_1 and X_2 is conjugate to q.

The conjugate direction search procedure finds two search optima and replaces the nth dimension of the quadratic surface by the direction specified by the two optima. Successively replacing the original dimensions in this way yields a new set of n dimensions which, if the original surface is quadratic, all turn out to be conjugate to each other. Thus, on the nth dimensional replacement, the optimum is reached using n single-factor searches.

Like all the other procedures, conjugate directions do not operate effectively unless the appropriate step size for the search is chosen. This is more critical with this method than some of the others because axis rotation takes place. Thus, a step size that is appropriate for one of the dimensions may not be so for one of the others. As rotation takes place, the best step size changes and becomes exceedingly difficult to estimate. Since partan does not rotate axes, the initial judgment of the best step size will remain so throughout the search.

The selection of a best search procedure to use is difficult to determine. If scaling problems are likely to occur, partan or steepest ascent is probably better than conjugate directions. If the surface does not closely approximate an ellipse, the conjugate direction method is preferred. Generally, trial and error is the only way to determine which procedure is best.

Two widely used search programs are those in the IBM 360 Scientific Subroutine Package. Two subroutines are available, either in single- or double-precision form. One method uses gradient techniques (steepest descent—it finds a minimum—and is based on a procedure given by Fletcher and Powell). The second uses a conjugate gradient approach and is essentially the same as what we have called the conjugate direction method. (This conjugate gradient is described in Fletcher and Reeves [1964].) Both routines in the Scientific Subroutine Package include procedures for determining the direction and step size on each iteration as well as for determining tolerable limits within which the analyst will accept the solution as the minimum.

We have now examined most of the important techniques that are relevant to simulation analysis. In the next chapter we try to put some of these ideas together through a case study simulation.

exercises

9–1 Design and run an experiment to determine which of the following dispatching rules reduces lateness to the greatest extent for the situation in Chapter 5.

Rule 1: Job in queue with shortest waiting time taken first (as in Chapter 5).

Rule 2: First come, first served.

Rule 3: Job in queue with earliest due time first.

Rule 4: Job in queue with lowest slack first, where

$$\text{slack} = \text{due time} - \text{remaining processing time}$$

Compare variance estimates of the solutions when runs use uncorrelated random numbers and when antithetic/correlation methods are used.

9–2 Choose an appropriate language, develop, debug, and run a simulator to represent the following single-item inventory situation:

- Orders have an interarrival time that is exponentially distributed with a mean of 10.

- It costs $5.00 to place an order and one week to receive the items after ordering. (Orders are placed and received after business at the end of each week.)

- Items cost $4.00 per week to hold in inventory.

- A lost sale represents a loss of $20.00.

Design and run a search on the two control variables: reorder point and quantity to find the optimum operating conditions. (Eliminate starting transients. Choose an observation period appropriate to the problem.)

Compare the results of the search with the theoretical optimum derived by standard operations research techniques.

references

Box, G. E. P., and K. B. Wilson, "On the Experimental Attainment of Optimum Conditions," *Journal of the Royal Statistical Society,* Vol. B13, 1951, pp. 1–45.

Brownlee, K. A., *Statistical Theory and Methodology in Science and Engineering,* Wiley, New York, 1960.

Burdick, D. S., and T. H. Naylor, "Design of Computer Simulation Experiments for Industrial Systems," *Communications of the Association for Computing Machinery,* Vol. 9, No. 5, May 1966, pp. 329–39.

Clough, D. J., "An Asymptotic Extreme-Value Sampling Theory for Estimation of a Global Maximum," *Canadian Operational Research Society Journal,* Vol. 7, No. 2, July 1969, pp. 102–15.

Davies, O. (ed.), *Design and Analysis of Industrial Experiments,* 2nd ed., Hafner, New York, 1960.

Emshoff, J., "A Simulation Model of Prisoner's Dilemma," *Behavioral Science,* Vol. 15, No. 4, July 1970.

Fishman, G. S., with P. J. Kiviat, *Input-Output Analysis,* RM–5540–PR, RAND Corp., Santa Monica, Calif., February 1968.

Fletcher, R., and M. Powell, "A Rapidly Convergent Descent Method for Minimization," *Computer Journal,* Vol. 6, No. 2, 1963, pp. 163–68.

Fletcher, R., and C. Reeves, "Function Minimization by Conjugate Gradients," *Computer Journal,* Vol. 7, No. 2, 1964, pp. 149–54.

Friedman, M., and L. J. Savage, "Planning Experiments Seeking Maxima," in *Techniques of Statistical Analysis* (Statistical Research Group of Columbia University), McGraw-Hill, New York, 1947.

Geisler, M. A., "The Size of Simulation Samples Required to Compute Certain Inventory Characteristics with Stated Precision and Confidence," *Management Science,* Vol. 10, No. 6, 1964, pp. 261–86.

Giese, C., "Determination of Best Kinetic Coefficients of a Dynamic Chemical Process by On-Line Digital Simulation," *Simulation,* Vol. 8, No. 3, March 1967, pp. 147–50.

IBM Application Program, *System/360 Scientific Subroutine Package (360A–CM–03X), Version III, Programmer's Manual,* H20–0205–3, New York, 1968, pp. 221–29.

Kempthorne, O., The Design and Analysis of Experiments, Wiley, New York, 1952.*

Shah, B. V., R. J. Buehler, and O. Kempthorne, *The Method of Parallel Tangents (Partan) for Finding an Optimum, Technical Rept. No. 2,* ONR Project, Iowa State University Statistical Laboratory, Ames, 1962.

Sisson, R. L., and R. L. Ackoff, "Toward a Theory of the Dynamics of Conflict," in *Conflict Resolution and World Education* (ed. by S. Mudd), Junk, The Hague, 1966.

Wheeling, R., "Heuristic Search: Structured Problems," in *Progress in Operations Research,* Vol. III (ed. by J. Aronofsky), Wiley, New York, 1969.

Wilde, D. J., *Optimum Seeking Methods,* Prentice-Hall, Englewood Cliffs, N.J., 1964, pp. 175–83.

Wilde, D., and C. Beightler, *Foundations of Optimization,* Prentice-Hall, Englewood Cliffs, N.J., 1967.

Zadeh, L., "On the Identification Problem," *IEEE Transactions on Circuit Theory,* Vol. CT–3, No. 4, December 1956, pp. 277–81.

*Requires mathematical sophistication.

a simulation model of a computer center's operations

introduction 10-1

This study was undertaken for the Computer Center of the University of Pennsylvania. At the time the center used an IBM 360/65 to process approximately 1000 jobs of various descriptions each day. There are three phases in processing a job; these are illustrated in Figure 10–1. In the input phase, jobs are read into the computer from card readers located in different places around the campus. These readers send the job to the Computer Center via telephone lines, and the job is merged with others on an input disc. The job waits on the input disc until its turn for the processing phase. When the system is free, a job is removed from the input disc, loaded into the central processing unit (CPU), and the program is compiled and executed. The output from the program is transferred from the CPU to an output disc, where it waits until printers and card punches are available. There are printers around the campus and each job request specifies where output should be sent. In the output phase, jobs are removed from the output disc when the requested device is free, and print–punch instructions are executed.

Of critical concern to the Computer Center staff at the time of the study were the scheduling rules for deciding when a job would be removed from the input disc and processed. Job scheduling was being done by placing each incoming job into one of fifteen different classes, based on the maximum processing time required, input–output requirements, peripheral devices needed, and the priority rate for processing time. Charges were higher for higher priorities. As a job was placed on the input disc, an identification of its class and time of entry was recorded. The scheduling rule in use was: "Process the jobs in the highest priority class (Class 15)

ch. 10
model of a computer
center's operations

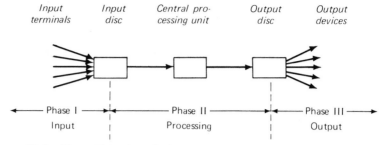

Input *Input* *Central pro-* *Output* *Output*
terminals *disc* *cessing unit* *disc* *devices*

←——— Phase I ———→|←——————— Phase II ———————→|←—— Phase III ——→
Input | Processing | Output

Figure 10–1 Flow of jobs through the computer center.

on a first-come, first-served basis; process the jobs in the next highest priority class (14) on a first-come, first-served basis whenever there are no jobs waiting in Class 15 . . . ; process the jobs in the lowest priority class (1) on a first-come, first-served basis whenever there are no jobs waiting in any of the other classes."

At the time of the study, the processing phase was performed on a sequential basis; that is, only one job was physically in the central processing unit at a time. This meant that turn-around time was quite good for high priority classes (less than an hour from submission to return for jobs in Class 15) but often took twenty-four hours or more for those in low priority classes.

The Computer Center staff was in the process of modifying the system to allow more than one job to occupy the CPU at the same time (multiprogramming). The new system is known as *multiprogramming with a fixed number of tasks* (MFT). This multiple-processing system was expected to significantly increase computing capability and thus reduce the expected turn-around time for users. However, the Computer Center staff felt that the full potential of the improved system would not be achieved unless they used an effective scheduling program for assigning processing priorities. Since the new system had not yet been implemented, there was no way in which the current facilities could be used to determine what the best scheduling rule should be. Thus, it was decided that a simulator of the MFT processing system would be developed and alternative scheduling rules would be tested on the simulator before implementing one on the system.

Two interconnected problems were posed by the Computer Center staff: (1) How many jobs should be permitted in the CPU at a time? (How many *partitions* of core?) and (2) What should be the rule for assigning jobs to the CPU as each job is completed? Since the answers to these questions about the processing phase are affected by the nature and timing of job input and, in turn, the processing affects the output phase (see Figure 10–1), the simulator must describe the interactions among all three phases of job flow.

An objective function is needed to evaluate alternative scheduling rules in a way that reflects the importance of each phase of the system. This problem is similar to that occurring in any job shop that is dominated by one critical process.

226

We review first the specification of the objective function and then turn
to the development of the simulation model.

sec. 10-2
the objective
function

the objective function 10-2

The Computer Center is primarily a service organization for the university community. Therefore, the objective function should reflect the
desires of the university users. Since it is hard to imagine how to measure
the individual user's objectives and values (much less combine them in any
meaningful way), we assumed that the Computer Center staff accurately
reflected the collective interests of the users and treated them as the
decision makers. They provided two objectives for effective operation
of the computer:

(1) To minimize the turn-around time of jobs being submitted (the
time between submission and receipt of the job by the user).

(2) To maximize the utilization of the computer; that is, to make sure
that the hardware was not idle when there were jobs that could be
worked on.

We decided not to try to combine the two objectives into a single-value
function. Discussions with the staff indicated that explicit trade-offs
between utilization and turn-around time would be difficult to construct;
furthermore, the staff *preferred* to see both measures and make the trade-
offs through discussion.

A weighted average of the turn-around time over all jobs in the fifteen
classes was used for the turn-around part of the objective function.
Weightings were needed because the high-priority classes of jobs (e.g.,
13, 14, and 15) were expected to have quick turn-around time. For jobs
in the low priority classes, however, longer turn-around was expected,
and penalties for delays were less serious. To assign the weights, we
asked the Computer Center staff to specify a desired turn-around time for
each class of jobs. We used the reciprocal of the desired time as the
weighting factor for turn-around time in each class. This objective was
defined, therefore, as follows:

$$\text{Turn-around objective} = \frac{\sum_{i=1}^{15} \sum_{j=1}^{N_i} \dfrac{t_{ij}}{D_i}}{\sum_{i=1}^{15} N_i} \qquad (10\text{--}1)$$

where t_{ij} = actual turn-around time for job j in class i

D_i = desired turn-around time for jobs in class i

N_i = number of jobs in class i

This measure will become larger as the performance deteriorates. Since
D_i will be small for high-priority jobs, the turn-around time of such jobs

will have a significant effect on the objective function. Low priority (with higher D_i's) will receive less emphasis.

For the computer utilization objective, we decided to concentrate on the efficiency of the central processing unit. This emphasis makes sense not only because the CPU is the most expensive piece of hardware in the system, but also because the proposed shift to MFT is designed to improve CPU efficiency. The Computer Center staff told us that the CPU was operated efficiently as long as computation was taking place on a job in the system. (As we will describe in detail later, it is possible for a job to be in the CPU and for no computation to be taking place; in this case, the CPU is in an *interrupt* status and is essentially idle.) The CPU efficiency should not be penalized when the CPU is idle because no job is available for processing. This leads to the following ratio:

$$\text{CPU utilization objective} = \frac{\tau}{T} \qquad (10\text{--}2)$$

where τ = the amount of time when at least one job is in the CPU and the CPU is computing

T = the amount of time when at least one job is in the CPU

For each run of the simulator, Equations 10–1 and 10–2 were computed. The scheduling rules that were not dominated (i.e., no other rule had yielded better performance in both objectives) were then presented to the Computer Center staff for their analysis and evaluation.

10-3 data requirements and sources

Accounting cards are collected at the Computer Center for each job that is run. These cards provide almost all the input information needed to run the simulator. From the information on the cards, it is possible to completely recreate a day's or week's operation at the Computer Center. Since this data source was so complete, we decided to recreate job arrivals exactly as they had been on several days of actual operation rather than to derive distributions for generating simulated jobs. (Distributions were developed for a GPSS simulator.) In this way, alternative scheduling rules would be compared under identical operating conditions (a way of introducing positive correlation).

Four types of information were obtained from the accounting cards:

(1) Arrival patterns. The priority class of an entering job and the actual time when the input phase was begun (the card reader activated).

(2) Input time. The time to read the program and data on to the input disc. (This phase will not be altered in the simulation model since no changes are made to affect the input phase.)

(3) Processing time. The time between initiation of reading into the CPU and conclusion of writing onto the output disc. (This time will vary in the simulator because processing time will change with

multiple processing. However, processing time under the current (sequential) system provides an estimate of how long it will take under the MFT system.)

(4) Output time. The time to print and punch the output from the output tape to the correct peripheral device. (This time will remain the same in the simulation model as on the accounting cards. However, times to obtain access to the peripheral devices may not be the same since the job sequence will be different.)

Two critical pieces of information were needed, but unavailable, about each job. The first was the input/output device for origin and destination of each job. Neither the accounting cards nor any other internal source could provide this information. Therefore, we decided to restrict our analysis of output to that which was printed at the three high-speed printers located in the Computer Center. Seventy-five percent of the total output was processed on these three devices. We approximated this situation by not attempting to simulate printing on the remote terminals. It was not possible to identify remote jobs, so the printing load was adjusted by reducing the print demands on each job by twenty-five percent.

The other information missing from available records concerned the processing phase. When only one job is in the central processor, either computation is taking place on the job or the CPU is in an interrupt state and no computation is taking place. Interrupts occur for many reasons determined by the nature of the job in the CPU. For example, whenever data are requested by the job or whenever output must be written, the processing is interrupted until the data transfer task is completed. Similarly, calls for special library subroutines result in interrupts. Each job is interrupted many times—sometimes more than a thousand—during its execution. An important characteristic of a job is the percentage of the time that it will be in an interrupt phase when it is in the CPU. As we shall soon see, this percentage has an effect on the efficiency of the MFT system and thus affects the performance of scheduling rules. Unfortunately, no data were available on interrupt frequencies for individual jobs, nor were estimates available for average interrupts for job classes.

With no a priori feel for what interrupt frequencies by class were likely to be, we treated them as parameters in the simulator. The interrupt frequency for each of the classes was changed between each of a series of runs. By comparing outputs, the sensitivity of the results to the assumptions about interrupt distributions could be checked. If results had been sensitive to values of the parameter, better methods of estimating it would have been needed. Fortunately, this was not the case.

subsystem analysis and flow charts 10-4

The simulator has three subprograms—input, processing, and output—which correspond approximately to the three processing phases. Segmenting the problem into subprograms makes model development easier

ch. 10
model of a computer
center's operations

because each subprogram operates fairly independently of the others. For example, the arrival of a new job at the input has no effect on the current activity of either the processing subprogram or the output. Completion of a job in the processor does change the status of the input (because a new job is called from the input disc) and also affects the status of the output. Completion of a job in the output subprogram causes summary statistics to be updated, but does not affect the status of either of the other subprograms.

Input Subprogram

In this subprogram of the simulator, descriptions of all the jobs to be processed in one run of the model are read into the system, put into a format, and placed on a file in order of arrival. This part is not a simulation, but a preparatory bookkeeping process. The file created represents the input disc and is used by the processing subprogram to select the next job. Control is not transferred to the processing phase until all the jobs have been read in (which deviates from the behavior of the real system). The time when the job actually did arrive is included on the file and is used to enter jobs into processing; thus, the processing subprogram starts processing each job at the proper time.

Since the input subroutine serves to organize input data for the rest of the simulator, it has no automatic time advance. Once the data files are established, control is transferred to the processing subroutine (and never returns to input). Figure 10–2 describes the seventeen parameters associated with each job that passed through the model. Figure 10–3 provides a flow chart of the input subprogram.

Job Parameter	Source	Information	Remarks
1	Input	Job number	Arbitrarily assigned
2	Input	Job type (priority class)	Accounting card data
3	Input	Job arrival time	Accounting card data
4	Input	Job output time	Accounting card data
5	Input	Number of cards read in	Accounting card data
6	Input	Number of output lines	Accounting card data
7	Input	Number of output cards	Accounting card data
8	Input	Total reader time	Accounting card data
9	Input	Execution time (old system)	Accounting card data
10	Input	Job print time	Accounting card data
11	Input	Job punch time	Accounting card data
12	Computed	Percentage time in interrupt	Computed in input subprogram
13	Computed	Job arrival time in core	Computed in processor subprogram
14	Computed	Job finish time in core	Computed in processor subprogram
15	Computed	Job arrival time at printer	Computed in output subprogram
16	Computed	Job finish time	Computed in output subprogram
17	Computed	Job turn-around time	P16 minus P3

Figure 10–2 Job parameter information for the simulator.

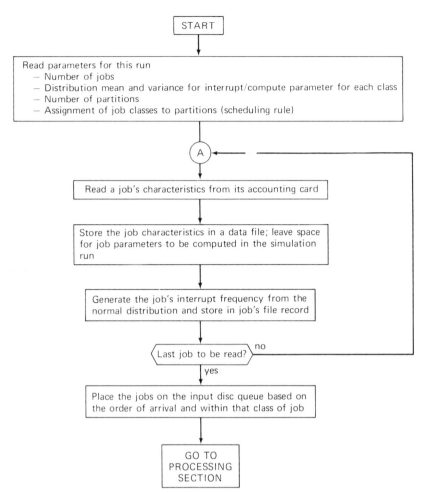

Figure 10–3   Flow chart of input subprogram.

Processing Subprogram

We will not attempt to describe the complexities of the MFT processing system; instead, we will illustrate the general sequence by means of an example. A complete description of the MFT processor is found in the *IBM System/360 Operating System Planning for Multiprogramming with a Fixed Number of Tasks, Version II* (Form C27–6939–0). For the sake of simplification, assume that the system is set up so only two jobs can occupy the computer core at the same time (two partitions). (The number of partitions is one of the decision variables to be investigated using the simulator.)

(Since each job must be small enough to fit into the partitioned area of the core, the MFT system cannot handle jobs as large as can a sequential processor with the same size core. An obvious implication of the MFT system is that as more jobs are permitted in the core at the same time, each

231

is allocated a smaller amount of working area and the processing of very large jobs cannot be undertaken. On the other hand, we shall show that increasing the number of jobs that can simultaneously occupy the core improves the efficiency of computer usage, and is useful in a university context where many jobs are small.)

Figure 10–4 shows how processing in a two-partition MFT system would take place. The partitions are assigned priorities that affect processing rates; we refer to the highest priority partition as P_1 and the second highest priority partition as P_2. Referring to the figure, a job in P_1 either can have computation being performed or can be in an interrupt state. (The main causes of interrupts were listed in the previous section.) The CPU can work only in one partition at a time; that is, at any instant of time only one of the partitions can be in a compute mode. (In this sense processing still takes place sequentially.) Therefore, the only time P_2 can be in a compute mode is when P_1 goes into an interrupt. The partition priority rule is that if more than one partition is ready for computation by the CPU, the partition with the highest priority is processed. This priority rule is the reason why P_2 is sometimes waiting for access to the CPU, but P_1 never waits. Since the partition priority rule applies for a more-than-two partition system, it is clear that the amount of waiting time increases when a job is placed in a lower priority partition. Consequently, the high-priority partitions yield faster turn-around times.

Figure 10–4
Sequence of typical processing phases for a two partition MFT system.

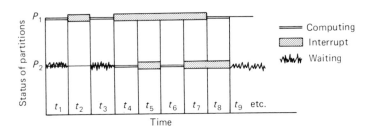

If only two partitions are used, the CPU has a reasonably good chance of being idle part of the time because both jobs are in the interrupt state. Idleness means that computer efficiency drops. In Figure 10–4, states t_5 and t_7 were idle periods for the CPU because it could have been computing on a third job if the job had been available. Obviously, additional partitions decrease the chances that all will be in interrupt at the same time, and thus leads to improved efficiency of the system. (The reader may wish to re-examine the efficiency objective, Equation 10–2, in the light of this discussion.)

For two reasons an explicit simulation model of the *compute, interrupt,* and *wait* stages of jobs in each partition was not attempted. First, such a model would have required two probability distributions; one of the time between the occurrence of interrupts and another of the interrupt duration for each type of job. Estimates of these distributions were not available. A second and more compelling reason for not attempting a microsimulation is that the running time of the simulator would probably have exceeded the real running time of the job being simulated. In such a situation, the least expensive way to determine the best scheduling rule would not be simulation; instead, test data would be fed directly into the computer and alternatives examined on the system. Direct experimentation costs less and is more accurate if the microlevel is to be studied.

To aggregate, we assumed that only the fraction of job-processing time spent in the interrupt state was important. Even with this assumption, historical estimates were unobtainable. As indicated in the data section, we parameterized the interrupt-compute ratio. It was assumed that this ratio was normally distributed with a mean and a variance dependent on the job class. Then the exact interrupt percentage for a particular job was determined by selecting a random variable from a normal distribution with the mean and variance appropriate for the job's class.

A probability model was developed to predict the rate at which jobs would be advanced in each of the partitions. We use the term *advance* to mean that the job is not in the wait state. Thus, the job in P_1 is always advancing and the rate of advance in lower priority partitions depends on the compute-interrupt ratios for jobs in the higher priority partitions. The basis of the model is illustrated in Figure 10–5, which is a decision tree of the possible states each of the two partitions can have. As shown in the figure, there are four possible states that can exist:

(1) Computing in P_1 and interrupt in P_2.
(2) Computing in P_1 and waiting in P_2.
(3) Interrupt in P_1 and computing in P_2.
(4) Interrupt in P_1 and interrupt in P_2.

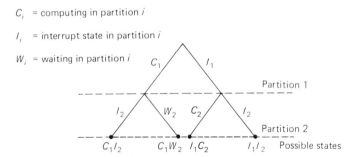

C_i = computing in partition i

I_i = interrupt state in partition i

W_i = waiting in partition i

Figure 10–5 Possible states of a two-partition MFT system.

The probability of advance for P_2 is the probability that the partition is not in a wait state, i.e., $1 - \{C_1 \text{ and } W_2\}$. This probability would have been easy to compute if events in partitions were independent because probabilities could be computed by multiplication. However, events in lower priority partitions clearly depend on higher order partition activity and therefore estimates of interaction effects are needed. Since no information on the degree of interaction between the partitions was available, an additional parameter was introduced into the simulation. This parameter's

233

ch. 10
model of a computer
center's operations

value could be set in a way that assumed anything between complete dependence to complete independence of events; in this way the sensitivity of the solution to this assumption could be determined.

Figure 10–6 presents a flow chart of the processing part of the simulator.

Output Subprogram

The output subprogram takes jobs that have completed processing, assigns them a position in a file simulating a queue that is waiting for the printers, and prints the output on a first-come, first-served basis on the three printers. The file represents jobs waiting in the output disc. When a job is removed from the disc and placed on a free printer, all others move up one position. The three printers have different processing rates; however, at the time of the study no attempt was being made to use rules to schedule what jobs would be assigned to printers. (It was on a first-come, first-served basis.)

The output simulator was programmed on an event-advance basis. A flow chart of this is presented in Figure 10–7. Two kinds of events are possible: an arrival of a job from the processing phase or completion of a job on one of the printers. If the event is an arrival, the job is placed either at the end of the output disc queue or, if a printer is free, the job goes directly there. If the event is the completion of printing on a job, the next one on the output disc is assigned to the printer, queue positions are advanced for other jobs waiting on the disc, and summary statistics are updated to include the job just completed.

Summary statistics on a job are obtained from the job parameters (see Figure 10–2). For the turn around time objective, the job counter for the job class of the job just completed must be incremented, and the turn-around time must be added to the total for that job class. From the intermediate information compiled in the job parameters, causes of turn-around delays can be analyzed: [(Parameter 13 – Parameter 3) + Parameter 8] is the delay to get into the processing phase; (Parameter 14 – Parameter 13) is the delay in processing; (Parameter 15 – Parameter 14) is the delay in obtaining a printer and (Parameter 16 – Parameter 15) is the delay in printing. Analysis of these specific delays provided clues to scheduling rules that would yield improved turn-around time.

Statistics on CPU utilization were calculated directly in the processing phase. Referring to Equation 10–2, τ is the amount time when the CPU is in a compute mode in any one of the partitions (or, as in Figure 10–4, the time when at least one partition is not in an interrupt state).

10-5 programming the simulator

Based on the subsystem flow charts, versions of the simulator were programmed in both FORTRAN IV and GPSS/360. These languages were selected because they represent respectively the most popular general-purpose programming language and the most popular simulation speciali-

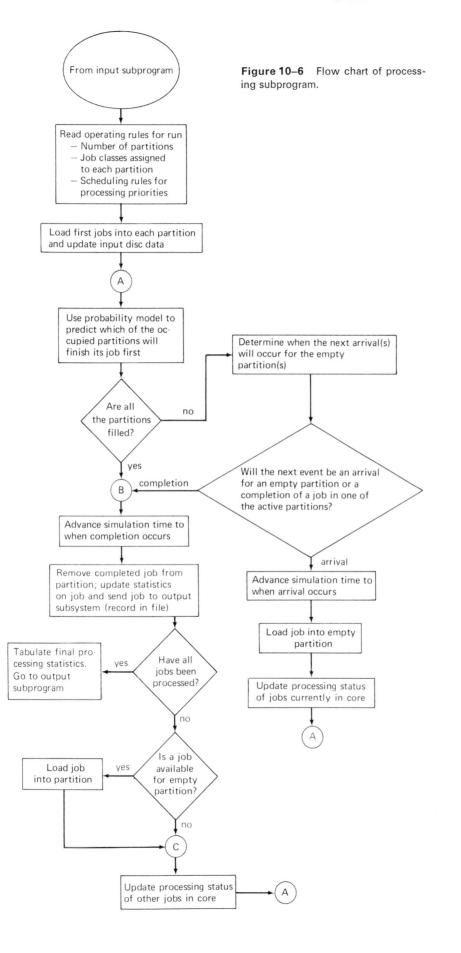

Figure 10–6 Flow chart of processing subprogram.

From input subprogram

Read operating rules for run
— Number of partitions
— Job classes assigned
  to each partition
— Scheduling rules for
  processing priorities

Load first jobs into each partition
and update input disc data

A

Use probability model to
predict which of the oc-
cupied partitions will
finish its job first

Determine when the next arrival(s)
will occur for the empty
partition(s)

Are all
the partitions
filled?

no

yes

B   completion

Will the next event be an arrival
for an empty partition or a
completion of a job in one of
the active partitions?

Advance simulation time to
when completion occurs

arrival

Remove completed job from
partition; update statistics
on job and send job to output
subsystem (record in file)

Advance simulation time to
when arrival occurs

Tabulate final pro-
cessing statistics.
Go to output
subprogram

yes

Have all
jobs been
processed?

Load job into empty
partition

Update processing status
of jobs currently in core

no

A

Load job
into partition

yes

Is a job
available
for empty
partition?

no

C

235

Update processing status
of other jobs in core

A

ch. 10
model of a computer
center's operations

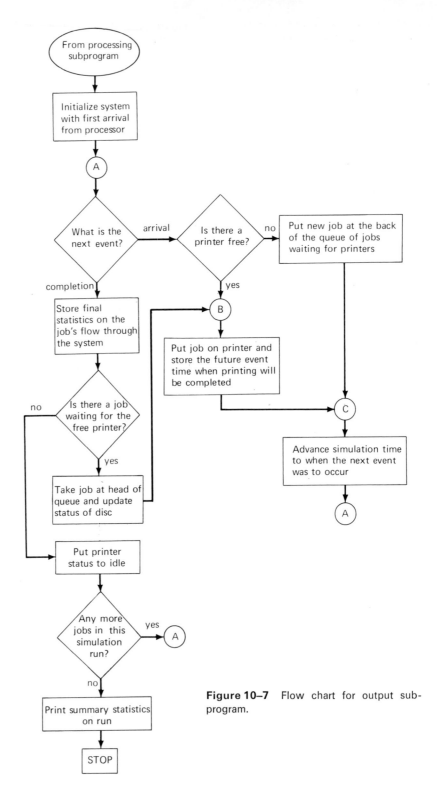

Figure 10–7 Flow chart for output sub-program.

zation language. Comments about programming and debugging time, computation efficiency, and general observations about the capabilities of each language are presented in this section.

FORTRAN Version

The FORTRAN simulator was programmed using the flow charts in Figures 10–3, 10–6, and 10–7. The program was nearly 600 statements long. To compile the program and simulate one day's activity of the Computer Center (about 1000 jobs) took 1.3 minutes on an IBM 360/65 (of which about 1.2 minutes was for compiling).

The simulator took about four man-weeks to program and another three man-weeks to debug. Most of the programming problems were encountered in coordinating the effects of events; that is, updating conditional event variables when another part of the system changed status. Debugging activity was primarily to account for unanticipated special situations where unusual kinds of jobs or special backlogs could not be handled by the existing program. For example, on occasions the computer systems group would run a special job for which no turn-around time was recorded (the clock was turned off). When data on such jobs were fed into the simulator, error messages were recorded because normal job logic did not apply.

The FORTRAN program was a direct translation of the flow chart and was used to analyze alternative scheduling rules. The initial simulator lacked some generality in the kinds of scheduling rules it would permit; for example, it did not permit scheduling a job class to a second partition when the primary one was too busy. The program was later modified to permit examination of a rule in which certain job classes went to any available partition.

GPSS/360 Version

When we described simulation languages in Chapter 6, we indicated that GPSS is an event-oriented language and that it uses a flow approach to describe the behavior of the system. Using this language to simulate the computer system created a few problems. In particular, the mechanism for generating jobs (or transactions as they are called in GPSS) that flow through the system is usually done by taking random samples from prespecified arrival distributions. Job characteristics are assigned to the arrival variates from other distributions. Although arrival times and characteristics of jobs can be read directly into a GPSS simulator, to do so requires advanced features of the language. Most of the effort was directed toward putting the FORTRAN simulator into operation; therefore, we decided to use the standard GPSS features. Distributions were developed to generate arrivals and assign processing characteristics to them.

To simplify the problem, only three types of jobs were to be generated in the GPSS simulator:

(1) High-priority jobs that demanded quick turn-around.

ch. 10
model of a computer
center's operations

(2) Input–output bound jobs that were expected to place heavy demands on data inputs and/or printer output (and thus would have a high percentage of time in interrupt).

(3) Compute bound jobs that were expected to spend a low percentage of time in interrupt because input–output requirements would be small.

Distributions were developed for each of the three classes for the following characteristics:

- interarrival time between jobs
- the execution time
- the percentage of the execution in an interrupt
- the amount of output printing
- the output device requested by the job

Using a distribution to assign input–output devices is a way to handle output directed to remote terminals. (This method differs from the approximation in the FORTRAN simulation.) In this case, more than the three Computer Center printers are analyzed by the simulator.

The GPSS simulator took about one man-week to program and debug. Debugging time was particularly short because the model was compiling very soon after programming was completed and test data enabled the analyst to examine the program for logic errors. Thus, programming effort for the GPSS model was about fifteen percent of that required for the FORTRAN model. The decrease would not have been as dramatic if the same input data and job classes had been used in the GPSS version.

The GPSS simulator was thirty statements long and required 0.38 minutes (IBM 360/65) to simulate one day's activity at the Computer Center.

10-6   validating the model

Most tests of validity (or credibility) of simulation models involve comparing the performance of the simulator under historical operating conditions with the actual performance of the system. Unfortunately, we were unable to apply this test because the MFT system was not in existence at the time the model was developed. All we could do was run the simulator as a single-partition system and compare its performance against the current sequential processing system. (A single-partition system processes only one job at a time and thus is equivalent to the current system.) This run was made and the figures generated by the computer on machine utilization and turn-around time were statistically equivalent to those observed in the actual system. This was no guarantee, however, that our model of MFT would accurately represent the behavior of that system. No independent predictions were available on how the new system might perform; therefore, we accepted our simulator as at least credible and began designing experiments to test scheduling rules.

experimental design 10-7

Because of the way the simulator is constructed, analysis is not required to determine such factors as when the transient effects have ended, when steady-state analysis can be applied, or how long a run is required for statistical stability. An actual eight-hour (prime time) day's arrival pattern is being supplied. The system begins empty, and queues build and recede as demands vary, just as in the actual system. We are interested in how well (in a relative sense) alternative scheduling rules can handle the same demand pattern. The only concern is whether the day chosen to test the rules is typical of arrival patterns that would be expected over a longer period. This question can be answered by sampling other days' activities and determining whether the relative performance of the scheduling rules shifts (a study subsequent to the effort report here).

In the problem-formulation section, we identified two interconnected decisions of interest to the Computer Center staff: (1) how many partitions to allow and (2) what rule to use in scheduling jobs into partitions. The decision on the number of partitions primarily affects computer utilization—more partitions means more utilization. (As we already pointed out, however, this also means less space for each program.) The Computer Center staff indicated they would be very pleased with a utilization of about ninety percent. Some mathematical analysis was performed using a probability model to predict the advance rate of jobs in the processing phase. This analysis showed that a graph of computer utilization as a function of the number of partitions took the form in Figure 10–8. (The simulation technique has the advantage of flexibility—those aspects of the problem that fit the assumptions of analytic models can be represented as such and the predictions from them combined with the simulation representation of the less structured aspects.) From the mathematical analysis, we concluded that more than three partitions would not be justified because there is little gain in utilization and a large cost in core

Figure 10–8 Computer utilization for different number of partitions.

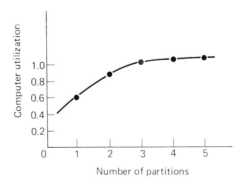

space available for each job. Using only two partitions sacrificed too much utilization. Therefore, we decided three partitions were optimal, and this variable was not changed in the simulator. (This recommendation was not difficult to sell to the Computer Center staff because they were of the opinion that three partitions were optimal even before we did our analysis.)

Two scheduling rules were proposed initially—one by the Computer Center staff and one by the analysts building the simulator. The Computer Center staff felt that jobs with high turn-around priority should be placed in the first partition in order to maximize turn-around. Jobs with a high percentage of interrupt should be scheduled into the second partition. The third partition would contain jobs with very little interrupt—thus making a nonutilization instance unlikely. The alternative, suggested by the analysts, was to place high priority jobs in Partition 2 and jobs with a high percentage of interrupt in Partition 1. From the model of processing rates, we felt the second scheduling rule would increase throughput; however, it also might increase the turn-around time of high-priority jobs. As a base case, we also decided to run the simulator using a rule that jobs are placed in the first free partition on a first-come, first-served basis, regardless of the job's priority. This is essentially a random allocation and shows how much improvement we can obtain with better schedules. It was expected that still more scheduling rules would be tested after the strengths and weaknesses of those already proposed had been analyzed.

Besides testing scheduling rules under one specific set of conditions, we had to test the sensitivity of the rules to changes in those conditions. Two parameters were built directly into the model—the fraction of time each job type was in interrupt and the degree of independence of events in processing—and ranges of these needed to be explored. The sensitivity of the solution to which day's operation is selected for input data had to be tested as well. Finally, we wanted to determine the sensitivity of the rules to changes in the current level of demand for the computer. Changes in demand rates could be introduced easily by decreasing interarrival times between jobs. A formula for doing so can be obtained by letting t_i be the arrival time of the ith job, and t'_i be the arrival time for the same job when demand is changed and arrivals are occurring faster. Then,

$$t'_i = t'_{i-1} + \frac{1}{1 + \alpha} (t_i - t_{i-1}) \qquad (10\text{--}3)$$

The parameter α can be set to change the arrival rate. Demand rates can be increased across the board, or increases can be made selectively for certain classes of jobs.

To avoid needless compounding of the number of runs, we initially tested the scheduling rules only under one set of the parameter values. Then we took the two best rules and did parameter sensitivity analysis and demand sensitivity analysis. If the relative positions of the rules remained invariant over the range of changes, we concluded that the results were insensitive to the variables. Where changes occurred, closer estimation of the likely ranges of values would be needed to determine the best rule.

When the simulator was run for the three scheduling rules already described, we found that the random partition allocation was significantly worse than either of the structured schedules. Placing jobs with high interrupt in the first partition did marginally better than placing high-priority jobs in the first partition. The more significant results of these runs came when we analyzed where and why delays were occurring for the scheduling rules.

It turned out that the MFT system effectively added an additional fifty percent to current computing capabilities. This additional capacity meant that the system could easily handle current demands—in fact, much of the time at least one of the partitions was idle. Periodically, however, large numbers of high-priority jobs would enter the system in rapid succession. When this happened, queues would build up for the partition assigned to these jobs while the other partitions remained relatively empty. The system thus acted almost like a sequential processor in removing the backlog. Further analysis into these peak demand periods revealed that classwork was often submitted in batches and, when this occurred, the peak loads would occur.

To compensate for these peak demands, we decided to test another, more flexible rule where any type of job could be assigned any available partition, but that jobs lined up to get partitions on a first-come, first-served basis *within their priority class;* that is, we used the same rule as was practiced when sequential processing was used and applied it to all three partitions. This scheduling rule has the advantage that batches of high-priority jobs have full utilization of the CPU and turn-around times are minimized.

When the rule was tested on the simulator, it substantially reduced the weighted turn-around measure. Utilization was a little worse than the other rules, but not significantly so.

When sensitivity analyses were run for the rules, we found that the only factor that could change the optimality of this new scheduling rule was the volume of jobs entering the system. As the rate of input was increased, the utilization objective became better in an absolute sense, but worse relative to using a rule of scheduling classes of jobs into separate partitions. By running the simulator at different demands, we determined when other rules become more efficient and presented this to the Computer Center staff. Our recommendation for current demand levels was to use the flexible rule: all partitions on a priority basis.

One final note on the way the solution was reached is worth emphasizing. The best alternative had not been conceived at the time the simulator was developed. It was only after we analyzed the details of how the system operated under specific schedules as predicted by the simulator that new alternatives became apparent. This sequential method of solving the problem is fairly typical of successful simulation studies. In fact, a simulator's greatest value in a research program is often that it facilitates a greater understanding of the alternative solutions that are possible.

ch. 10
model of a computer
center's operations

Because these solutions may not be apparent at the time the simulation is constructed, we suggest that all simulation studies have some time devoted to general exploration of the behavior of the system. If the simulator is used only as a tool for evaluating predetermined alternative solutions, new operating procedures are not likely to be discovered.

simulation models of human behavior

the need for models that explain behavior 11-1

The previous chapters in this book describe the use of simulation to improve decision making at operational levels. The purpose of this chapter is to examine its use to aid decision making at higher levels of management and also in functions other than production and distribution. Models in these areas are difficult to develop because they must include the representation of the behavior of people not directly supervised by the decision-making organization. Simulation is becoming a vital tool in creating the required models of such behavior; indeed, the simulation of behavior may be a most significant technique for extending operations research to top-management, long-range planning problems.

Figure 11–1 is a schematic representation of the areas in which operations research has been and can be applied. Along the bottom are the functional areas, starting with production and distribution (the areas that are constrained largely by physical processes) and extending through more behavioral functions to research, which is largely an individual, creative process.

On the vertical axis are levels of organizational complexity. At the lowest level is the process; cutting metal, storing and moving goods, the actual transferring of funds, and so on. Next is operations management which deals with the minute-by-minute and day-to-day direction of processing. The middle-management level is concerned with establishing the rules by which the operations-management proceeds, and to some extent with changes in the structure of the operational-process system. It includes, for example, decisions to acquire new equipment or to redesign the information-processing system. Top management deals with decisions that have long-range consequences, including: the introduction of new

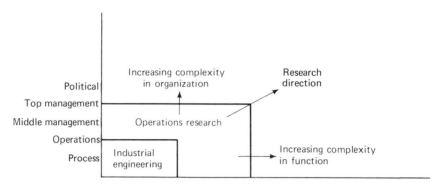

Figure 11–1   Areas of application of operations research.

product lines and new marketing areas, changes in the system's structure (such as major technological process innovations), or changes in the organizational assignments to carry out these processes. Top management decides who makes which decisions at the middle and operational levels. Finally, there is the political level at which organizations and individuals interact to make major interenterprise decisions.

Operations research has had great success applying symbolic models to the production, distribution, and some financial decisions made at the operations- and middle-management levels. (The design of production and distribution processes is a part of the industrial engineer's area of concern and expertise.)

The techniques developed for operations research are now being used on a routine basis in most progressive firms. The *research* efforts in operations research are being devoted to expanding the boundaries of application both upward and to the right. The operations research literature includes many studies of marketing problems. Operations researchers are also beginning to work in the areas of personnel management and in education (both public and industrial). There are also increasing numbers of studies of such top-management decision problems as the selection of new products and the restructuring of organizations to improve efficiency.

All of these research areas involve, in a significant way, human beings whose activities cannot be controlled in any direct way by the organization. In marketing we must predict the behavior of customers; in personnel management area we have to deal with the way people behave in relation current employees to policies and operating procedures; in the top-management area we have to deal with the way people behave in relation to organizational structure, policy, and methods of operation and with competitors' behavior. Thus there is an increasing need to forecast not only present but future behavior of people in reaction to changes in the nature of products, services, or organizations.

It is possible to get clues to the behavior of people by direct experimentation. Many marketing studies consist of exposing a selected group of potential customers to either advertising messages or to new products. The group reaction to the stimulus is then estimated, either through individual statements (surveys) or by observing changes in the purchasing behavior of the group after the exposure. This kind of experimentation, however, is not directly generalizable to other consumer groups nor to other products. The behavior patterns seem to change, not only over time, but also as a result of changes in the competitive situation in which the products are introduced. Furthermore, experimentation is expensive research.

What is sought, then, is a general model that represents the stable characteristics of behavior so that predictions in a particular situation can be deduced. To obtain this general model we do not necessarily want to trace every mental manipulation that a person goes through to arrive at a particular action or communication. The models should be as abstract as possible and still be predictive. Behavioral models are especially needed where experimentation is physically or economically infeasible, such as, in conflict situations or in a study of a product still on the drawing board.

The problem of representing behavior can be described by means of Figure 11–2. We imagine the person or a group as a black box. The inputs to this mysterious box are messages from other people and from media, the actions of others and the actions in nature (for example, weather). The outputs are the messages (spoken or written) and actions taken. It is particularly important to recognize that the black box has within it what seems to be a very complex, long-term memory. This memory makes the process of developing a model very difficult because it means the output messages and actions are often a function of inputs that occurred many years ago in apparently unconnected situations.

Figure 11–2 The problem of modeling behavior.

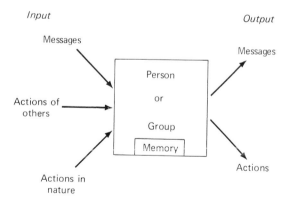

gaming 11-2

There are two approaches to the study of behavior: one is experimental, using a laboratory experiment rather than a natural experiment; the other is modeling. The first of these is called gaming. A simulation is created, but the behavioral component is played out by a real person. The actions and communications of the person are observed in an effort to understand his behavior. In this section we will discuss gaming, and in the next section we will discuss all-computer simulation models of behavior. (We are not talking about gaming for the purpose of educating the player, although that is certainly a valid use of a game.)

In dealing with behavioral problems it is extremely difficult to create a true laboratory experiment, and it is extremely difficult to observe and comprehend the mental process of interest. The game has evolved as an intermediate form of research vehicle with two different uses: (1) it can be viewed as a difficult-to-control laboratory, an *artificial reality,* or (2) it can be viewed as a model of real-world processes. In the first use, the game is considered as a real world, but, being a game, is somewhat under the control of the experimenter. The research then alternates between study of the game and development of a symbolic or simulation model until such time as the model makes good predictions *of the game activity.* Finally, when a model is constructed that works well in complex games, it must be tested in the real world [Sisson and Ackoff, 1966].

A game may also be used not as an artificial reality to be modeled, but as a model of reality. One of the components of this model is rather difficult to control—namely, the human player—but it can be considered a model nevertheless. A game is constructed and played. Its predictions are tested against the real-world observations. The game is modified and this process is repeated until the game is a good predictor—that is, a valid model.

Description of a Game

A game is a simulation except that some of the subroutines are executed by the human. Many of the factors of simulation that we have already mentioned apply. It is not the intention of this book to investigate the art of gaming extensively, but we will review briefly these factors in terms of the eight basic dimensions of a simulation described in Section 1–6.

State–Dynamic. Games are always dynamic since static behavior is essentially meaningless.

Aggregate–Detailed. Games may represent either highly aggregate or very detailed phenomena. For example, some games have been played to represent the key foreign policy decisions made by nations [Guetzkow et al., 1963] using aggregate models. On the other hand, games have been used to study the individual buying decisions of a single product by one consumer. A key problem in the use of games is to direct the player's attention to the appropriate level of detail; otherwise he may not observe and process the appropriate aggregate or detailed variables as he would in the real situation being represented.

Physical–Behavioral. The human in the game is obviously intended to represent the behavioral aspects of the process; however, the overall simulation may contain computer subroutines that represent the physical processes. For example, studies have been made of how humans control aircraft by using simulations in which the human plays the pilot's role, with the remainder of the aircraft and aerodynamic environment simulated by a computer.

Computer–Human. By definition a game contains at least some human component.

Recursive–quasi-equilibrium. Both of these approaches are used in games. Most games are recursive; that is, the conditions at the end of one simulated time period are the starting conditions for the next time period. At the beginning of each time period the human player is given data produced by the game at the end of the last period. For example, if the player is playing the role of a production manager, he would be given those production reports that the manager would normally receive at the beginning of each reporting period. (The reports summarize the current consequences of past decisions.) On the other hand there are very complex simulations in which the researcher may make some adjustment or special inputs between each time period [Bloomfield and Whaley, 1965]. This is particularly true in simulation games used by political scientists to study long-term political processes (such as activities leading to a revolution). The researcher observes the results of the simulation at the end of one time period, then introduces new conditions before the start of the next simulation period. One reason for doing this is to represent a period of time that is not simulated. Thus, each play will be considered a quasi-equilibrium process. There is an analogy between the economic equilibrium and some political processes, such as negotiations between parties that yield an equilibrium point—that is, an agreement.

Continuous–Discrete. We do not know whether the human brain processes information discretely or continuously. The computer simulation part of the game can be either continuous or discrete. Aggregate models (like those of an entire national economy) tend to be continuous; however, models of greater detail (such as a game to study a person's job shop scheduling decisions) are likely to be discrete.

Size of Time Quanta. Time in a game may proceed on a uniform basis or on an event-advance basis. If it proceeds on a uniform basis, the time unit may be short, such as a fraction of a second, or very long, such as a decade. The shortest time unit occurs in games intended to observe a human's physiological reactions, such as piloting an aircraft. Here time units of fractions of a second might be appropriate.

Time need not advance uniformly. In some games used to study political phenomena, the referees cause time to advance from event-to-event (an event might be the start of a major negotiation or the outbreak of conflict) [Bloomfield and Whaley, 1965].

Deterministic–Stochastic. Because it is expensive to run a game, most complex games are run only once and thus are treated as deterministic. However, in some studies the games are repeated many times, and a distribution of outputs is obtained. A game is, in one sense, naturally stochastic, since it is impossible to control the exact procedures used by the human player. Therefore, if the game is replicated, different results will invariably occur. When used as a research tool, the games should always be treated as a stochastic process; constraints on the number of replications are usually dictated by the research budget.

Initial Conditions and Transient Behavior

In addition to these eight dimensions, there are several other factors which we have discussed before and which are particularly critical in a game. The greatest difficulty in setting up a game as a realistic model is in creating appropriate initial conditions. In a game it is necessary to establish the initial conditions for both the mechanical and human components of the simulation. The initial conditions for the computer part are established in the usual way; that is, by establishing appropriate variable values in each data array. It is much more difficult, however, to establish the appropriate initial conditions in the human. The human not only comes to the simulation already "programmed," but also with a memory full of information and data, the contents of which are inaccessible to the researcher. Usually the analyst tries to establish the appropriate initial conditions by having the player learn a set of instructions and a scenario that describes the way the simulated world is at the time at which the game is to start. Obviously there is no assurance that the game participant has absorbed this statement of initial conditions.

The researcher is faced with a major problem when he writes the scenario for the players. On one hand, it must be definitive enough to ensure that each player starts the game with a perception of the situation that is consistent with the intent of the game. On the other hand, the scenario should not be so restrictive that the player has (or feels he has) no real choices during the play of the game. Perhaps the single greatest weakness in the use of games as a research tool is the problem of setting the initial conditions in a way that can be replicated from run to run with different players (even with the same players) and yet does not prevent the player from considering alternative decisions.

As with other simulations, there may be an initial transient phase that is not typical of the process and therefore should be ignored in collecting data. There are two basic ways of avoiding transient effects. One is to establish the initial conditions so that (with as high a probability as possible) the game starts in the desired steady-state process. The other way is to play the game for a number of periods during which information is not collected but the simulation—including the player's behavior—settles down to a steady state. Because of the expense of running games, the former method is usually used.

Many simulations are designed to study the transient phase. This seems to be particularly true with games. For example, in the use of games in political science it is the transients or dynamic behaviors leading up to such events as wars or revolutions that the political scientist wants to study. In this case, the play immediately before the major event is of great interest (but the problem of establishing initial conditions becomes severe).

Games have all of the problems related to experimental design. Because they are so expensive, statistically reliable experimental designs are not often found. Researchers make every effort to replicate the games and to run them under various conditions according to a planned design. As far as we know, no one has used a game to find an *optimum* behavior pattern. Games are usually used as descriptive models or as situations that are then modeled by other means.

There is one other peculiarity of games that is most important. That is the problem of role-playing. A player in a game may be asked to play himself or to play the role of some other person. The last mode is extremely difficult to justify. For example, suppose we asked a United States college undergraduate to assume the role of a Russian general in a simulation game. First, we have the problem of knowing whether the player is really trying to play the role of the general, i.e., does he become *involved*. Second, there is the question that, even if the player is properly involved, does he know enough about how a Russian general will behave to play the game out in a predictive fashion. If the player is being asked to play himself, the problem of whether he knows the role or not does not arise. However, every person is capable of playing a large number of roles and it is not clear if the person will play out a game situation the same way he would have played the real situation. Nevertheless, this is the assumption made when using games, particularly when using games as models.

Recall that one common purpose of a simulation is to provide a decision maker with insights about the environment with which he is dealing. To the extent that this is the goal, games can be extremely useful. In business, for example, games have been used successively to provide a management labor relation team with insights about how the dynamics of a negotiation would proceed. One game was arranged so that some members of the management team played the labor union negotiators' role. Several plays through the game showed how different tactics and negotiation bargaining positions could occur, increasing the insight of the management team and leading to their increased effectiveness in the actual negotiations.

the state of the art of simulations of behavior* 11-3

Since we have pointed out that all-computer simulations are becoming an effective tool for modeling behavior, we would like to review briefly the state of the art and encourage the interested reader to use the references at the end of this chapter for a more detailed study of this technique.

The Importance of Simulating Behavior

The literature demonstrates that directed, technical behavior can be simulated; for example, a foreman dispatching jobs according to a scheduling rule [Conway et al., 1963], a trust officer making decisions [Clarkson

* Adapted with permission from Chapter 2, "Simulation: Uses," in *Progress in Operations Research*, Vol. III (ed. by Julius Aronofsky), Wiley, New York, 1969.

in Cyert and March, 1963] and even a psychologist interpreting job applicant test data [Smith and Greenlaw, 1967]. Researchers are, however, only beginning to explore the use of simulators to represent behavior that is not under management direction. There are two basic difficulties in representing this behavior: the inaccessibility of the phenomena and the discontinuity of the processes.

Inaccessibility of Behavioral Phenomena

Simulation permits us to explore the consequences of the interactions of a large number of subprocesses, each of which we understand. In simulating a distribution system, the analyst makes assumptions about the logical relationships and physical constraints that operate at each key point; for example, warehouse and reordering procedures, transportation delays, rules for product allocation, and customer-ordering patterns. The interactions between various subsystems are, however, discontinuous and nonadditive. They follow logical rules, but different rules apply over different ranges of the variables. To produce a simulation, the analyst models each of the subsystems. He then integrates these into a model of the entire system. The simulation can then predict system variables such as frequency of stock shortages and operating costs. Data for the model are obtained by observation (past or present) of the subsystems in operation.

In behavior it is necessary to represent phenomena wherein the subsystems are inaccessible. Presumably these subsystems are embedded in some neurological process in the brain. When the subsystems are not observable it is impossible to study their details and combine them into subsystem models. An alternative is the *black box* approach in which the subprocess models are derived indirectly. This problem occurs not only in the study of a single individual but in studies of groups of individuals. In the latter case we may be able (given enough research money) to understand those subsystems that involve communication between the people, since this communication is, to some extent, publicly observable. That part of the process which goes on in each individual's head is, however, still inaccessible.

The black box approach starts with observation of input-output relationships. From these the researcher tries to deduce a model of the process which must be operative in the box. Sometimes the black box is known to contain a system constrained by physical phenomena (which we understand fairly well) or, more generally, contains something about which we have independent information. In this case determining the submodel process (from the input-output relationships) is feasible, although more difficult than synthesizing from subsystem models. When we know essentially nothing about the inside of the black box, however, the problem of determining the model is extremely difficult. The formulation of the model in this way confounds two normally distinct phases: the definition of the structure of the model and the determination of the parameters of the model. The researcher hypothesizes a model structure to explain the output-input relationships. Next he takes some portion of actual output-input history and performs a search to find model parameters. In this search, the controllable variables are the parameters of the model and the objective is to minimize the difference between the output produced by the model and the output produced in actual experimentation or history. If a close match is obtained, it is hypothesized that the structure, with the determined parameters, is a good model of the black box. Note that the structure and the parameters are developed simultaneously. If the model is not a good predictor, it is difficult to tell whether the parameters are wrong or whether the structure is wrong, and, if so, which part. If prediction is good, we may then confirm the model with further experimentation. This process is feasible—chemical processes are often modeled in this way [Giese, 1967]—but it is not neat.

Econometricians have developed this parameter search procedure to a fine art [Goldberger, 1964; Thiel, 1965]. In socioeconomic studies the search procedure often consumes all available historical data, and statistically good fits between simulated and real outputs may be difficult to obtain. Additional difficulties arise in many behavioral models. For example, some variables may be discrete, and the search over the discontinuous surfaces thereby generated is difficult. In representing behavior there is an even more important form of discontinuity, which will be discussed next.

Discontinuity in Model Structure

To explain the discontinuity problem we will use an analogy with computer processing. Imagine behavior as a series of computer programs, that is, procedures for information processing. Basic principles equivalent to the physical laws of conservation have not been found for information processing. (There is, of course, a limit on communication capacity as given by information theory.) This means that the information process can be subject to true discontinuities. To continue the analogy, think of behavior as a system of programs containing two kinds of subsystems, one or more *control* routines and a collection of *operational* routines. The control routine determines which operational routine is active at any time, in a manner similar to a computer executive routine. The system can, through its control routine, change the operative operational routine instantaneously. This means that the system has not only discontinuities in functional relationships, but also *discontinuities in complete model structure.* It is not hard to imagine the difficulties in modeling such a situation, and it is, in fact, surprising that some progress has been made. Yet

"computer simulation of psychological processes has proved itself an important tool in the development of psychological theory. A number of successful programs parallel human problem solving, pattern recognition or other behavior [Feigenbaum and Feldman, 1963]. The different functions in which computer simulation can be of value [are]: First, computer programs can serve as unambiguous formulations of a theory. . . . Second, computer simulation is a means to demonstrate and test the consistency and sufficiency of a theory . . . running the program under a variety of conditions may generate consequences which can be tested against new evidence. These consequences may be quite important such as the discovery of performance fluctuations without the introduction of stochastic elements [Feigenbaum, 1959]. . . . Third, computer simulation may serve as a heuristic in the search for models" [Frijda, 1967, p. 59].

251

The next section summarizes some of the major work in simulating behavior.

11-4 a review of simulations involving behavior

Most of the reported uses of simulation contain a simple behavioral component. The model of managerial behavior assumes that the manager performs specified algorithm (and, therefore, could be replaced by a computer). This assumption is common in the extensive work on job shop sequencing. A model that contains a dispatching rule of say, "Select the job in the queue with the shortest processing time for this machine," is, in effect, assigning this decision behavior to a foreman. In real shops foremen and workers do not always follow such behavior, and some analysts have made an effort to take into account these deviations. In simulating antisubmarine warfare it is assumed that the commanders follow prescribed tactical procedures. In traffic simulators elementary rules about the driving behavior are used.

Simulation of General Management Behavior*

Above the lowest level of management it is more difficult to represent behavior. Some efforts have been made to simulate such behavior, largely for the purposes of explicating theories of administration. The classical work is that of March and Cyert [Cyert and March, 1963], under whose direction a number of simulations have been performed. They have been able to represent middle-level managers such as retail store buyers [Cyert, Ch. 7] or trust officers [Cyert, Ch. 10]. The simulations that result are not general, but do seem to model the behavior of the specific manager reasonably well; it is possible to predict his decisions in a given situation.

The simulations are developed by detailing decision-making computations. For example, the decision of a trust investment officer, as modeled by Clarkson, contains a procedure for determining the kind of investment account to select. A model of a manager's decision process is then built up by postulating how he organizes incoming and recalled data and how he chooses alternative actions on the basis of this data.

This work represents the technical aspects of a job. This is true of most models of managers' decision processes. His own goals and aspirations and their effect on his decisions are not included. Work is just starting on simulations that will merge psychological simulations (to be described) with the technical decision making to obtain an overall model of the human managers.

Early studies, such as the work Cyert and March, concentrated on the manager himself. In the last two years there has been some experimentation with enterprise models. These are simulators that combine an operational model of a firm with a model of the middle-level managers.

* See Bonini, 1963; Cyert and March, 1963; Meier, 1964; Rome and Rome, 1961; Smith and Greenlaw, 1967.

Enterprise models thus include the effects of the decisions made by the middle managers in predicting the operation of the enterprise. Enterprise models (see pages 273–296 for an example) should be useful for top management, since they permit them to study the effects of their decisions as interpreted by middle management and executed by the system that these managers in turn operate.

Simulations of Economic Behavior (Econometric Models)*

Economics made a basic assumption about behavior; that people will try to select a package of goods so as to maximize a hypothesized utility function within disposable income. This single assumption about behavior has permitted economics to become one of the most successful behavioral sciences. (It must be admitted, however, that economics deals largely with man-made, that is, legal and traditional, interactions, which are more clear-cut and accessible than other forms of behavior.) Economists are beginning to recognize that if they wish to develop more detailed models they must model individual behavior of people in various roles. Modern econometric models involve hundreds of equations and represent a number of behavioral phenomena, including allocation between savings and consumption, industrial allocation between capital and labor, government tax and interest-level decisions, and other aggregate behavior [Klein, 1964]. These models have been successful in forecasting gross economic trends, such as unemployment rates and GNP, for several quarters into the future. Econometric models must be judged successful in representing economic behavior in the aggregate. Progress is being made toward developing useful models that will make predictions about individual sectors of the economy.

Simulations of Mass Behavior†

Behavioral assumptions made in studies of consumer behavior and political science are similar to those made in economics but concern other human activities. In these cases interest centers on the behavior of aggregate population. The behavior is characterized by one or two variables, for example, how will people vote, or whether they will purchase a particular item. Models are used to express the relationship between these variables and other complex variables such as the kind of information presented to a group in the form of advertising or political statements. Some progress has been made in modeling such relationships. Models to predict the effect of political statements on voting were developed for the Kennedy campaign [Pool, 1961]. This work has been extended to other public affairs

* Cohen and Cyert, 1961; Evans, 1967; Forrester, 1961; Holland, 1963; Klein, 1964; Orcutt et al., 1961; Stone, 1962; Stonebraker and Murphy, 1966; Thiel, 1965.

† Abelson and Bernstein, 1963; Amstutz and Claycamp, 1964; Bloomfield and Whaley, 1965; Coleman, 1965; Greenlaw, 1961; Guetzkow et al., 1963; Kotler, 1965; McPhee, 1961; Moshman, 1964; Pool and Abelson, 1961; Rosenthal, 1965; Wells and Chinsky, 1965.

matters, for example, voting on the fluoridation of water in a small town [Abelson and Bernstein, 1963]. Similar techniques are being used for marketing-decision studies [e.g., Amstutz and Claycamp, 1964; Kotler, 1965]. A number of marketing researchers have used Markov brand switching models. These models contain a very large number of free parameters that must be derived from the data; such models contain very little explanation of behavior. They do pinpoint very clearly the discontinuous nature of the behavior referred to previously. More explanatory (but mathematically less tractable) models, explored through simulation, are advancing the study of consumer behavior.

Simulations of Small Group Behavior*

Since the early 1950's social psychologists have been exploring the nature of the interactions within small groups by means of simulation. Until very recently most of these simulations were games (which present a problem with regard to validity). Recently some efforts have been made to develop computer simulation models to replicate the behavior observed in gaming situations [Rapoport and Chammah, 1965]. We have noted the value of conceiving of a game as an artificial reality—that is, a world to be studied. An all-computer simulation of that game may then be regarded as the first step toward a theoretical model of behavior [Sisson and Ackoff, 1966]. The objective in the early stages of such research is to produce computer simulations that model the gaming behavior reasonably well. The advantage of using games is that the artificial history can be produced rapidly. This type of behavioral simulation has all of the difficulties alluded to in Section 11–3. In particular, it is very difficult to develop models with a small number of parameters. Most behavioral models have so many parameters that the process is more nearly curve fitting than model building.

One of the earliest simulations of the social situation was the Gullahorns' model [Gullahorn and Gullahorn, 1963]. The situation involves supervisors of three similar departments. One of the supervisors is effective and the other two are marginal. The model focuses on the good supervisor's behavior when approached for assistance by one of the others. The effective man must weigh whether or not he will help on the basis of his previous experience with the requestor and his own workload. (The paper describes the model; results of its use have not been reported in the literature.)

We have modeled the players of a prisoner's dilemma game (a 2×2 nonzero sum situation) [Emshoff, 1970]. The basic flow chart for one version of this simulator is shown in Figure 11–3. This model reproduced the general behavior of the players given estimates of the four free parameters that represent the player's previously learned dispositions. (The model, however, has not been quantitatively validated, and work is continuing.)

* Clarkson and Simon, 1960; Coe, 1964; Guetzkow, 1962; Gullahorn and Gullahorn, 1963; Hare, 1961; McWhitney, 1964; Popkin, 1965; Siegel et al., 1964; Sisson and Ackoff, 1966.

Simulations of Individual Behavior*

The study of individual behavior is the study of psychology. Psychologists began in the very recent past to use simulations as a tool for the development of models. This work, however, is embryonic. As they emerged from the qualitative era, psychologists have become engrossed with mathematical models deriving from game theoretic concepts. The principal difficulty with game theory is its static nature, whereas the interesting behavior is dynamic. Simulation would appear to be a fruitful tool for modeling dynamic behavior, recognizing the very difficult problems we have mentioned; those involving inaccessibility and discontinuity.

Where an individual has been placed in the role of a controller of a physical system, simulations have been quite successful in modeling his physiological and sensory data processing behavior [Gregg, 1965]. The problems become almost insurmountable, however, as the individual being studied does more complex tasks, which are a function of streams of information other than those related to a system bound by physical dynamics. Much of the simulation research that bears on understanding individual behavior derives from the effort to build an artificial intelligence, independent of any particular human personality. This area will be discussed in the next section.

Artificial Intelligence†

Studies of artificial intelligence involve creating units that exhibit human-like behavior. These efforts have gone on in increasingly more complex environments, but generally in those constrained by logical rules. The artificial behavior is exercised in the context of games (e.g., checkers), puzzles, or theorem-proving. Simulations have been developed of the information storage and retrieval processes, which it is presumed must go on in an artificial intelligence.

Computers and Thought [Feigenbaum and Feldman, 1959] is a collection of the key papers describing early success in limited forms of artificial intelligence. Their general outlook for further progress is optimistic. *Alchemy and Artificial Intelligence* [Dreyfus, 1965] presents a reaction to these developments.

"Attempts to simulate cognitive processes . . . have . . . run into greater difficulties than anticipated. . . ."

"An examination of these difficulties reveals that the attempt to analyze intelligent behavior in digital computer language systematically excludes three fundamentally human forms of information processing."

* Abelson and Carroll, 1965; Colby, 1965, 1967; Feigenbaum, 1959; Frijda, 1967; Gregg, 1965; Gyr et al., 1962; Harmon, 1960; Hoveland and Hunt, 1960; Hunt, 1962, Ch. 6; Laughery and Gregg, 1962; Ozkaptan and Gettig, 1963; Reitmain, 1965; Simmons and Simmons, 1961; Simon, 1962; Tomkins and Messick, 1963.

† Dreyfus, 1965; Feigenbaum and Feldman, 1963; Feldman et al., 1963; Minsky, 1965; Neisser, 1963; Newell, 1962, 1964.

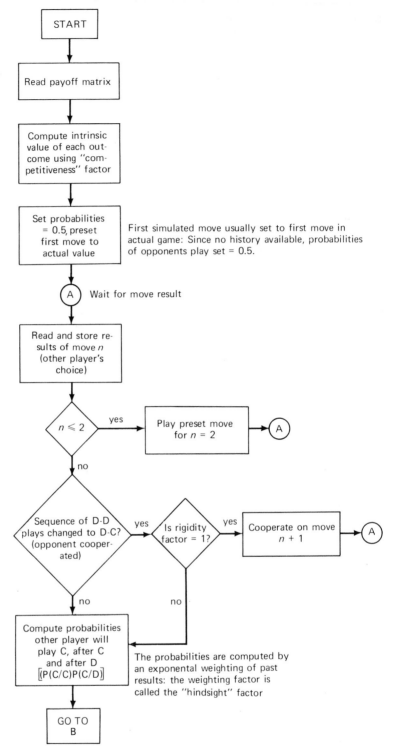

First simulated move usually set to first move in actual game: Since no history available, probabilities of opponents play set = 0.5.

The probabilities are computed by an exponental weighting of past results: the weighting factor is called the "hindsight" factor

Figure 11–3   Flow chart of simulation of prisoner's dilemma player.

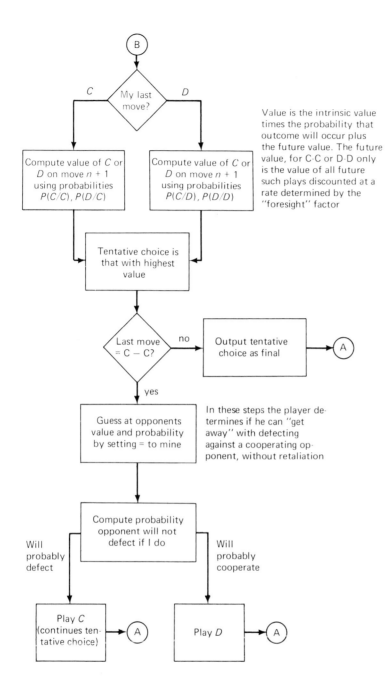

Value is the intrinsic value times the probability that outcome will occur plus the future value. The future value, for C-C or D-D only is the value of all future such plays discounted at a rate determined by the "foresight" factor

In these steps the player determines if he can "get away" with defecting against a cooperating opponent, without retaliation

Figure 11–3 (continued)

257

These forms are:

"fringe consciousness . . . or . . . marginal awareness."

"essence/accident discrimination . . . or . . . a grasp of the essential structure of the problem."

"ambiguity tolerance."

"Fringe consciousness makes us aware of cues in the context which are too numerous to be made explicit. A pragmatic sense of what is essential in a given context allows us to ignore as irrelevant certain possible parsings of sentences and meanings of words . . . . Ambiguity tolerance then allows us to use this information about goals and context to narrow down the remaining spectrum of possible . . . meanings as much as the situation requires."

It is probably too pessimistic to say we will never be able to simulate these human processes, but it will require efforts many times that already invested in artificial intelligence. However, "Man *and* computer is capable of accomplishing things that neither of them can do alone." [Rosenblith in Greenberger, 1962]. "Problems of Computer Simulation" [Frijda, 1967] reviews the use of simulation in behavioral science, taking a middle-of-the-road attitude as to the difficulties involved. "The computer simulation . . . seems to be essential to carry process analysis beyong a purely verbal state . . . a helpful technique in psychological research." [Frijda, 1967].

Minsky (in the oral presentation of his 1965 paper) pointed out that it may well be possible to simulate nonspecific, "intelligent" behavior; but without a general theory of mental processes, these simulations will be electronic complexes that are just as confusing as biological ones. We may be able to duplicate our thinking but without gaining any understanding of it. Nevertheless, such simulations would have value to decision makers as an aid in predicting behavior (a possibility requiring ethical contemplation). Such intelligence simulators can also serve to bring an inaccessible phenomena to visibility, which is perhaps a step toward a general theory of intelligence.

To summarize, there has been some success in simulating behavior of large numbers of unorganized people, such as consumers or the totality of managers in the industrial sector. There has been success in predicting the behavior of a single person in regard to a single activity (e.g., a management decision). In the other areas, successful simulations (indeed any models) are rare, because hypotheses upon which they might be built are practically nonexistent. The availability of simulation for precise representation of how people think appears to be hastening the development of valid hypotheses of behavior, and, hence, of better psychological and sociological theory. This in turn provides a basis for forecasting the environment of a business and leads to more effective management decisions.

references/bibliography

Abelson, R. P., and A. Bernstein, "A Computer Simulation Model of Community Referendum Controversies," *Public Opinion Quarterly*, Spring 1963, pp. 93–122.

Abelson, R. P., and J. Carroll, "Computer Simulation of Individual Belief Systems," *American Behavioral Scientist*, Vol. 8, No. 5, 1965, pp. 24–30.

Abt, C., "War Gaming," *International Science and Technology*, Vol. 32, 1964, pp. 29–37.

Amstutz, A. E., "Management Games—A Potential Perverted," *Industrial Management Review*, Vol. 4, Fall 1963, pp. 29–36.

Amstutz, A. E., and H. J. Claycamp, "The Total Market Environment Simulation, "*Industrial Management Review,* Vol. 4, Spring 1964, pp. 47–60.

Bloomfield, L., and B. Whaley, "The Political-Military Exercise: A Progress Report," *Orbis*, Vol. 8, No. 4, Winter 1965, pp. 845–70.

Bonini, C., "Simulation of Organizational Behavior," in *Management Controls; New Directions in Basic Research* (ed. by C. P. Bonini, R. K. Jaedicke, and H. M. Wagner), McGraw-Hill, New York, 1963, pp. 91–101.

Clarkson, G., and H. Simon, "Simulation of Individual and Group Behavior," *American Economic Review,* Vol. 50, No. 5, December 1960, pp. 920–32.

Coe, R., "Conflict, Interference and Aggression: Computer Simulation of a Social Process," *Behavioral Science,* Vol. 9, No. 2, April 1964, pp. 186–97.

Cohen, K., and R. Cyert, "Computer Models in Dynamic Economics," *Quarterly Journal of Economics,* Vol. 75, No. 1, February 1961, pp. 112–27.

Colby, K. M., "Computer Simulation of Neurotic Processes," in *Computers in Biomedical Research* (ed. by R. W. Stacy and B. D. Waxman), Academic Press, New York, 1965.

Colby, K. M., "Computer Simulation of Change in Personal Belief Systems," *Behavioral Science*, Vol. 12, No. 3, May 1967, pp. 248–53.

Colby, K. M., and J. P. Gilbert, "Programming a Computer Model of Neurosis," *Journal of Mathematical Psychology*, Vol. 1, 1964, pp. 405–17.

Colby K. M., J. Watt, and J. P. Gilbert, "A Computer Method of Psychotherapy," *Journal of Nervous and Mental Diseases,* 1966, Vol. 93, pp. 148–52.

Coleman, J., "The Use of Electronic Computers in the Study of Social Organization," *European Journal of Sociology*, Vol. 6, No. 1, 1965, pp. 89–107.

Conway, R., W. Maxwell, and L. Miller, *Theory of Scheduling*, Addison-Wesley, Reading, Mass., 1967.

Cyert, R., and J. March, *A Behavioral Theory of the Firm*, Prentice-Hall, Englewood Cliffs, N.J., 1963.

Dill, W. R., "Management Games for Training Decision Makers," in *Studies in Personnel and Industrial Psychology* (ed. by E. A. Fleischman), Dorsey Press, Homewood, Ill., 1961, pp. 219–30.

Dreyfus, H., *Alchemy and Artificial Intelligence*, P–3244, RAND Corp., Santa Monica, Calif., October 1959.

Emshoff, J. R., "A Simulation Model of the Prisoners Dilemma," *Behavioral Science,* Vol. 15, No. 3, July 1970.

Feigenbaum, E., *An Information Processing Theory of Verbal Learning,* P–1817, RAND Corp., Santa Monica Calif., October 1959.

Feigenbaum, E., and J. Feldman (eds.), *Computers and Thought,* McGraw-Hill, New York, 1963.

Feldman, J., F. Tonge, and H. Kanter, "Empirical Explorations of a Hypothesis-Testing Model of Binary Choice Behavior," in *Symposium on Simulation Models: Methodology and Applications to the Behavioral Sciences* (ed. by A. C. Hoggatt and F. E. Balderston), South-Western Publishing, Cincinnati, 1963, pp. 55–100.

Forrester, J. W., *Industrial Dynamics,* M. I. T. Press, Cambridge, Mass., 1961.

Frijda, N., "Problems of Computer Simulation," *Behavioral Science,* Vol. 12, January 1967, pp. 59–67.

Giese, C., "Determination of Best Kinetic Coefficients of a Dynamic Chemical Process by On-Line Digital Simulation," *Simulation,* Vol. 8, No. 3, March 1967, pp. 147–50.

Goldberger, A. S., *Econometric Theory*, Wiley, New York, 1964.

Greenberger, M. (ed.), *Computers and the World of the Future*, M.I.T. Press, Cambridge, Mass., 1962.

Greenlaw, P. S., "Marketing Simulations: Problems and Prospects," *Marketing: A Maturing Discipline* (ed. by M. L. Bell), American Marketing Association, Chicago, 1961, pp. 68–74.

Gregg, L., "On Computer Simulation of Human Operator Performance," *Simulation*, Vol. 5, July 1965, p. 61.

Guetzkow, H. (ed.), *Simulation in Social Science*, Prentice-Hall, Englewood Cliffs, N.J., 1962.

Guetzkow, H., et al., *Simulation in International Relations*, Prentice-Hall, Englewood Cliffs, N.J., 1963.

Gullahorn, J. T., and J. E. Gullahorn, "A Computer Model of Elementary Social Behavior," *Behavioral Science*, Vol. 8, 1963, pp. 345–63. (Reprinted in Feigenbaum and Feldman, 1963.)

Gyr, J., J. Thatcher, and G. Allen, "Computer Simulation of a Model of Cognitive Organization," *Behavioral Science*, Vol. 7, January 1962, pp. 111–16.

Hare, A. P., "Computer Simulation of Interaction in Small Groups," *Behavioral Science*, Vol. 6, July 1961, pp. 261–65.

Harmon, R., *The Computer as a Research Instrument in the Behavioral Sciences*, SP–411, System Development Corp., Santa Monica, Calif., 1960.

Holland, E., *Experiments on a Simulated Underdeveloped Economy*, M.I.T. Press, Cambridge, Mass, 1963.

Hoveland, C. I., and E. B. Hunt, "Computer Simulation of Concept-Attainment," *Behavioral Science*, Vol. 5, July 1960, pp. 265–67.

Hunt, E., *Concept Learning: An Information Processing Problem*, Wiley, New York, 1962.

Hunt, E., J. Marin, and P. Stone, *Experiments in Induction*, Academic Press, New York, 1966.

Klein, L., "A Postwar Quarterly Model: Description and Applications," in *Models of Income Determination* (National Bureau of Economic Research), Princeton University Press, Princeton, N.J., 1964.

Kotler, R., "The Competitive Marketing Simulator—A New Management Tool," *California Management Review*, Vol. 8, Spring 1965, pp. 49–60.

Laughery, K. R., and L. W. Gregg, "Simulation of Human Problem-Solving Behavior," *Psychometrika*, Vol. 27, September 1962, pp. 265–82.

McPhee, W. N., "Note on a Campaign Simulator," *Public Opinion Quarterly*, Summer 1961, pp. 184–93.

McWhitney, W. H., "Simulating the Communication Network Experiments," *Behavioral Science*, Vol. 9, No. 8, January 1964, pp. 80–84.

Meier, R. L., "Explorations in the Realm of Organizational Theory. IV: The Simulation of Social Organization," *Behavioral Science*, Vol. 10, No. 2, July 1964, pp. 232–48.

Minsky, M., "Matter, Mind and Models," *Proceedings of IFIP Congress, 1965*, Sparton, Baltimore, 1965, pp. 45–50.

Moshman, J. R., "Elections and Computer Projection," *Datamation*, Vol. 8, October 1964, pp. 30–37.

Neisser, U., "The Imitation of Man by Machine," *Science*, Vol. 139, 1963, pp. 193–97.

Newell, A., "Computers in Psychology," in *Handbook of Mathematical Psychology*, Vol. I (ed. by R. D. Luce, R. R. Bush, and E. Galanter), Wiley, New York, 1964, pp. 361–428.

Newell, A., and H. A. Simon, "Computer Simulation of Human Thinking," *Science*, Vol. 134, 1962, pp. 2011–17.

Orcutt, G., et al., *Microanalysis of Socioeconomic Systems*, Harper & Row, New York, 1961.

Ozkaptan, H., and R. Gettig, "Computer Simulation of Man-Integrated Systems," *Behavioral Science*, Vol. 8, July 1963, pp. 259–66.

Pool, I. deS., and R. Abelson, "The Simulmatics Project," *Public Opinion Quarterly*, Summer 1961, pp. 167–83.

Popkin, S., "A Model of a Communication System," *American Behavioral Scientist*, Vol. 8, No. 9, May 1965, pp. 8–11.

Rapoport, A., and A. Chammah, *Prisoner's Dilemma*, University of Michigan Press, Ann Arbor, 1965.

Reitman, W. R., *Cognition and Thought: An Information Processing Approach*, Wiley, New York, 1965.

Rome, S., and B. Rome, "The Leviathan Technique for Large-Group Analysis," *Behavioral Science*, Vol. 6, No. 2, April 1961, pp. 186–92.

Rosenthal, H., "Electronic Simulation," *European Journal of Sociology*, Vol. 6, No. 1, 1965, pp. 21–42.

Siegel, A. I., et al., *Digital Simulation of Submarine Crew Performance: I. Logic of a Psychological "Model" for Digitally Simulating Crew Performance*, Applied Psychological Services, Wayne, Penna., 1964.

Simmons, P. L., and R. F. Simmons, *The Simulation of Cognitive Processes—An Annotated Bibliography*, SP590/002/00, System Development Corp., Santa Monica, Calif., 1961.

Simon, H., "Simulation of Human Thinking," in *Computers and the World of the Future* (ed. by M. Greenberger), M.I.T. Press, Cambridge, Mass., 1962, pp. 94–131.

Sisson, R. L., and R. L. Ackoff, "Toward a Theory of the Dynamics of Conflict," in *Conflict Resolution and World Education* (ed. by S. Mudd), Junk, The Hague, 1966.

Smith, R., and P. Greenlaw, "Simulation of a Psychological Decision Process in Personnel Selection," *Management Science*, Vol. 13, No. 8, April 1967, pp. B409–B419.

Stone, R., *A Program for Growth: A Computable Model of Economic Growth*, M.I.T. Press, Cambridge, Mass., 1962.

Stonebraker, G., and E. Murphy, *The Uses of Systems Analysis in Manpower Adjustment*, National Bureau of Standards, Institute of Applied Technology, Washington, D.C., January 25, 1966.

Thiel, H., "Econometrics and Management Science," *Management Science*, Vol. 11, No. 10, June 1965, pp. B200–B212.

Tomkins, W. S., and S. Messick, *Computer Simulation of Personality*, Wiley, New York, 1963.

Wells, W. D., and J. M. Chinsky, "Effects of Competing Messages: Laboratory Simulation," *Journal of Marketing Research*, Vol. 2, May 1965, pp. 141–45.

the future of simulation

introduction 12-1

Simulation will have a major impact on the way people manage. It is being used with increasing frequency by decision makers to provide both insights into complex problems and quantitative estimates of the consequences of specific actions. The result is improved decision making. In the future simulation might have limited use for decision making; that is, where the implemented values of the controllable variables would be those found by search for optimum using the model. But the major use will be support for the human decision process. In this chapter we extrapolate some current trends in the creation and use of simulation models to provide a picture of the future as further background for those who wish to make full use of the technique.

current uses of simulation 12-2

Before we indicate future applications of simulation, it is well to review the surprisingly diverse and extensive areas in which it is now used. Figure 11–1 showed that simulation is being used to expand the functional areas being analyzed by formal models. Simulation also facilitates such analysis at higher organizational levels.

The technique has been used to a greater or less extent for almost every combination of function and level. We could add a third dimension representing the type of industry. If we did this, we would find that simulation analysis is used to study different functions in different industries, the functions being those that are most critical to the industry. Metal forming and manufacturing industries tend to use simulation extensively

Air traffic control queuing
Aircraft maintenance scheduling
Airport design
Ambulance location and dispatching
Assembly line scheduling
Bank teller scheduling
Bus (city) scheduling
Circuit design
Clerical processing system design
Communication system design
    Computer time sharing
    Telephone traffic routing
    Message system
    Mobile communications
Computer memory-fabrication test-facility design
Consumer behavior prediction
    Brand selection
    Promotion decisions
    Advertising allocation
    Court system resource allocation
Distribution system deisgn
    Warehouse location
    Mail (post office)
    Soft drink bottling
    Bank courier
    Intrahospital material flow
Enterprise models
    Steel production
    Hospital
    Shipping line
    Railroad operations
    School district
Equipment scheduling
    Aircraft
Facility layout
    Pharmaceutical center
Financial forecasting
    Insurance
    Schools
    Computer leasing
Insurance manpower hiring decisions
Grain terminal operation
Harbor design

Industry models
    Textile
    Petroleum (financial aspects)
Information system design
Intergroup communication (sociological studies)
Inventory reorder rule design
    Aerospace
    Manufacturing
    Military logistics
    Hospitals
Job shop scheduling
    Aircraft parts
    Metals forming
    Work-in-process control
    Shipyard
Library operations design
Maintenance scheduling
    Airlines
    Glass furnaces
    Steel furnaces
    Computer field service
National manpower adjustment system
Natural resource (mine) scheduling
    Iron ore
    Strip mining
Parking facility design
Numerically controlled production facility design
Personnel scheduling
    Inspection department
    Spacecraft trips
Petrochemical process design
    Solvent recovery
Police response system design
Political voting prediction
Rail freight car dispatching
Railroad traffic scheduling
Steel mill scheduling
Taxi dispatching
Traffic light timing
Truck dispatching and loading
University financial and operational forecasting
Urban traffic system design
Water resources development

Table 12–1. Areas in Which Simulation Methods Are Currently Being Used

for production planning and for predicting the effects of production facility changes. Insurance companies are more likely to use simulation in financial planning and personnel management.

Table 12–1 is a summary of some of the many ways in which simulation has been used. Several bibliographies [e.g., IBM, 1966; Malcolm, 1960] are available that index the simulation literature and can be used to find information on specific applications and techniques. The examples and exercises throughout this book have been chosen to be representative of the most typical applications of simulation.

From a user's point of view, one of the most significant changes in computer technology is the on-line computer terminal. The on-line computer terminal connected to a properly designed computer system provides the user with extremely rapid response to his inputs. Data or programming fed into a terminal is processed and the results are displayed in a matter of seconds. The most rapid response is obtained with a cathode ray tube (CRT) terminal; less rapid response is achieved from a typewriter terminal. There are two aspects of simulation model building that can benefit from such a high response system:

- greatly reduced time for the preparation and debugging of the simulation program
- fast output from a run that permits the user to explore what-if questions and search for optimal operating conditions

Let us examine in more detail each of these possible benefits of quick response terminals.

On-Line Program Preparation

The process of preparing the program for a simulation model requires that the programmer keep in mind at the same time an organized and logical representation of many factors. If the programming effort is interrupted, the process of resuming it at some later time requires a relearning of the logic (e.g., recalling various conditions for change or the variable names). When the program must be debugged on a batch system, the interruptions in the programming effort are unavoidable. After each series of modifications to the program, it must be submitted to the computing center and hours, or perhaps a day, may pass before the results are available. This interruption slows down the programming process not only because of physical delays but also by lengthening the time required on the part of the programmer to reorient himself. Both types of delays are eliminated by on-line programming and debugging. After each change is inserted in the program, it is submitted to the computer and the results are obtained quickly. (The program is translated and run to the point where the additions can be tested.) Thus debugging time is reduced but, also, on-line program preparation may yield a higher quality program—one that runs more efficiently or that uses less core. This is because the programmer works in an environment that encourages continuity of thought.

A typewriter terminal is adequate for most program debugging, even though a lengthy program requires that many steps be typed out for review. A CRT display can present material faster then the programmer can react to it; thus this high-speed capability may not be justified for debugging purposes. Where on-line terminals are accessible, we would strongly recommend that the analysts arrange to have the simulation language translator placed in the on-line system, and the terminals made available to the analyst. One note of caution—putting any computer language onto an on-line system is not a trivial effort. It requires the co-operation of, and manpower from, the system's programming group.

On-Line Use of a Simulator

Running a simulator on-line is more controversial than using it for de-bugging purposes. On the one hand it would reduce the overall processing time and, therefore, reduce analysis time by eliminating delays encountered in batch processing of jobs. Reducing these delays should aid the analyst in planning experiments with the simulator to find the best solution to the problem or to explore interesting relationships. However, the advantage is greatly reduced because most simulators require considerable computing time, even on a fast computer. For example, the simulation of a small enterprise described in the Appendix requires three to ten minutes to simulate one year of activity (when programmed in GPSS on an IBM 360/65). It does not seem reasonable that an analyst can benefit from the on-line terminal if he has to wait five to ten minutes after every set-up before the results are obtained. Five to ten minutes is long enough to distract his attention from the problem. A batch-processing system with a turn-around time of half an hour (or even two hours) would probably be as good, and considerably less expensive. Typewriter terminals would be further slowed if the simulator output is lengthy. Thus, for many analytic purposes the batch mode is preferred, simply because the on-line mode does not add any advantages and is more expensive.

There are two situations in which on-line use of simulation might be justified. One case is where the simulation proceeds very quickly and the analyst is trying to perform a heuristic search for an optimum. In this instance the analyst has to keep in mind, on a more or less continuous basis, the nature of the response surface that he is studying—that is, the performance variations in relation to controllable variable values. It is unlikely that this combination of a sophisticated search and a fast-running program will occur, since the simulation for complex situations is likely to have a long running time. The other case in which on-line computation might be justified is where the manager is using the simulation directly. The simulation might be fairly aggregate, or it might be a small part of the enterprise so that computations proceed quickly. It is likely that the manager will prefer to gain the benefits from using the simulator in a one or two hour uninterrupted period rather than spending a few minutes every half day or so in such a study. Thus, to encourage the use of simula-tion by the manager himself, an on-line system appears desirable.

At least three institutions are currently making extensive use of on-line simulation. One of the most advanced groups in the application of simula-tion is a group at the Norden Division of United Aircraft under the direction of Julian Reitman. They have arranged to be able to debug and use GPSS simulators with an on-line terminal (see Figure 12–1). They feel the on-line use is justified, not only for debugging but also for some analysis. In their situation the decision-maker is often involved in the analysis and undoubtedly benefits from the rapid response. MITRE also has adapted

Figure 12–1
CRT on-line
terminal:
(a) being used
to correct a
GPSS program;
(b) displaying
the output of a
GPSS simula-
tion. (Photos
courtesy of
Norden Division
of United Air-
craft)

GPSS to an on-line system [Ziegler, 1968]. M.I.T. has explored the use of on-line simulation and has developed a language called OPS (on-line programming system) especially for this purpose [Greenberger, 1965; Jones, 1968].

The corporate staff of General Electric has assisted a number of its departments to explore the use of on-line simulation. They have prepared relatively simple but useful simulations. One is a model of demand and production to assist in exploring the effects of the timing and the extent of plant capacity increases. These simulators run on-line. A terminal is provided at the department manager's office; he or his staff can use it to explore various alternative decisions. This system has been an effective tool for introducing the ideas of simulation to the top management of the company.

12-4 simulation packages

A simulation package is a simulator that has been designed so that it can represent any specific case of a class of situations through the insertion of proper parameter values (usually by control cards). The most famous simulator package is the job shop simulator [Rowe, 1959], which is actually a predecessor to several simulation language development efforts. By changing a few dozen parameters this program can be made to simulate any of a wide range of job shops varying in size, in structure, and in dispatch rules. Simulation packages have the obvious benefit of reducing the time necessary for preparing a simulator essentially to zero. They are faster than using a simulation language since no model deisgn or programming is required. Therefore the analyst should examine the applicability of all simulation packages before resorting to the development of a separate simulator for his problem. Some effort must be made to determine that the model implied by the package will be suitable to the situation under analysis. If the package is not suitable, then some programming effort is required, either to modify the package or to build a model with an appropriate simulation language. The flexibility of recently developed simulation languages has tended to make the original packages obsolete.

In many areas of application, however, simulation has now passed beyond the development stage and, as a result, relatively stable models are evolving. This is especially true in the production and distribution areas. In these circumstances it is possible to conceive of simulation packages that represent a type of situation that can be set by parameters to represent specific situations. We would foresee such packages becoming available in the near future.

One interesting effort, reported in "Programming by Questionnaire" [Markowitz and Kiviat, 1964] improves the useability of the job shop simulator package. In their version the parameters are inserted by means of a questionnaire. In other words, the answers to a series of questions are used to provide parameters to set up the package simulation model. This feature makes the package easy to use; it amounts to putting the instructions for the use of the package into a programmed text form.

Perhaps the most important development in the simulation field will be improvements in simulation languages. Many such improvements already exist. SIMSCRIPT I.5 is a major improvement over SIMSCRIPT I. SIMSCRIPT II is really an entirely new and improved language. GPSS/360 is an improvement over GPSS/III, which in turn is an improvement over its predecessors. Both of these languages have arrived at a fairly stable form (much as FORTRAN IV has stabilized) since each, for the use for which it is intended, seems to be applicable with a minimum of restrictions.

The kinds of language developments we expect to see in the next few years are now discussed. IBM is experimenting with an activity-oriented language (see Section 6–4) called NSS (new simulation system). The improvements in GPSS and SIMSCRIPT permit them to simulate almost any situation, whether activity based or event oriented. There may be, however certain situations in which these languages are awkward, and a language such as NSS would be useful. Every language requires a translator and that users be trained. Because these are expensive steps, it is unlikely that NSS will become a common language in the near future.

PL/I, IBM's newest multipurpose language, is gradually gaining acceptance. It has many features that make it suitable for preparing simulations. In particular, it has list-processing features to facilitate the storage and retrieval of data. If PL/I becomes more widely accepted and if translators are written to incorporate all PL/I features, then a PL/I-based simulation language may evolve. Such a language would probably consist of a number of subprograms to be used with PL/I to assist in preparing the simulation program (as GASP is for FORTRAN, see Section 6–4). The subprograms, of course, will perform functions such as time advance, random number and random variate generation, array entry and retrieval processes, and output preparation. Gradually subprograms that represent specific kinds of activities (like the subprograms within the GPSS system) may become available.

Work is nearing completion on SIMSCRIPT II, a complete new language for both procedural and simulation use (see Chapter 6). If successful, it would provide a very flexible language system for ordinary problem solving as well as for simulation preparation. Again, this development is proceeding slowly because of the difficulty of preparing and implementing translators and training analysts in the language itself. The language and translator are available, however.

There are a number of situations wherein the most suitable model is part continuous and part discrete. It is possible that discrete plus continuous systems would be best represented by a new language. We know of no effort in this direction, but foresee it as a long-range possibility.

Finally, languages will become oriented toward simulations for specific areas. These might be considered halfway between a general simulation language and a simulation package. For example, work is proceeding at the University of Toronto, under Professor Richard Judy, in the development of simulations of universities. Several models have been developed, one of the undergraduate part of the university and another of the medical school. This work has shown the researchers what kinds of operators and data arrays are required for effective simulators of university systems. This knowledge is now being incorporated in a language system. Such a language system would be directed specifically toward the simulation of universities (and other institutions of higher learning), but within that context would be quite general. Similar specialized languages might evolve in other commonly used areas, such as for health, political, and economic systems, and consumer-marketing systems. In other words, languages might evolve in any area where one kind of problem arises many times for different enterprises and even many times, but in different ways, for the same enterprise. Simulation languages will evolve when there are commonly accepted models of the basic underlying phenomena, and a high interest in improving decision making in an area. These were the conditions under which GPSS, a language suitable for the representation of many types of production, communication, and distribution systems, was developed. The structures in the other areas just mentioned are sufficiently different, both from GPSS and from each other, to justify their own language. However, each system is very complex and time will be required to develop a basic understanding of the common structural elements.

12-6 some comments on games

This book has not concentrated on the use of gaming techniques. However, we do want to mention that such methods are useful for education and for some applied studies. For example, we foresee management making more use of game simulations to study areas where behavioral factors cannot be fully represented by an all-computer simulation. Such areas include the one mentioned in Chapter 11 (i.e., the preparation of management-labor negotiations), as well as studies of marketing processes and organizational changes (personnel reassignments). Although the use of games as an educational tool is expensive, it is likely to continue to grow as a part of management training programs, if for no other reason than the fact that the demand for managers is so great that any aid to help them quickly comprehend the situations they may face is useful.

In our opinion, it is unlikely that games will find much use as models for analysis. The use of humans as parts of a model introduces too much variability. Games may find increasing use as artificial realities (see Section 11–2) to help advance research in behavior.

12-7 simulators as adaptive aids to management decision making

Perhaps the most exciting potential for simulation is as a direct aid to management decision making and to the continuing education of the manager. The progressive manager of the future (and not too distant future) should have a simulation model directly accessible. He will learn how to insert parameters (by filling out a form or through direct access on a computer terminal) that make the model represent the conditions he wishes to study. He will know how to interpret the results, which can be presented in formats resembling his ordinary management reports or as graphs and tables, as he desires. By running the simulator he will be able to explore a wide range of "blue sky" as well as obvious alternatives. He will also learn to examine and evaluate the realism of the assumptions upon which the model rests.

The decision maker will profit in several ways by such interaction with the simulator:

(1) He will gain insights into the way his environment would behave under conditions that he might not be able to test directly. (Incidentally, should one of these insights prove somewhat inaccurate as the result of later experience, the improved knowledge can be built into the evolving simulation.)

(2) The decision maker can obtain a better understanding of the trends and future situations he may face; that is, the simulation becomes an early warning system.

(3) He can find, both by his own intuitive search and with the help of formal search procedures, optimum operating conditions for specific decision situations.

Perhaps the most important requirement is for feedback from the decision maker to the model. The decision maker, living in the real world, continually gains insights. He can then introduce these (or have them introduced by the analyst) into the model. The model thus evolves continually or *adapts* to the decision maker's understanding of the real system. At any time the model represents the best understanding of the system being managed. This can include many relationships that the decision makers may have forgotten. The value of such an adaptive model is obvious. It is also clear that such a model would become valuable in training personnel to move up to management positions.

If, in fact, the business being modeled is fairly stable, the simulation may prove to be sufficiently educational so that, after a time, it is no longer needed! In other words, the simulation has become a tool to bring the manager to a new level of intuitive insights that he can then apply on a day-to-day basis without specific reference to the model. However, if the model includes phenomena that bear on infrequent strategic decisions such as plant location, organizational change, or product selection, its use would probably continue. The reason for this is that the manager does not remember from one such decision to the next all the factors involved, even if he has used the simulator previously to educate himself. The simulation thus becomes a repository of the enterprise's knowledge.

The state of the art of simulation has advanced to the point where every manager, from the line supervisor to the chairman of the board, should begin an investigation of the development of a simulation model that can adapt in the manner just described. This initial investigation should proceed at two levels. First, the manager himself should become fully acquainted with simulation techniques (including learning how to program a computer). Second, the manager should employ (on a part-time basis if necessary) an analyst who can start the development of the first adaptive model. We strongly recommend that the first model be in an aggregate form so it is not large yet includes all of the parts of the enterprise or activity under the control of the manager. At first every effort should be made to avoid going into great detail, even though it is obvious that many decisions depend on predicting such details. Once the basic aggregate model is developed, the manager and analyst can explore its use. The initial model usually pays for itself by assisting in some decisions. The manager can then proceed to have more detailed models developed that reflect his more detailed comprehension of the world. The details added should be those most likely to bear on important decisions. The evolution of more complex models should continue as long as the manager feels that the simulation is providing new insights and requires more improvement. Every effort should be made to make it easy for the manager to use the model directly since it must be *his* decision-making tool. Nevertheless, most managers will require assistance to work out some of the technical details.

Such an adaptive simulation program may well become a competitive advantage to the progressive manager. Any manager who wants to run his activity so that he controls its changes, rather than reacting to changes, cannot avoid investigating simulation.

references

Greenberger, M., et al., *On Line Computation and Simulation, The OPS–3 System,* M.I.T. Press, Cambridge, Mass., 1965.

IBM, *Bibliography on Simulation,* Report 320–0924–0, IBM, White Plains, N.Y., 1966.

Jones, M., *Incremental Simulation of a Time-Shared Computer,* Project MAC Report MAC–TR–48 (thesis), Massachusetts Institute of Technology, Cambridge, Mass., January 1968.

Malcolm, D. G., "Bibliography on the Use of Simulation in Management Analysis," *Operations Research*, Vol. 8, March 1960, pp. 169–77.

Markowitz, H., and P. J. Kiviat, *Programming by Questionnaire : The Job Shop Simulation Program Generator,* RM–5162, RAND Corp., Santa Monica, Calif., 1964.

Rowe, A., "Toward a Theory of Scheduling," *Contributions to Scientific Research in Management,* Proceedings of a Conference, Western Data Processing Center, Graduate School of Business, University of California, Los Angeles, January 29–30, 1959.

Ziegler, E., "The GPSS On-Line Monitor," *IEEE Transactions on Systems Science and Cybernetics,* Vol. SSC–4, No. 4., November 1968, pp. 438–41.

appendix

an example

To review and emphasize some of the points made in the text we will describe a company-wide simulation study made by the authors. The company studied is small, and it probably could not have afforded such an analysis from its own resources. (Support was provided by the Management and Systems Engineering Group of the University of Waterloo and by the cooperation of students there.) By choosing a small company, it was possible to show how a complete enterprise can be modeled, and yet have the resulting simulation documentation be compact enough for publication.

The company in question is a distributor of industrial equipment. Some of the units sold are large pieces of equipment that cost thousands of dollars. Most of the sales, however, are in smaller items sold in quantity. Some of these items cost several hundred dollars and are sold in units of one or two at a time. Other items are small replaceable parts that are sold in quantities of dozens at frequent intervals. Most of the sales are to local outlets who are close to the ultimate consumer. Sales are made by five salesmen (including the president of the company) who travel the company's sales areas. A small office staff runs the remainder of the business. The business is seasonal, reaching a peak in July and August and a lull in December and January. Several thousand items are carried in inventory.

Problem Definition

Discussions with the company's president and with the man responsible for financial management indicated that the company made two key operating decisions and was, because of rapid growth over the past few years, about to be faced with several strategic decisions. The day-to-day operating decisions are:

- inventory reordering
- financial cash flow decisions (acquisition and use of cash)

The inventory decisions are the classical ones: to order so as to minimize carrying costs and yet not antagonize customers by being out of stock. This distributor, of course, has competitors, and to retain his customers must provide the goods when his customers need them. Inventory decisions are complicated by the seasonality of the business and by occasional specials when special discounts are given for a short period of time in order to attract business. Price changes occur from time to time, and before each there is a flurry of orders.

The cash flow decisions are made so that the company operates with as little idle cash as possible. By carefully estimating potential accounts receivable and by choosing when to pay accounts payable, it finds it can operate with a minimum of cash. To tide it over during certain phases of the season when inventories must be built up, it may borrow from the bank. The financial decision rule should minimize the cost of bank loans, the risk of antagonizing the bank by not being able to repay the loan as scheduled, and the risk of antagonizing suppliers by not paying them within a reasonable time.

Two imminent strategic decisions are when and how to expand warehousing facilities and when and in what territory to extend sales efforts by the addition of more salesmen. In this analysis we will concentrate on the tactical operating decisions. Simulation studies of the sales effort problem would require models of salesman and consumer behavior.

Problem Formulation

Understanding of the company and its operation was developed by both a flow and a functional analysis. The material flow analysis did not help much because many processes of interest are not directly related to the flow of materials through the company. Thus, we developed a functional analysis that shows both information and material processing. This analysis was developed in cooperation with the senior members of the company. The functions include the marketing functions (soliciting sales and receiving and editing customer orders), the inventory control functions such as checking stock and filling back orders and accounting functions (adjusting accounts receivable, cash and accounts payable at appropriate times). There are two key decision points: calculating the reorder quantity (implicitly utilizing a reorder point) and determining when to pay accounts payable and how to adjust the bank loan. At this point we have the problem defined since we can formulate the decision question, "What combination of inventory reorder and financial decision rules will provide the company with the highest expected profit under the assumed future environmental conditions?" Furthermore, a start has been made toward developing the model in the form of the functional flow diagram.

Some time was spent in determining how to represent the market and the selling process. Ultimately it would be desireable to relate actual customer orders to various determining factors: general economic conditions, total demand for the products that are made by the equipment sold, the effectiveness of the company's salesmen both in creating good will (some orders were unsolicited in any direct way) and in terms of closing sales. Modeling the market would require a major design and data collection effort. Therefore, it was decided that this first model would exclude such considerations and would assume a simpler market representation. The market would generate orders at rates and with order product requirements determined by frequency distribution. These distributions are based on past data plus managers' subjective estimates of how they would change in the future. At some future time, a more sophisticated market model could be added that would compute these frequency distributions from more basic considerations.

Estimating Parameters

At this point in the study it was recognized that several key groups of data would be needed to set the parameters of the model. It would be necessary to obtain distributions of customer order characteristics, to obtain the distribution of lead-times on shipments from suppliers, and it would be desirable to obtain the existing management decision rules. These latter were never stated explicitly (as is true in most small companies) and would probably have to be deduced from actual behavior. This in turn would make it necessary to obtain some information about actual reorder patterns, accounts payable, and bank loan activities.

In this company none of the data was in machine-readable form, which presented an immediate problem of data gathering and reduction. The main data gathering effort was to analyze one year's invoices. To indicate typical data gathering problems we will describe how these data were obtained and used to produce customer order quantity. It should be recognized that invoice data are not a direct representation of customer orders since the invoice is prepared when the order is edited and may not include orders that were lost or rejected early in the process. The invoices do not indicate the time between the customer order and the checking of stock. However, they were the only data available on customer order activity. In this particular case the company assured the analysts that practically no orders were received that were not indicated in some way on the invoices.

The data reduction process for analyzing these invoices was designed to achieve the following information:

- a distribution of sales by product line by month
- a distribution of sales by product line by salesmen (perhaps by month)
- a distribution of sales within each product line by dollar amount and by quantity of order
- an indication of the number of invoices and the number of invoice items by product line per month

Two decisions were made in order to simplify this initial model. First, it was decided not to try to distinguish between customers, so that the market was represented as one large order-producing entity. Thus, a distribution by customer activity was not required in this first analysis. Second, it was decided to group 5000 individual stocked items into five product classes in order to avoid handling a massive product file. The company tended to make its decisions in terms of product lines or classes rather than by individual items, although the results of this first analysis would undoubtedly lead to requirements for more detailed data. Since the company was being managed by pure intuition at this point, any model, even grossly aggregated by product class, would provide additional, and hopefully useful, information.

The steps in the data analysis were as follows: One year's worth of invoices were obtained from the company. These were scanned visually. It was observed that there were two different sequences of invoice serial numbers (because of an earlier merger of two companies) and that there were many special cases such as the following:

- Some invoices represented returns for credit.
- Many invoices had back-ordered items indicated on them.
- Invoices with just one item did not have totals.
- All prices were given as list prices with the discount taken after groups of items or at the end of the invoice, so that the invoice total was the net price.

At this point, card layouts were created; three for each invoice.

(1) A header card that contained the invoice number, the customer's name, the salesman's name, the date of the invoice.

(2) A card for each invoice item that repeated the invoice number and and had the quantity, item identification (part number), item description, back-order quantity, price, and the amount.

(3) A third card that gave the net amount for the invoice and repeated the invoice number.

Each card had, in column one, a type code. This type code also indicated when an invoice was a return for credit. Reasonably careful instructions were worked out for the keypunch group; however, in the first batches there was some confusion as to whether quantity columns would be justified right or left. This created additional problems in the editing program.

While cards were being keypunched, an edit program was written that would transfer the data from card to tape and in the process would accumulate certain statistics. The general procedure was to obtain overall statistics during the edit run and obtain product line statistics after the data had been put on tape. One reason for this was that it was difficult to determine how to group items into product lines. Therefore, the tape with one year's worth of data was sorted by item identification and listed. This list was analyzed to help make decisions as to to how to group items into product lines. The company made direct use of its supplier's item identifications, in general, and had provided the analysts with supplier's catalogues to assist in making this grouping. Once the data were on tape, they were sorted and listed. Statistics were accumulated in various ways.

The analyst chose to write these editing programs in FORTRAN, partly because the FORTRAN translator was easily accessible and because he knew the language. The choice of a language with more format control, such as COBOL or RPG, might have been more suitable in this editing step. Because of the way the data were written on invoices, there were a number of fields in which alphabetic data occasionally appeared, such as the dimension *in.* for inches in a quantity field or *N/C* for no charge in a price field. In any case it became necessary to make two editing runs. For each month's invoices, one run assumed all data as alphanumeric and listed them. A clerk could then quickly go through the data and pick out the alphanumeric data in the quantity columns. These cards were corrected, and then the data were rerun with a program that read the quantities properly as numeric values. The left-adjusted quantity fields were corrected during this editing.

Another confusion that arose was that the cards for each month were returned by the keypunch group with all the header cards grouped together, all the item cards grouped together, and then, all the total cards together. This was accommodated easily by creating a program that retained the header information in a FORTRAN array and then reassigned it to the appropriate item cards as the data were processed. This was made possible because we had made the fortunate choice of having invoice numbers repeated on all cards (a suggestion of the director of the keypunch group). In any case, this data analysis produced the required distributions.

Developing the Simulation Program

The model was being developed in parallel with this data reduction effort. It was decided to write the model in GPSS. The analysts knew this language, and a translator was available on the computer. This problem was of the type that could be handled by GPSS in such a way that the programming time would be reduced significantly.

The transactions of GPSS have different meanings as they flow through the simulator, but they start off representing customer orders. We will not explain the program in detail; Figure A–1 is an annotated listing.

This model went through several stages of debugging, first to remove obvious bugs and then to assure us that the model represented the situation as we understood it. In order to debug, the model was set up to represent existing situations. The main form of validation was to produce outputs—company profits, financial levels, and inventory levels—that reproduced the financial manager's recollection of actual situations. Comparisons were made with such data as were available.

The preliminary use of the model was to explore, heuristically, inventory or financial decision rules.

277

Figure A–1 shows the model with a very simple inventory decision rule and a more complicated and realistic financial decision process. The inventory rule is to order three times the minimum level whenever the minimum level is reached. The minimum levels were set subjectively on the basis of the company's experience.

The financial decision has two parts: a daily part and a monthly part. In the daily part, money is borrowed on any day in which the bank balance (cash on hand) would go below zero; enough is borrowed to create a $10,000 balance.

Each month, the entire financial situation is forecast. If the forecasted accounts receivable do not cover the forecasted accounts payable, an effort is made to expedite future accounts receivable by offering a discount. If this is not sufficient, a bank loan is made. If a surplus occurs in any month, bank loans are repaid. The expression of the logic of the financial decision in GPSS is quite awkward; this is a deficiency in the language. It is possible to write assembly-level or even FORTRAN subroutines for GPSS but this requires rather sophisticated knowledge of the GPSS system.

As an illustration, this simulation was run four times. Two of the runs represented a very simplified parameter search. The second pair of runs explored the desirability of a new financial decision rule.

Parameter Identification

In the simulation model it is hypothesized that the probability that an order will be lost if backlogged is $a + bx/y$, where a is a constant representing initial impatience with having to wait, x is the quantity on back-order, and y is the normal reorder quantity. Thus, if b is properly chosen, bx/y represents the increasing probability of a lost order as the estimated wait for delivery increases. Suppose that there is doubt about the value of a, but that b and other parameters of the model are known reasonably accurately. The model can then be run with various values of a to determine which fits historical data most closely. In a complete example a search for the best fit to both a and b may be required. To illustrate, the model was run at two values of $a = 0.02$ and 0.2.

Financial Decision

The monthly financial decision is a complex computation; is this complexity justified? Suppose the daily borrowing decision were made to maintain an adequate cash position. To examine the effect of the monthly decision, the simulation was run using it and not using it.

Example Results

The results of these four runs are shown in Table A–1. The monthly financial decision does appear to pay off. Also, the output is very sensitive to the choice of a. This factor will have to be fit carefully with historical results.

- validate the choice of the balking model: $a + bx/y$
- try other financial and inventory decision rules, replicating each with different random numbers to investigate statistical confidence in apparent differences in the use of different rules
- extend the model to include a more sophisticated market submodel, including the relating of sales to the number and quality of salesmen
- represent product lines in more detail

	Run			
Balking Level (a)	0.200	0.200	0.020	0.020
Financial Decision	Full	Daily only	Full	Daily only
End Inventory	276,822	276,822	221,313	221,313
Start cost	293,270	293,270	151,251	151,251
Change in inventory	−16,448	−16,448	70,062	70,062
Profit	44,277	38,817	45,872	42,280
Asset change	27,829	22,369	115,934	112,342

Table A–1. Analysis of Equipment Wholesaler Simulation Runs

```
BLOCK
NUMBER   *LOC    CPERATICN   A,B,C,D,E,F,G                 CCMMENTS
                 SIMULATE
         *
         *
         *       SIMULATE EQUIPMENT SUPPLY COMPANY
         *
         *          FUNCTION LISTING
         *
           1 FUNCTION   RN1,D5            PRODUCT LINE DEMAND DISTRIBUTICN     FUNCTIONS
  .C1   1     .26   2     .51   3      .76   4     1.0   5                     permit defining
           2 FUNCTION   P1,D5             MIN. INVENTCRY LEVELS                arbitrary
  1.    0     2.    396   3.     990   4.     660   5.     528                 relationships
         *                                                                    between the
           3 FUNCTICN   P1,D5             UNIT SELL PRICE                      first variable
  1.    1000  2.    100   3.     50    4.     10    5.     1                   after the word
         *                                                                    FUNCTION and
           4 FUNCTION   P1,D5             UNIT CCST PRICE                      the result
  1.    950   2.    95    3.     47    4.     9.6   5.     .99                 (called FN/)
         *
           5 FUNCTION   RN2,D5            CUSTOMER PAYMENT TERMS
  .1    10    .3    30    .7     60     .9    90    1.     120
         *
           6 FUNCTION   P1,D5             SUPPLIER PAYMENT TERMS
  1.    10    2.    90    3.     90     4.    60    5.     30
         *
           7 FUNCTION   P1,D5             AVERAGE NUMBER OF ITEMS PER SALES CRD
  1.    1     2.    2     3.     5      4.    10    5.     20
         *
           8 FUNCTION   P7,D12            SEASCNAL FACTOR
  1.    .6    2.    .5    3.     .6     4.    .75   5.     1.    6.    1.35
  7.    1.4   8.    1.5   9.     1.4    10.   1.35  11.    1.    12.   .75
         *
           9 FUNCTION   P1,D5             MINIMUM SALES CRDER SIZE
  1.    0     2.    0     3.     0      4.    0     5.     C
         *
          10 FUNCTICN   P1,D5             MINIMUM PURCHACE CRDER SIZE
  1.    0     2.    0     3.     0      4.    50    5.     1C0
         *
          11 FUNCTION   RN3,D14           CUMULATIVE NORMAL CURVE              RNX is a generated
  .C2   -20   .05   -18   .1     -13    .2    -8    .3     -5    .4    -3      random number
  .5    0     .6    3     .7     5      .8    8     .9     13    .95   15
  .98   2C    .999  30
         *
          12 FUNCTION   RN4,D5            SALES PER SALESMAN CISTRIBUTION
  .2    6     .4    7     .6     8      .8    9     .999   10
         *
          13 FUNCTICN   P1,D5             CRDER DEL TIME PER PRCDUCT LINE      Relationship given
  1.    21    2.    15    3.     15     4.    5     5.     2                   as x₁,y₁;x₂,y₂, etc.
         *
         *
         *
         *
         *
         *
         *
         *
         *       TIME UNITS
         *
         *   1       -10MINUTES
         *   48      -1 DAY                                 Time units
         *   1152    -1MCNTH
         *   13824   -1 YEAR
         *
         *          ***DCCUMENTATION***
         *
         *       PARAMETER  LISTING                    Parameters associated with
         *                                             each transaction
         *   P1    PRODUCT LINE
         *   P2    QUANTITY SALES CRDER
         *   P3    QUANTITY  PURCHASE CRDER
         *   P4    DCLLAR TGTAL AMCUNT SALES ORDER
         *   P6    ORDER DAY
         *   P7    CRDER MCNTH
         *   P8    SALESMAN NUMBER
         *   P10   TEMPCRARY STCRAGE
         *   P11   A/R CELAY
         *   P12   A 1 HERE INDICATES A PC TRASACTICN
         *   P13   PROFIT CN CRDER
         *   P14   RECEIPT QUANTITY
         *
         *
         *       VARIABLE LISTING (NCT ALL VARIABLES)
         *
```

Figure A–1 GPSS program to simulate an equipment wholesale firm.

```
CRDQ    FVARIABLE   FN7-FN9             AVERAGEORDER    QUANTITY
ADDQ    FVARIABLE   V$CRDQ*FN11*781/10000    VARIABLE PART CF ORDER QUAN
CNTY    FVARIABLE   (FN7+V$ADDQ)*FN8        ORDER QUANTITY
SAMT    FVARIABLE   V$QNTY*FN3              DOLLAR SALES AMOUNT
CAMT    FVARIABLE   V$QNTY*FN4              DOLLAR COST AMOUNT
PROF    FVARIABLE   (FN3-FN4)*P2           DOLLAR PROFIT PER SALE
SCOST   FVARIABLE   MX1(1,P1)*FN4          COST OF STOCK CN HAND
DAY     VARIABLE    ((C1+K1)/K48)*K48      TIME AT END OF DAY
CDAY    VARIABLE    (C1/K48+K1)'K24   DAY OF MONTH
MTH     VARIABLE    ((C1+K1)/K1152)*K1152  TIME AT END CF MONTH
CMTH    VARIABLE    ((C1/K1152)+K1)   MONTH
CATE    VARIABLE    X13'K288+K1            DAY NUMBER
CVHD    FVARIABLE   K5000                  CONSTANT OVERHEAD EXPENCES PER MONTH
*
*
* VARIABLES FCR FINANCIAL DECISICN
*
FDV1    VARIABLE    (X13+P10)'K288+K1   DAY IN NEXT MONTH
FDV2    VARIABLE    X10+X1                 R+B
FDV3    VARIABLE    X11+K10000             P+S
FDV4    VARIABLE    (X13+P10+K24)'K288+K1  MONTH AFTER NEXT
FDV5    FVARIABLE   V$FDV2+.3*V12          R+B+.3RF
FDV6    FVARIABLE   X12*282/1000           NET FROM FUTURE A/R
FDV7    FVARIABLE   V$FDV3-V$FDV2-V$FDV6   AMT. TO BORRCW
FDV8    FVARIABLE   MX2(V$FDV4,3)*3/10     REDUCTION IN FUTURE A/R
FDV9    FVARIABLE   X15*5/1000             INTEREST - LOW RATE
FDV10   FVARIABLE   X16*75/10000           INTEREST - HIGH
FDV11   VARIABLE    X15+X16                TCTAL LOAN
FDV12   VARIABLE    K10000-X1              AMT TC BORRCW - DAILY
FDV14   VARIABLE    V$FDV2-V$FDV3          R+B-(P+S) SURPLUS
*
*           SAVEVALUE DEFINITICNS
*
*   X1    BANK BALANCE
*   X2    CUMULATIVE PROFITS
*
* FACTORS FOR FINANCIAL DECISICN
*
* X10   SUM OF NEXT 24 DAYS EST. A/R    = R
* X11   SUM OF NEXT 24 DAYS EST. A/P    = P
* X12   SUM OF DAYS 25 - 48  A/R        = RF
*
* X13   DAY NUMBER
*
* X15   LOAN AT LOW RATE
* X16   LOAN AT HIGH RATE
* LOGIC SW. 10   LAST ACTICN INDICATOR,SET = BCRROW
*
*           MATRIX MSAVEVALUE LIST
*
1       MATRIX      X,5,5
*   K1    PRODUCT LINE  1 - 5         INVENTORY RECCRD
*     1 QUANTITY OF STOCK CN HAND
*     2 QUANT ON ORDER
*     3 QUANTITY CF DAILY BACK ORDERS
*     4 COST CF STOCK CN HAND
*     5 LOST REVENUE CN LOST SALE
*
2       MATRIX      X,290,7
*   ACCOUNTS RECCRD
*     1-DAY  2-MON  3- A/R  4- A/P  5- CASH  6- CUM: PRCFIT
*                7- $ SALES
*
*     1 DUE DATE
*
*
*     *** CRDER TRANSIT MATRIX ***
3       MATRIX      X,290,7
*   K3 1-2 DAY , MONTH
*   K3   PRODUCT LINE 3-7 DAILY CRDERS
*     1 DUE DATE
*
4       MATRIX      X,4,5
*   K4    PRODUCT LINE  1 - 5      MARKET SALES RECORD BY PRODUCT LINE
*     1 TCTAL QUANTITY SCLC
*     2 TCTAL DOLLAR AMOUNT
*     3 TCTAL  DOLLAR PRCFIT
*     4 TCTAL LOST PROFIT
*
5       MATRIX      X,2,5
```

These are arithmetic subroutines to be used in the main program

K24 = 24 = a constant (either notation is used)

SAVEVALUES (*x*'s) are general storage locations

MATRIX SAVEVALUES are two-dimensional arrays

281

Figure A–1   (continued)

```
*      K5   SALESMAN  1 - 5        MARKET RECORD BY SALESMAN
*           1 TOTAL DOLLAR AMOUNT
*           2 TOTAL DOLLAR PROFIT
*
*     ****  INITIALIZE MXSAVEVALUES  ****
*
            INITIAL     MX1(1,2),1188    INVENTORY LEVELS
            INITIAL     MX1(1,3),2970
            INITIAL     MX1(1,4),1980
            INITIAL     MX1(1,5),1584
            INITIAL     MX2(18,4),252450   INITIAL A/P
            INITIAL     MX2(276,4),19008
            INITIAL     MX2(246,4),1568
            INITIAL     MX1(4,2),112860   COST OF INVENTORY
            INITIAL     MX1(4,3),139590
            INITIAL     MX1(4,4),19008
            INITIAL     MX1(4,5),1568
            INITIAL     X1,K10000          INITIAL BANK BALANCE
            INITIAL     X13,K216           START IN FOURTH QUARTER.
            INITIAL     MX2(217-240,3),1000   INITIAL A/R
            INITIAL     MX2(217-240,4),1000   INITIAL A/P          Simulation starts
*                                                                  by generating
1           GENERATE    1,,,,,I5,H       GENERATE ONE ORDER EVERY 10 MINUTES  orders
*
2           ASSIGN      6,V$CDAY         ASSIGN DAY COUNTER
3           ASSIGN      7,V$CMTH         ASSIGN MONTH COUNTER
*
*
4           ASSIGN      1,FN1            ASSIGN PRODUCT LINE TO ORDER    Order is created
5           ASSIGN      2,V$QNTY         ASSIGN SALES QUANTITY TO ORDER
*
6           TEST L      P2,K1,ZERO
7           ASSIGN      2,K1
*
8    ZERO   ASSIGN      4,V$SAMT         ASSIGN DOLLAR SALES AMOUNT
9           ASSIGN      8,FN12           ASSIGN SALESMAN NUMBER TO ORDER
10          ASSIGN      13,V$PROF        ASSIGN PROFIT
*
11          TEST E      P1,K1,TRY        PRODUCT LINE 1
12          MSAVEVALUE  K1+,2,P1,P2      ADD TO ON ORDER
13          MSAVEVALUE  3+,V11,3,P2      IF PL 1 , PLACE ORDER - V11 BELOW
14          TRANSFER    ,BACKO           SEND PL1 TRANS. TO BO QUE
15   TRY    TEST L      P2,MX1(1,P1),BACKQ   CHECK ORDER QTY AGAINST STOCK
*
16          MSAVEVALUE  K1-,1,P1,P2      DECREASE STOCK ON HAND
*
*     ****  UPDATE SALES RECORDS  ****
*
17          MSAVEVALUE  K1,4,P1,V$SCOST     COST OF STOCK ON HAND
18          MSAVEVALUE  K4+,1,P1,P2      VOLUME SOLD PER PRODUCT LINE
19          MSAVEVALUE  K4+,2,P1,P4      $ VOLUME SOLD PER PRODUCT LINE
20          MSAVEVALUE  K2+,V$DATE,7,P4   $ SALES TO OUTPUT
21          MSAVEVALUE  K4+,3,P1,P13     $ PROFIT SOLD PER PRODUCT LINE
22          SAVEVALUE   2+,P13           ACCUMULATE PROFIT
*
     51 VARIABLE   P8-K5                 REDEFINES SALESMAN NUMBER
23          MSAVEVALUE  K5+,1,V51,P4      $ AMOUNT PER SALESMAN
24          MSAVEVALUE  K5+,2,V51,P13     $ PROF PER SALESMAN
*
*
     2  VARIABLE   (FN5+X13)'K288+K1    A/R DELAY
25          ASSIGN      11,V2
26          TEST E      P1,K1,LAAP       TEST FOR P.L.1
     3  VARIABLE   (K10+X13)'K288+K1    PAYMENT DAY FOR P. L. 1
27          ASSIGN      11,V3            IF P.L.1 REDEFINE DAY VARIABLE
28   LAAP   MSAVEVALUE  K2+,P11,3,P4     ADD $ SALE AMT TO A/R MATRIX
*
29          TRANSFER    ,TERM            TRANSFER TO RECORDS
*
30   BACKQ  LOGIC S     P1               BACKORDER RELEASE SWITCH
31          TRANSFER    .V$BALK,NEXT,LOST  CUSTOMERS BALK IF WAIT IS TOO LONG
*
*     BALK CAUSES PROBABILITY OF LOSING BACK ORDER
*     TO BE PROPORTIONAL TO FRACTION OF REORDER LEVEL
*     WHICH IS ON BACKORDER.
     BALK   FVARIABLE   (MX1(3,P1)*1000)/(3*FN2)+20 ──────────── Varied to represent
32   NEXT   SPLIT       1,BAK            CREATE BO TRANSACTION         different balking
33          MSAVEVALUE  K1+,3,P1,P2      INCREASE BACK ORDER QUANTITY  behavior
34          TRANSFER    ,TERM
35   BAK    QUEUE       BLOG                                           Backlog queue
```

Figure A-1   (continued)

```
36              ASSIGN      12,K1           INDICATE BO TRANS.
37              GATE UR     P1              WAIT FOR RECEIPT OF GOODS
38              DEPART      BLOG
39              MSAVEVALUE  K1-,3,P1,P2      DECREASE BO QUAN
40              TRANSFER    ,TRY                              Return to main process
        *
41     LOST     MSAVEVALUE  K4+,4,P1,P13     ADD LOST PROFIT TO OUTPUT
42              TRANSFER    ,TERM            TRANSFER TO CHECK END OF DAY
        *
        *   ****   CHECK FOR DAY OR MONTH END ****
        *
        30      VARIABLE    C1+K1
43     TERM     TEST NE     P12,K1,BOUT      IF BO TRANS., TERMINATE.
44              TEST NE     V$DAY,V30,EDAY   CHECK FOR END OF DAY
45     MON      TEST NE     V$MTH,V30,EMON    CHECK FOR END OF MONTH
46              TERMINATE   1
47     BOUT     TERMINATE
        *
        *
        *
48     EDAY     ASSIGN      1,K5             ASSIGN LOOP PARAMETER       Transactions now
        *                                                               represent processing
        *          CYCLE THROUGH ALL PRODUCT LINES                      triggers (for day end
        *                                                               or month end) rather
        * DAILY PROCESSING                                              than orders
        *
        *
        *   ****   R E - O R D E R   R U L E  ****
        *
        40      VARIABLE    MX1(1,P1)+MX1(2,P1)   ON ORDER + ON HAND
49     EDAY1 TEST NE       P1,K1,HERE       IF PL1, SKIP REORDER PROCESS.
50           TEST L        V40,FN2,HERE      TO HERE  IF NO ORDER NEEDED.
        *
       PURQ  FVARIABLE    3*FN2
       PCOST FVARIABLE    P14*FN4
        *
        *
        9  FVARIABLE    P1+K2        +2 PUTS INTO CORRECT COL IN MATRIX
        11     VARIABLE    (FN13+X13)'K288+K1  DELIVERY DUE DATE
51              ASSIGN      9,V11
52              MSAVEVALUE  K3+,P9,V9,V$PURQ   PLACE PUR QTY IN TRANSIT MATRIX
53     SKIP1 MSAVEVALUE    K1+,2,P1,V$PURQ   ADD PURQ. QUAN. TO ON ORDER.
        *
        *   ORDER RECEIPT PROCESSING
        *
        *
54     HERE     ASSIGN      14,MX3(V$DATE,V9)    ASSIGN DAILY RECEIPTS
55              MSAVEVALUE  K1,4,P1,V$SCOST   COST OF STOCK ON HAND
56              MSAVEVALUE  K1+,1,P1,P14      ADD DAILY RECEIPTS TO INVENTORY
57              MSAVEVALUE  K1-,2,P1,P14      SUBT. RECEIPTS FROM ON ORDER.
        21      VARIABLE    (FN6+X13)'K288+K1  PAYMENT DUE DATE
58              ASSIGN      9,V21
59              MSAVEVALUE  K2+,P9,4,V$PCOST    ENTERS $ PUR. AMT TO OUTPUT
60     SKIP2 LOOP         1,EDAY1
61              SAVEVALUE   1+,MX2(V$DATE,3) ADD DAILY A/R TO BANK BAL.
62              SAVEVALUE   1-,MX2(V$DATE,4) SUBT. DAILY A/P FROM BANK BAL.
        *
63              MSAVEVALUE  K2,V$DATE,6,X2   PUT CUM. PROFIT IN OUTPUT
64              MSAVEVALUE  K2,V$DATE,1,P6   ENTER DAY IN ACCOUNTS RECORD
65              MSAVEVALUE  K2,V$DATE,2,P7   ENTER MONTH IN ACCOUNTS RECORD
66              MSAVEVALUE  K3,V$DATE,1,P6   ENTER DAY IN ORDER TRANSIT MATRIX
67              MSAVEVALUE  K3,V$DATE,2,P7   ENTER MONTH IN ORDER TRANSIT MATRIX
        *
68              ASSIGN      1,K5
        *
        *   PHASE  TWO  BACK ORDER PROCESS
        *
       BOAT  FVARIABLE    P2*FN3
       BOPT  FVARIABLE    P2*(FN3-FN4)
        *
69     EDAY2 TEST G       MX1(1,P1),K0,NOSTK    HAVE STOCK
70              LOGIC R     P1              ALLOW BO'S TO BE PROCESSED.
        *
71     NOSTK LOOP         1,EDAY2
72              TEST L      X1,K0,EDAY3      IS BANK BAL NEG.
73              SAVEVALUE   14,V$DAY
74              PRINT       1,16,X,N
        *
        * BORROW SO BAL. WILL NOT GO NEG.
75              SAVEVALUE   16+,V$FDV12      BORROW AT HI RATE
76              LOGIC S     10              LAST ACTION = BORROW        283
```

Figure A-1   (continued)

```
77              SAVEVALUE   1,K10000          10000 IN BANK
78      EDAY3 MSAVEVALUE   K2,V$DATE,5,X1    ENTER BANK BAL.
79              SAVEVALUE   13+,K1            ADVANCE DATE NUMBER BY ONE.
80              TRANSFER    ,MON
        *
        *                   UPDATE MONTHLY RECORDS
        *
81      EMON    SAVEVALUE   1-,V$CVHD         SUBT MO C.H. FROM BANK BAL.
82              SAVEVALUE   1-,V$FDV9         SUBTRACT INTEREST
83              SAVEVALUE   1-,V$FDV10
84              SAVEVALUE   2-,V$CVHD         SUBT. CH FROM PROFIT
85              SAVEVALUE   2-,V$FDV9         SUBT. INTEREST
86              SAVEVALUE   2-,V$FDV10
        * FINANCIAL DECISION
87      FIN51 TEST NE      P7,K12,FIN40      IF DEC. SKIP FIN. DECISION
88              SAVEVALUE   10,K0             CLEAR TO ACC. NEXT MO. A/R
89              SAVEVALUE   11,K0             A/P
90              SAVEVALUE   12,K0             MO. AFTER NEXT A/R
91              ASSIGN      10,K24            DC 24 DAYS
92      FIN1    SAVEVALUE   10+,MX2(V$FDV1,3)   R
93              SAVEVALUE   11+,MX2(V$FDV1,4)   P
94              SAVEVALUE   12+,MX2(V$FDV4,3)   RF
95      FIN3    LOOP        10,FIN1
96      FIN5    TEST L      V$FDV2,V$FDV3,FDOK   R+B (LT) P+S
97              TEST G      V$FDV5,V$FDV3,FDN    R+B+.3RF (GT) P+S
        * THIS PATH IF MUST BORROW
98              GATE LR     10,FIN10          LAST ACTION BORROW TO 10
99      FIN11 SAVEVALUE   15+,V$FDV7         BORROW AT LOW PRICE
100             LOGIC S     10
101             TRANSFER    ,FIN20
102     FIN10 TEST G      V$FDV11,K100000,FIN11   ABOVE CRITICAL AMT.
103             SAVEVALUE   16+,V$FDV7         BORROW AT HIGH RATE
104             LOGIC S     10
105     FIN20 SAVEVALUE   1+,V$FDV7          ADD TO BANK BAL.
        * THIS PATH IF FUTURE A/R USED
106     FDN     SAVEVALUE   1+,V$FDV6         ADD MOVED UP A/R TO BAL.
107             ASSIGN      10,K24
108     FIN2  MSAVEVALUE   K2-,V$FDV4,3,V$FDV8   REDUCE FUTURE A/R
109             LOOP        10,FIN2
110             SAVEVALUE   14,V$DATE          SIGNAL TO INDICATE MONTH END LOAN
111             PRINT       1,16,X,N           PRINT IF LOAN
112             TRANSFER    ,FIN40
113     FDOK    ASSIGN      10,V$FDV14        PUT AVAIL IN P10
114             TEST G      X16,P10,FIN31     LOAN (GT) SURPLUS
115             SAVEVALUE   16-,P10           PAY HIGH RATE LOAN
116             SAVEVALUE   1-,P10            REDUCE BAL
117             LOGIC R     10
118             TRANSFER    ,FIN40
119     FIN31 SAVEVALUE   1-,X16             REDUCE BAL.
120             ASSIGN      10-,X16           REDUCE SURPLUS
121             SAVEVALUE   16-,K0            REDUCE LOAN
122             TEST G      X15,P10,FIN32     LOAN (GT) SURPLUS
123             SAVEVALUE   15-,P10           REDUCE LOAN
124             SAVEVALUE   1-,P10            REDUCE BAL.
125             LOGIC R     10               LAST ACTION = REPAY
126             TRANSFER    ,FIN40
127     FIN32 SAVEVALUE   1-,X15             REDUCE BAL.
128             SAVEVALUE   15,K0             CLEAR LOAN
129             LOGIC R     10
130     FIN40 MSAVEVALUE   2,V$DATE,5,X1     ENTER BANK BAL.
131     OUT     TERMINATE   1                                              End of program
        *
                START       3456              RUN FOR INITIAL STARTUP PERIOD
        *   THREE MONTHS
        *                                                                  Runs for 3 months
                RESET                         CLEAR TOTALS FOR MAIN RUN
                INITIAL     X2,K0
                INITIAL     MX1(1-5,5),K0     CLEAR DATA ACCUMULATION SAVEVALUES
                INITIAL     MX2(217-288,1-7),K0
                INITIAL     MX3(217-288,1-7),K0
                INITIAL     MX4(1-4,1-5),K0
                INITIAL     MX5(1-2,1-5),K0
                START       13823
                END
```

Annotations in right margin:
- Lines 88–91: End-of-month financial decision process
- Line 131: End of program
- Runs for 3 months

Figure A–1 (continued)

Partial output after 3 months (3456 time units)

RELATIVE CLOCK
BLOCK COUNTS

BLOCK	CURRENT	TOTAL
1	0	11
2	0	11
3	0	11
4	0	360
5	0	360
6	0	360
7	0	360
8	0	360
9	0	360
10	0	360

3456   ABSOLUTE CLOCK   3456

BLOCK	CURRENT	TOTAL		BLOCK	CURRENT	TOTAL		BLOCK	CURRENT	TOTAL		BLOCK	CURRENT	TOTAL		BLOCK	CURRENT	TOTAL
1	0	3456		11	0	3456		21	0	3446		31	0	89		41	0	4
2	0	3456		12	0	36		22	0	3446		32	0	170		42	0	4
3	0	3456		13	0	36		23	0	3446		33	0	85		43	0	3535
4	0	3456		14	0	36		24	0	3446		34	0	85		44	0	3456
5	0	3456		15	0	3499		25	0	3446		35	0	85		45	0	3456
6	0	3456		16	0	3446		26	0	3446		36	0	85		46	0	3453
7	0	660		17	0	3446		27	0	26		37	0	79		47	0	79
8	0	3456		18	0	3446		28	0	3446		38	0	79		48	0	72
9	0	3456		19	0	3446		29	0	3446		39	0	79		49	0	360
10	0	3456		20	0	3446		30	0	89		40	0	79		50	0	288

BLOCK	CURRENT	TOTAL		BLOCK	CURRENT	TOTAL		BLOCK	CURRENT	TOTAL		BLOCK	CURRENT	TOTAL		BLOCK	CURRENT	TOTAL
51	0	72		61	0	360		71	0	3		81	0	3		91	0	3
52	0	72		62	0	72		72	0	3		82	0	3		92	0	72
53	0	72		63	0	0		73	0	3		83	0	3		93	0	72
54	0	72		64	0	0		74	0	3		84	0	3		94	0	72
55	0	72		65	0	0		75	0	3		85	0	3		95	0	72
56	0	72		66	0	0		76	0	3		86	0	3		96	0	3
57	0	72		67	0	0		77	0	3		87	0	3		97	0	1
58	0	72		68	0	72		78	0	3		88	0	3		98	0	0
59	0	360		69	0	72		79	0	3		89	0	3		99	0	0
60	0	339		70	0	72		80	0	3		90	0	3		100	0	0

BLOCK	CURRENT	TOTAL		BLOCK	CURRENT	TOTAL		BLOCK	CURRENT	TOTAL		BLOCK	CURRENT	TOTAL
101	0	0		111	0	1		121	0	2		131	0	3
102	0	0		112	0	1		122	0	2				
103	0	0		113	0	2		123	0	0				
104	0	0		114	0	2		124	0	0				
105	0	0		115	0	0		125	0	0				
106	0	1		116	0	0		126	0	2				
107	0	1		117	0	0		127	0	2				
108	0	24		118	0	0		128	0	2				
109	0	24		119	0	2		129	0	2				
110	0	1		120	0	2		130	0	3				

Figure A–1   (continued)

Conditions at Start of Full One-Year Run

MATRIX FULLWORD SAVEVALUE   1

	COLUMN	1	2	3	4	5	Product line
ROW	1	7	848	2450	1894	779	Quantity (units) on hand
	2	6	C	C	0	C	Quantity on order
	3	C	C	C	0	0	Quantity on back order
	4	6650	8C560	115150	18182	771	Cost of stock on hand; value of inventory
	5	C	0	0	0	C	Lost revenue

```
*   THREE MONTHS
*
    RESET
    INITIAL    X2,KC                  Clear totals for main run (transient
    INITIAL    MX1(1-5,5),KO               period is over)
    INITIAL    MX2(217-288,1-7),KO
    INITIAL    MX3(217-288,1-7),KO
    INITIAL    MX4(1-4,1-5),KO
    INITIAL    MX5(1-2,1-5),KO
    START      13823
```

CONTENTS OF FULLWORD SAVEVALUES (NCN-ZERC)
SAVEVALUE	NR,	VALUE	NR,	VALUE	NR,	VALUE	NR,	VALUE	NR,	VALUE
	1	-1651C5	2	4330	10	68455	11	279343	12	70966
	13	305	14	864						

CONTENTS OF FULLWORD SAVEVALUES (NCN-ZERO)
SAVEVALUE	NR,	VALUE	NR,	VALUE	NR,	VALUE	NR,	VALUE	NR,	VALUE
	1	152264	2	-2120	10	93435	11	278061	12	70728
	13	36C	14	73	16	161003				

CONTENTS OF FULLWORD SAVEVALUES (NCN-ZERC)
SAVEVALUE	NR,	VALUE	NR,	VALUE	NR,	VALUE	NR,	VALUE	NR,	VALUE
	1	-4S114	2	3214	10	93435	11	278061	12	70728
	13	378	14	4368	16	161C03				

Figure A–1   (continued)

Above messages occur whenever a loan is taken:

Savevalue	Contents
1	Bank balance (before loan)
2	Cumulative profits
10	Estimated accounts receivable due next month
11	Estimated accounts payable due next month
12	Estimated accounts receivable due month after next
13	Day number
14	(No significance)
16	Loan outstanding

End-of-run output

RELATIVE CLOCK 13823 ABSOLUTE CLOCK 17279

BLOCK COUNTS

BLOCK	CURRENT	TOTAL		BLOCK	CURRENT	TOTAL		BLOCK	CURRENT	TOTAL		BLOCK	CURRENT	TOTAL		BLOCK	CURRENT	TOTAL
1	0	13823		11	0	13823		21	0	13709		31	0	1410		41	0	120
2	0	13823		12	0	125		22	0	13709		32	0	2580		42	0	120
3	0	13823		13	0	125		23	0	13709		33	0	1290		43	0	15119
4	0	13823		14	0	125		24	0	13709		34	0	1290		44	0	13823
5	0	13823		15	0	14994		25	0	13709		35	0	1290		45	0	13823
6	0	13823		16	0	13709		26	0	13709		36	0	1296		46	0	13811
7	0	1882		17	0	13709		27	0	123		37	0	1296		47	0	1296
8	0	13823		18	0	13709		28	0	13709		38	0	1296		48	0	288
9	0	13823		19	0	13709		29	0	13709		39	0	1296		49	0	1440
10	0	13823		20	0	13709		30	0	1410		40	0	1296		50	0	1152

BLOCK	CURRENT	TOTAL		BLOCK	CURRENT	TOTAL		BLOCK	CURRENT	TOTAL		BLOCK	CURRENT	TOTAL		BLOCK	CURRENT	TOTAL
51	0	79		61	0	288		71	0	1440		81	0	12		91	0	11
52	0	79		62	0	288		72	0	288		82	0	12		92	0	244
53	0	79		63	0	288		73	0	2		83	0	12		93	0	264
54	0	1440		64	0	288		74	0	2		84	0	12		94	0	264
55	0	1440		65	0	288		75	0	2		85	0	12		95	0	264
56	0	1440		66	0	288		76	0	2		86	0	12		96	0	11
57	0	1440		67	0	288		77	0	2		87	0	12		97	0	1
58	0	1440		68	0	288		78	0	288		88	0	11		98	0	0
59	0	1440		69	0	1440		79	0	288		89	0	11		99	0	0
60	0	1440		70	0	1438		80	0	288		90	0	11		100	0	0

287

BLOCK	CURRENT	TOTAL	BLOCK	CURRENT	TOTAL	BLOCK	CURRENT	TOTAL	BLOCK	CURRENT	TOTAL
101	0	0	111	0	1	121	0	0	131	0	12
102	0	0	112	0	1	122	0	0			
103	0	0	113	0	10	123	0	0			
104	0	0	114	0	10	124	0	0			
105	0	0	115	0	10	125	0	0			
106	0	1	116	0	10	126	0	0			
107	0	0	117	0	10	127	0	0			
108	0	24	118	0	10	128	0	0			
109	0	24	119	0	0	129	0	0			
110	0	1	120	0	0	130	0	12			

CONTENTS OF FULLWORD SAVEVALUES (NON-ZERO)

SAVEVALUE NR,	VALUE	NR,	VALUE	NR,	VALUE	NR,	VALUE	NR,	VALUE
1	375354	2	40044	10	258880	11	51268	12	258001
13	576	14	4368	16	110510				

QUEUE	MAXIMUM CONTENTS	AVERAGE CONTENTS	TOTAL ENTRIES	ZERO ENTRIES	PERCENT ZEROS	AVERAGE TIME/TRANS	$AVERAGE TIME/TRANS	TABLE NUMBER	CURRENT CONTENTS
BLOC	83	7.223	1296	11	.8	77.050	77.709		

$AVERAGE TIME/TRANS = AVERAGE TIME/TRANS EXCLUDING ZERO ENTRIES

Statistics on queue of back orders. There were 1296 back orders (an average of 7.2 at a time and a maximum of 83 at one time). The average back order waited 77 time units or about a day and a half.

Conditions at Start of Full One-Year Run

MATRIX FULLWORD SAVEVALUE 1

	COLUMN 1	2	3	4	5	Product line
ROW 1	1	1299	397	743	1117	Quantity on hand
2	9	0	2970	0	0	Quantity on order
3	6	0	0	0	0	Quantity on back order
4	950	123405	18659	7132	1105	Cost of inventory
5	0	0	0	0	0	Lost revenue

Financial Data

	COLUMN	1	2	3	4	5	6	7
ROW	Day Number	Day	Month	A/R	A/P	Cash	Cum. Profit	$ Sales
	1	1	1	13840	0	375354	193	4486
	2	2	1	13093	114428	68407	404	4408
	3	3	1	17857	0	72365	628	4073
	4	4	1	10285	1900	73345	831	4405
	5	5	1	9104	8550	73696	1004	3937
	6	6	1	10883	950	77446	1242	4995
	7	7	1	8251	141158	77978	1441	4871
	8	8	1	13570	2518	79856	1692	5658
	9	9	1	8140	0	82953	1916	4938
	10	10	1	16065	0	87509	2176	5643
	11	11	1	8804	19007	90191	2480	6553
	12	12	1	13163	0	93306	2815	7235
	13	13	1	9734	19007	76663	3124	7505
	14	14	1	9878	0	79792	3457	6253
	15	15	1	12787	2518	79208	3711	4790
	16	16	1	8686	0	82025	3912	5131
	17	17	1	14598	0	85111	4090	3536
	18	18	1	12411	254018	10000	4330	5888
	19	19	1	12373	950	13157	4607	4730
	20	20	1	11876	950	17100	4832	5117
	21	21	1	12705	950	21983	5031	4459
	22	22	1	10738	950	25151	5314	4292
	23	23	1	14743	1900	27921	5531	4814
	24	0	1	15206	19007	33017	5739	3201
	25	1	2	11628	1568	28690	−377	4146
	26	2	2	13100	0	32003	−110	4715
	27	3	2	7565	1568	33974	168	4704
	28	4	2	11129	0	39225	393	3491
	29	5	2	12554	950	41380	647	4570
	30	6	2	11576	0	45041	863	4514
	31	7	2	6442	950	46390	1076	3325
	32	8	2	10647	0	50271	1260	4095
	33	9	2	7241	1568	51617	1479	3881
	34	10	2	8837	0	55550	1692	4211
	35	11	2	6041	113810	56795	1844	3079
	36	12	2	11116	950	58972	2068	4372
	37	13	2	8987	0	62300	2257	3420
	38	14	2	10857	950	64372	2450	4476
	39	15	2	7301	160165	66814	2642	3474
	40	16	2	9889	950	69787	2870	4506
	41	17	2	10360	19007	55258	3080	3573
	42	18	2	9632	0	59058	3341	5584
	43	19	2	8592	950	62698	3586	4628
	44	20	2	13265	0	66960	3793	3850
	45	21	2	6005	0	69746	3978	3955
	46	22	2	8375	0	73718	4182	3266
	47	23	2	7720	0	77546	4445	5006
	48	0	2	8029	0	81108	4584	3629
	49	1	3	10272	950	66245	−1537	5935
	50	2	3	10482	0	72619	−1255	4572
	51	3	3	10174	0	76414	−1003	4201
	52	4	3	9069	2518	78092	−753	4635
	53	5	3	9404	950	82977	−552	4110
	54	6	3	10922	0	87319	−337	3312
	55	7	3	9409	0	92319	−31	5269
	56	8	3	9175	950	95615	204	4487
	57	9	3	10910	0	100787	579	5188
	58	10	3	9946	19007	105496	768	4093
	59	11	3	12235	950	110197	1045	5194
	60	12	3	9308	950	113685	1204	3673
	61	13	3	7778	0	118591	1556	7418
	62	14	3	5811	0	122771	1860	5140
	63	15	3	6497	0	126648	2130	4527
	64	16	3	5790	2518	127573	2318	4787
	65	17	3	6101	950	130818	2592	4965
	66	18	3	7391	21857	112545	2827	5159
	67	19	3	8218	0	118782	3038	4892
	68	20	3	6538	950	123118	3263	4498
	69	21	3	7554	0	127919	3472	3541
	70	22	3	7084	2850	129037	3638	4624
	71	23	3	8263	950	135156	3850	5059
	72	0	3	7023	113810	138526	4087	4818
	73	1	4	5991	0	156787	−1817	6447
	74	2	4	5447	950	160441	−1568	4319
	75	3	4	6777	0	164810	−1182	6519
	76	4	4	5532	139590	169613	−867	4586
	77	5	4	2980	1568	170200	−620	6963

Figure A–1   (continued)

78	6	4	5367	0	174126	−368	7431
79	7	4	5749	0	178598	−69	7787
80	8	4	6023	0	182736	247	5941
81	9	4	4744	0	185842	506	6854
82	10	4	7416	950	189999	747	4925
83	11	4	5120	0	194099	1039	5406
84	12	4	5282	0	197723	1340	6387
85	13	4	5038	950	200327	1606	4327
86	14	4	7231	0	205174	1914	7162
87	15	4	5516	2518	206988	2143	5942
88	16	4	9079	950	211505	2410	5288
89	17	4	5118	113810	102171	2683	5901
90	18	4	6880	950	105564	3008	6697
91	19	4	6033	159547	10000	3214	5325
92	20	4	6226	0	15599	3496	6265
93	21	4	5110	0	19765	3737	6472
94	22	4	5230	0	23376	4131	8697
95	23	4	4297	0	27138	4461	5863
96	0	4	9508	1568	34021	4715	4337
97	1	5	5135	950	29828	−1384	8321
98	2	5	3814	0	33221	−1013	7110
99	3	5	2351	0	35383	−645	6178
100	4	5	3811	0	38746	−269	8599
101	5	5	5006	0	43193	102	8997
102	6	5	4414	0	46984	552	6269
103	7	5	4371	0	50663	847	5433
104	8	5	5513	950	54787	1310	9412
105	9	5	3242	0	57472	1739	9442
106	10	5	4425	2518	59043	2058	7051
107	11	5	5386	1900	61497	2496	8455
108	12	5	3920	0	65425	2910	7975
109	13	5	3937	0	68271	3241	7320
110	14	5	4548	0	72350	3604	7972
111	15	5	3528	0	75457	4127	6060
112	16	5	4256	950	78707	4455	7807
113	17	5	3718	0	82267	4766	6552
114	18	5	3661	1568	84043	5201	6492
115	19	5	3897	0	87223	5624	8184
116	20	5	4815	950	90000	6019	9152
117	21	5	3771	0	93126	6346	7663
118	22	5	3939	0	96594	6759	8372
119	23	5	4547	19007	81489	7111	6237
120	0	5	2909	950	83036	7446	7433
121	1	6	3596	2518	76495	1336	12520
122	2	6	3472	0	79967	1879	14771
123	3	6	5935	0	85902	2379	10008
124	4	6	5194	950	90146	2897	10042
125	5	6	5746	0	95892	3441	9148
126	6	6	4846	0	100738	3884	8295
127	7	6	4026	1900	102864	4466	9443
128	8	6	4046	0	106910	4973	14489
129	9	6	6380	1568	111722	5545	13072
130	10	6	5062	0	116784	6063	10460
131	11	6	6690	0	123474	6597	10255
132	12	6	5838	4750	124562	6739	4737
133	13	6	7357	0	131919	6868	3363
134	14	6	6082	0	138001	7091	6313
135	15	6	7270	0	145271	7153	2348
136	16	6	3408	1568	147111	7971	20351
137	17	6	8962	0	156073	9574	31446
138	18	6	7500	0	163573	9920	9085
139	19	6	8620	0	172193	10503	10201
140	20	6	7742	0	179935	10973	11397
141	21	6	8510	0	188445	11337	10966
142	22	6	5654	950	193149	11794	8429
143	23	6	7092	22475	177766	12560	13452
144	0	6	8114	0	185880	13040	11792
145	1	7	3335	950	178853	6966	9879
146	2	7	5845	0	184698	7350	10952
147	3	7	7834	0	192532	7960	10430
148	4	7	6881	0	199413	8600	11462
149	5	7	6427	1568	204272	9058	9880
150	6	7	8434	0	212706	9669	15687
151	7	7	9127	950	220883	10308	14199
152	8	7	8115	0	228998	10635	4897
153	9	7	6993	0	235991	10975	7440
154	10	7	8178	0	244169	11832	15345
155	11	7	5296	1568	247897	12319	8976
156	12	7	7909	0	255806	12862	8460
157	13	7	8757	1900	262663	13270	9252
158	14	7	11996	950	273709	13893	13008

Figure A–1   (continued)

159	15	7	7293	2518	278484	14571	13685
160	16	7	10849	950	288383	15370	13889
161	17	7	11511	950	298944	16053	13291
162	18	7	3783	0	302727	16503	8396
163	19	7	4865	132817	174775	16853	8761
164	20	7	9485	1568	182692	17272	11261
165	21	7	6650	1900	187442	17978	13020
166	22	7	9659	0	197101	18289	11046
167	23	7	9584	1900	204785	18373	3199
168	0	7	9476	950	213311	18468	2737
169	1	8	12563	3468	184296	12047	2874
170	2	8	8811	950	192157	12809	19213
171	3	8	6240	0	198397	13105	6947
172	4	8	7587	139590	66394	14844	33667
173	5	8	9022	0	75416	15206	10434
174	6	8	9055	2518	81953	15895	11906
175	7	8	10504	0	92457	16685	16203
176	8	8	9844	0	102301	17291	16388
177	9	8	6309	19007	89603	17839	11302
178	10	8	6253	2518	93338	18407	13397
179	11	8	4355	950	96743	19185	12234
180	12	8	8432	0	105175	19792	13855
181	13	8	7265	0	112440	20295	11997
182	14	8	14435	0	126875	20847	11128
183	15	8	7586	3468	130993	21330	13106
184	16	8	12152	0	143145	22000	15256
185	17	8	9539	1900	150784	22586	14265
186	18	8	10561	0	161345	22917	10327
187	19	8	6289	1568	166066	23499	9739
188	20	8	8207	0	174273	23989	8522
189	21	8	8311	0	182584	24692	14951
190	22	8	10393	19957	173020	25347	13437
191	23	8	11957	1568	183409	25969	12529
192	0	8	9701	0	193110	26553	10065
193	1	9	4693	4750	182104	20902	11818
194	2	9	15348	0	197452	21380	6467
195	3	9	6196	1568	202080	21876	9095
196	4	9	8942	0	211022	22441	11746
197	5	9	20081	0	231103	22856	10018
198	6	9	9393	1900	238596	23211	5305
199	7	9	11357	0	249953	23463	6879
200	8	9	8545	1568	256930	23852	7793
201	9	9	9770	0	266700	24972	25489
202	10	9	10718	23757	253661	25338	8396
203	11	9	11528	950	264239	25560	6428
204	12	9	8642	2518	270363	25773	4176
205	13	9	14302	0	284665	25933	2869
206	14	9	8486	2850	290301	28274	46302
207	15	9	11177	0	301478	28821	12169
208	16	9	9518	950	310046	29249	9424
209	17	9	11773	1568	320251	29764	11823
210	18	9	14111	0	334362	30335	13394
211	19	9	9426	2850	340938	30850	15809
212	20	9	13033	0	353971	31344	11173
213	21	9	12432	20575	345828	31994	12391
214	22	9	12090	0	357918	32638	10772
215	23	9	8604	2850	363672	33150	8209
216	0	9	20369	2518	381523	33707	12904
217	1	10	12179	950	361221	28066	13106
218	2	10	10163	950	370434	28595	11488
219	3	10	10096	0	380530	29054	10962
220	4	10	16681	0	397211	29485	8726
221	5	10	13064	1568	408707	30073	12872
222	6	10	5865	950	413622	30719	13906
223	7	10	10159	0	423781	31356	12559
224	8	10	5829	20907	408703	31723	11884
225	9	10	9058	112860	304901	32128	7968
226	10	10	16650	141158	180393	32510	8282
227	11	10	12871	0	193264	33028	11517
228	12	10	5368	0	198632	33610	10389
229	13	10	6932	950	204614	34389	13487
230	14	10	11965	1568	215011	34832	9111
231	15	10	14477	950	228538	35104	8597
232	16	10	21830	0	250368	35516	7675
233	17	10	12867	0	263235	35616	2157
234	18	10	7285	20575	249945	36432	15830
235	19	10	11639	950	260634	36722	7308
236	20	10	14939	950	274623	36987	6158
237	21	10	12444	950	286117	37182	3740
238	22	10	13073	0	299190	38733	21550
239	23	10	12808	1568	310430	39432	10219

Figure A–1 (continued)

240	C	10	9656	950	319136	40297	16520
241	1	11	15536	950	300122	34529	6939
242	2	11	10036	950	309208	35022	11785
243	3	11	6288	6318	309178	35444	8159
244	4	11	11069	19097	301240	35773	6056
245	5	11	10194	0	311434	36152	6925
246	6	11	9806	0	321240	36544	7517
247	7	11	11259	1568	330931	37039	13262
248	8	11	12002	950	341983	37468	8621
249	9	11	13455	0	355438	37898	9044
250	10	11	11152	1900	364690	38273	8740
251	11	11	10498	0	375188	38526	5501
252	12	11	13035	1568	386655	38872	8495
253	13	11	8872	0	395527	39295	7945
254	14	11	6133	0	401660	39981	9518
255	15	11	7430	19007	390083	40329	7033
256	16	11	13699	3468	400314	40663	7247
257	17	11	11716	0	412030	41006	8243
258	18	11	5386	0	417416	41531	10706
259	19	11	7493	112860	312049	42044	7767
260	20	11	11218	1568	321699	42483	7242
261	21	11	12283	140540	193442	42941	9410
262	22	11	10563	0	204005	43346	9600
263	23	11	5898	0	209903	43806	9199
264	C	11	7349	0	217252	44400	11615
265	1	12	5825	20575	180854	38769	6150
266	2	12	24280	0	205134	39035	4367
267	3	12	12380	0	217514	39442	6069
268	4	12	14442	950	231006	39936	10294
269	5	12	13000	0	244006	40263	6213
270	6	12	12424	3468	252962	40552	6796
271	7	12	13683	0	266645	40862	5403
272	8	12	9930	2850	273725	41192	6869
273	9	12	9772	2850	280647	41482	4931
274	10	12	13086	0	293733	41758	6186
275	11	12	7715	0	301448	42073	6261
276	12	12	8204	22475	287177	42341	5435
277	13	12	11922	1900	297159	42646	5857
278	14	12	16748	0	313947	43035	6421
279	15	12	10484	1900	322531	43254	5637
280	16	12	12158	950	333739	43506	3898
281	17	12	8121	0	341860	43731	5192
282	18	12	7613	0	349473	44016	6217
283	19	12	10125	3468	356130	44386	6074
284	20	12	11807	0	367937	44640	5305
285	21	12	9330	0	377267	45056	5973
286	22	12	7633	950	383950	45380	7559
287	23	12	6838	1900	388888	45627	6390
288	C	12	11301	19007	381182	45872	5331
289	C	0	0	0	0	0	0
290	C	0	0	0	0	0	0

Final profit

Production Data

MATRIX FULLWORD SAVEVALUE 3

Quantity due from vendor on given day

	COLUMN 1	2	3	4	5	6	7
Day Number	Day	Month	←	Product Line	→		
ROW 1	1	1	0	0	2970	0	0
2	2	1	1	0	0	0	0
3	3	1	0	0	0	0	1584
4	4	1	0	0	0	0	0
5	5	1	1	0	0	0	0
6	6	1	1	0	0	1980	0
7	7	1	0	0	0	0	0
8	8	1	2	0	0	0	0
9	9	1	1	0	0	0	1584
10	10	1	1	0	0	0	0
11	11	1	1	0	0	0	0
12	12	1	2	0	0	0	0
13	13	1	2	0	0	0	0
14	14	1	0	0	0	0	0
15	15	1	0	0	0	0	0
16	16	1	0	0	0	0	0
17	17	1	1	0	0	0	0
18	18	1	0	0	0	0	0
19	19	1	1	0	0	0	0
20	20	1	0	0	0	0	0

Figure A–1 (continued)

21	21	1	1	0	0	0	0
22	22	1	0	0	0	0	1584
23	23	1	0	0	0	0	0
24	0	1	0	0	0	0	0
25	1	2	1	0	0	0	0
26	2	2	1	0	0	0	0
27	3	2	0	0	0	0	0
28	4	2	1	0	0	0	0
29	5	2	0	0	0	0	0
30	6	2	1	0	0	0	0
31	7	2	0	0	0	1980	0
32	8	2	0	0	0	0	0
33	9	2	1	0	0	0	0
34	10	2	0	0	0	0	1584
35	11	2	0	0	0	0	0
36	12	2	0	0	0	0	0
37	13	2	0	0	0	0	0
38	14	2	0	0	0	0	0
39	15	2	1	0	0	0	0
40	16	2	0	0	0	0	0
41	17	2	0	0	0	0	0
42	18	2	1	0	0	0	0
43	19	2	1	0	0	0	0
44	20	2	0	0	0	0	0
45	21	2	0	0	0	0	0
46	22	2	1	0	0	0	0
47	23	2	0	0	0	0	1584
48	0	2	0	0	0	0	0
49	1	3	1	0	0	0	0
50	2	3	1	0	0	0	0
51	3	3	0	0	0	0	0
52	4	3	0	0	0	0	0
53	5	3	0	0	0	0	0
54	6	3	1	0	0	0	0
55	7	3	1	0	0	0	0
56	8	3	3	0	0	0	0
57	9	3	0	0	0	0	1584
58	10	3	1	0	0	0	0
59	11	3	0	0	0	1980	0
60	12	3	3	0	0	0	0
61	13	3	1	0	0	0	0
62	14	3	1	0	0	0	0
63	15	3	0	0	0	0	0
64	16	3	1	0	0	0	0
65	17	3	0	0	0	0	0
66	18	3	0	0	0	0	1584
67	19	3	0	0	0	0	0
68	20	3	0	0	0	0	0
69	21	3	0	0	0	0	0
70	22	3	0	0	0	0	0
71	23	3	0	0	0	0	0
72	0	3	1	0	0	0	0
73	1	4	0	1188	0	0	0
74	2	4	0	0	0	0	0
75	3	4	1	0	0	0	0
76	4	4	0	0	0	0	1584
77	5	4	1	0	0	0	0
78	6	4	1	0	0	0	0
79	7	4	1	0	0	0	0
80	8	4	1	0	0	0	0
81	9	4	1	0	0	0	0
82	10	4	0	0	2970	0	0
83	11	4	0	0	0	1980	0
84	12	4	0	0	0	0	1584
85	13	4	0	0	0	0	0
86	14	4	0	0	0	0	0
87	15	4	1	0	0	0	0
88	16	4	0	0	0	0	0
89	17	4	0	0	0	0	0
90	18	4	0	0	0	0	0
91	19	4	0	0	0	0	1584
92	20	4	0	0	0	0	0
93	21	4	0	0	0	0	0
94	22	4	1	0	0	0	0
95	23	4	0	0	0	0	0
96	0	4	1	0	0	0	0
97	1	5	2	0	0	0	0
98	2	5	0	0	0	0	0
99	3	5	0	0	0	0	1584
100	4	5	0	0	0	0	0
101	5	5	0	0	0	0	0

Figure A–1 (continued)

1C2	6	5	1	0	0	C	0
1C3	7	5	0	0	0	198C	0
1C4	8	5	0	0	0	C	0
1C5	9	5	0	0	0	C	0
1C6	1C	5	1	0	0	C	1584
1C7	11	5	0	0	0	C	0
108	12	5	0	0	0	C	0
109	13	5	0	0	0	C	0
110	14	5	1	0	0	C	0
111	15	5	1	0	0	0	0
112	16	5	0	0	0	C	0
113	17	5	0	0	0	0	1584
114	18	5	1	0	0	C	0
115	19	5	0	0	0	C	0
116	20	5	0	0	0	0	0
117	21	5	2	0	0	198C	0
118	22	5	0	C	0	C	0
119	23	5	0	0	0	C	1584
12C	0	5	0	0	0	C	0
121	1	6	0	0	0	C	0
122	2	6	5	0	0	C	0
123	3	6	0	0	0	C	0
124	4	6	0	0	0	C	0
125	5	6	0	0	0	C	1584
126	6	6	C	0	0	0	0
127	7	6	0	0	0	C	0
128	8	6	0	0	0	C	0
129	9	6	0	0	0	C	1584
130	1C	6	0	0	0	198C	0
131	11	6	0	0	0	0	0
132	12	6	1	C	0	0	0
133	13	6	2	0	0	0	0
134	14	6	0	0	0	C	1584
135	15	6	1	1188	0	0	0
136	16	6	0	0	2970	C	0
137	17	6	C	0	0	C	0
138	18	6	0	0	0	C	0
139	19	6	0	0	0	0	1584
14C	20	6	0	0	0	C	0
141	21	6	1	0	0	0	0
142	22	6	0	0	0	1980	0
143	23	6	0	0	0	C	0
144	0	6	0	0	0	0	1584
145	1	7	0	0	0	0	0
146	2	7	0	0	0	0	0
147	3	7	2	0	0	C	0
148	4	7	1	0	0	0	1584
149	5	7	1	0	0	C	0
150	6	7	1	0	0	C	0
151	7	7	1	0	0	C	0
152	8	7	0	0	0	C	0
153	9	7	1	0	0	198C	1584
154	1C	7	0	0	0	0	0
155	11	7	2	0	0	0	0
156	12	7	0	0	0	0	0
157	13	7	2	0	0	0	1584
158	14	7	1	0	0	0	0
159	15	7	2	0	0	0	0
160	16	7	1	0	0	0	0
161	17	7	0	0	0	0	1584
162	18	7	0	0	0	C	0
163	19	7	0	0	0	C	0
164	2C	7	1	0	0	1980	0
165	21	7	0	0	0	C	1584
166	22	7	0	0	0	C	0
167	23	7	0	0	0	C	0
168	0	7	1	0	0	C	0
169	1	8	1	1188	0	C	0
170	2	8	0	0	0	0	1584
171	3	8	0	0	2970	C	0
172	4	8	0	0	0	0	0
173	5	8	2	0	0	0	0
174	6	8	0	0	0	198C	1584
175	7	8	2	0	0	0	0
176	8	8	0	0	0	C	0
177	9	8	C	0	0	0	0
178	1C	8	0	0	0	0	0
179	11	8	0	0	0	C	1584
18C	12	8	1	0	0	C	0
181	13	8	0	0	0	C	0
182	14	8	0	0	0	C	0

Note increasing order frequency during peak sales period

Figure A–1 (continued)

183	15	8	5	0	0	0	1584
184	16	8	0	0	0	1980	0
185	17	8	0	0	0	0	0
186	18	8	0	0	0	0	1584
187	19	8	0	0	0	0	0
188	20	8	2	0	0	0	0
189	21	8	0	0	0	0	0
190	22	8	0	0	0	0	0
191	23	8	0	0	0	0	1584
192	0	8	5	0	0	0	0
193	1	9	1	0	0	0	0
194	2	9	1	0	0	0	0
195	3	9	0	0	0	1980	0
196	4	9	3	0	0	0	1584
197	5	9	0	0	0	0	0
198	6	9	1	0	0	0	0
199	7	9	0	0	0	0	0
200	8	9	0	1188	0	0	1584
201	9	9	3	0	0	0	0
202	10	9	0	0	0	0	0
203	11	9	0	0	0	0	0
204	12	9	0	0	0	0	1584
205	13	9	3	0	2970	1980	0
206	14	9	1	0	0	0	0
207	15	9	1	0	0	0	0
208	16	9	1	0	0	0	0
209	17	9	0	0	0	0	1584
210	18	9	0	0	0	0	0
211	19	9	0	0	0	0	0
212	20	9	1	0	0	0	0
213	21	9	0	0	0	0	1584
214	22	9	2	0	0	0	0
215	23	9	0	0	0	0	0
216	0	9	0	0	0	1980	0
217	1	10	0	0	0	0	1584
218	2	10	0	0	0	0	0
219	3	10	1	0	0	0	0
220	4	10	0	0	0	0	0
221	5	10	1	0	0	0	0
222	6	10	0	0	0	0	1584
223	7	10	0	0	0	0	0
224	8	10	0	0	0	0	0
225	9	10	1	0	0	0	0
226	10	10	1	0	0	0	1584
227	11	10	1	0	0	0	0
228	12	10	0	0	0	1980	0
229	13	10	0	0	0	0	0
230	14	10	1	0	0	0	1584
231	15	10	1	0	0	0	0
232	16	10	1	0	0	0	0
233	17	10	5	1188	0	0	0
234	18	10	0	0	0	0	0
235	19	10	0	0	0	0	1584
236	20	10	0	0	0	0	0
237	21	10	0	0	2970	0	0
238	22	10	1	0	0	0	0
239	23	10	0	0	0	1980	0
240	0	10	2	0	0	0	1584
241	1	11	0	0	0	0	0
242	2	11	0	0	0	0	0
243	3	11	0	0	0	0	0
244	4	11	0	0	0	0	0
245	5	11	0	0	0	0	0
246	6	11	2	0	0	0	1584
247	7	11	0	0	0	0	0
248	8	11	0	0	0	0	0
249	9	11	0	0	0	0	0
250	10	11	0	0	0	0	0
251	11	11	1	0	0	0	0
252	12	11	0	0	0	1980	0
253	13	11	0	0	0	0	1584
254	14	11	0	0	0	0	0
255	15	11	0	0	0	0	0
256	16	11	0	0	0	0	0
257	17	11	0	0	0	0	0
258	18	11	1	0	0	0	0
259	19	11	0	0	0	0	0
260	20	11	2	0	0	0	1584
261	21	11	0	0	0	0	0
262	22	11	3	0	0	0	0
263	23	11	3	0	0	0	0

Figure A–1   (continued)

264	C	11	0	0	0	C	0
265	1	12	0	0	0	C	0
266	2	12	2	0	0	0	1584
267	3	12	2	0	0	1980	0
268	4	12	0	0	0	C	0
269	5	12	2	0	0	C	0
270	6	12	1	1188	0	0	0
271	7	12	0	0	0	0	0
272	8	12	0	0	0	C	0
273	9	12	2	0	0	0	0
274	10	12	0	0	2970	0	0
275	11	12	0	0	0	C	0
276	12	12	1	0	0	0	1584
277	13	12	2	0	0	C	0
278	14	12	0	0	0	0	0
279	15	12	0	0	0	0	0
280	16	12	0	0	0	C	0
281	17	12	0	0	0	0	0
282	18	12	1	0	0	0	0
283	19	12	6	0	0	0	1584
284	20	12	1	0	0	0	0
285	21	12	0	0	0	0	0
286	22	12	0	0	0	1980	0
287	23	12	0	0	0	0	0
288	0	12	0	0	0	0	0
289	0	0	0	0	0	0	0
290	0	0	0	0	0	0	0

Cumulative Results

MATRIX FULLWORD SAVBVALUE   4

	COLUMN	1	2	3	4	5	Product Line
ROW	1	156	7579	18737	38449	73669	Quantity sold
	2	145099	795426	974813	395723	73260	$ Sold
	3	7800	37895	56211	14118	5	$ Profit
	4	450	205	405	128	0	Lost profit on lost sales

MATRIX FULLWORD SAVBVALUE   5

	COLUMN	1	2	3	4	5	Salesman
ROW	1	487830	466199	477431	482781	470080	$ Sales
	2	24113	22145	23939	22546	23286	$ Profit (includes 3 month transient period)

Figure A–1   (continued)

296

Page numbers in *italic* contain the basic definition or explanation of the term; an asterisk indicates use of the term in an example.